ENCYCLOPEDIA *of* DISCOVERY

Skywatching

ENCYCLOPEDIA *of* DISCOVERY

Skywatching

CONSULTANT EDITORS
Robert Burnham, Dr John O'Byrne

FOG CITY PRESS

Published by Fog City Press
814 Montgomery Street
San Francisco, CA 94133 USA

Copyright © 2004 Weldon Owen Pty Ltd
Reprinted 2005, 2006, 2007
Chief Executive Officer: John Owen
President: Terry Newell
Publisher: Lynn Humphries
Managing Editor: Angela Handley
Design Manager: Helen Perks
Editorial Coordinator: Jennifer Losco
Production Manager: Louise Mitchell
Production Coordinator: Monique Layt
Sales Manager: Emily Jahn
Vice President International Sales: Stuart Laurence

Editorial Coordination: Jessica Cox, Jennifer Losco
Project Editors: Helen Cooney, Kathy Gerrard
Project Designers: Avril Makula, Cliff Watt
Consultant Editors: Robert Burnham, Dr John O'Byrne
Indexing: Puddingburn Publishing Services

ISBN-13: 978-1-87701-989-0
ISBN-10: 1-87701-989-5

Color reproduction by SC (Sang Choy) International Pte Ltd
Printed by SNP Leefung Printers Limited
Printed in China

A Weldon Owen Production

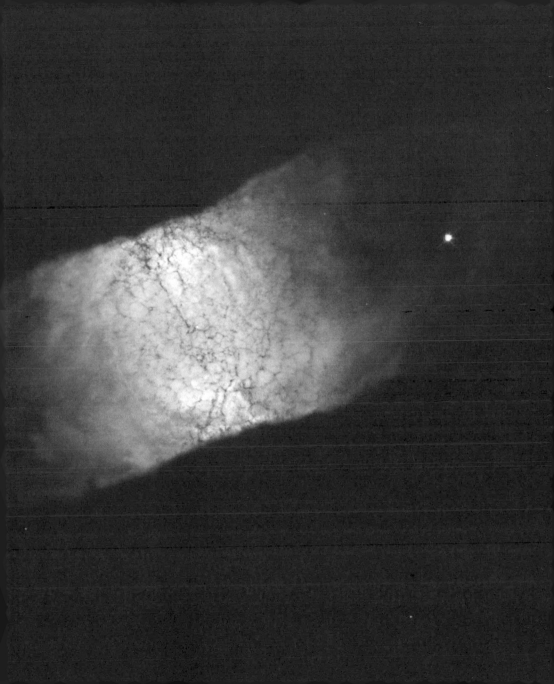

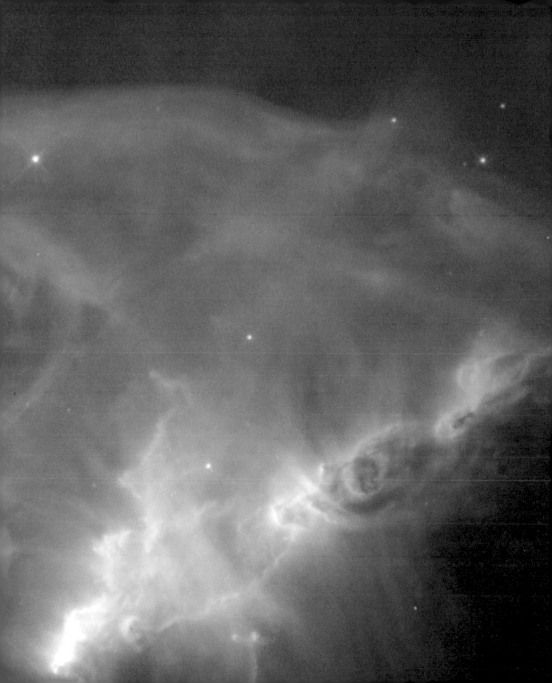

CONTENTS

PROBING THE
UNIVERSE

*Presenting the universe in
all its majesty, mystery and
infinite variety.*

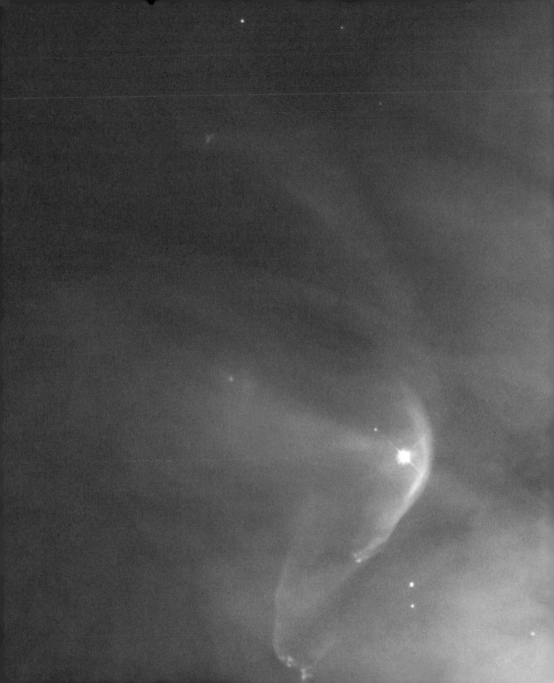

Understanding
the Universe

THE UNIVERSE

We think Earth is a big place, but trying to picture the sheer vastness of the universe is a real challenge. The Moon, our closest neighbor, is about 240,000 miles (385,000 km) from us; the Sun, 93 million miles (150 million km); and the nearest bright star, Alpha Centauri, a staggering 25 billion miles (40 billion km). The nearest large galaxy to our own, Andromeda, is about a million times farther away. The most distant galaxies yet known are more than 10 million times farther still.

THE HOME GALAXY

Along with eight other planets, Earth orbits the Sun. This Solar System is a tiny dot in the Milky Way Galaxy, a spiral galaxy of 400 billion stars that stretches 100,000 light-years from side to side.

In turn, the Milky Way is just one of billions of star-filled

OUR HOME Earth sits third in line from our star, the Sun, among the other rocky planets. Neptune and Pluto mark the outer edge of the Solar System.

OUR GALAXY The Solar System is a speck within the Milky Way Galaxy. Relatively nearby are two small galaxies, the Large and Small Magellanic Clouds.

galaxies, the building blocks of the universe. Despite its size, our Galaxy is tiny compared with the universe as a whole. Light from the nearby Andromeda Galaxy, for example, takes about 2.5 million years to reach us.

INTERSTELLAR SPACE

The Milky Way and Andromeda are the largest members of a small gathering of at least 35 galaxies called the Local Group. Our galactic family lives on the outskirts of a dense cluster of thousands of galaxies called the Local Supercluster. Astronomers believe that thousands of such superclusters are scattered throughout the universe.

What lies beyond? The Hubble Space Telescope has seen galaxies 10 billion light-years away, so far away that they appear merely as smudges near the edge of the observable universe.

OUR UNIVERSE The Milky Way (bottom left) is just one among many billions of galaxies. It is tiny compared with the universe as a whole.

MEASURING DISTANCE

Beyond our world lies a gulf in space too large to measure in miles and kilometers. Two main measurements are used instead: Astronomical Units and light-years.

A useful measure in our Solar System is the Astronomical Unit (AU), the average distance between Earth and the Sun—about 93 million miles (150 million km).

For measuring distances beyond the Solar System, we use the light-year. This is defined as the distance light travels in a vacuum in a year. A light-year is about 6 trillion miles (10 trillion km).

The Big Bang

■ In 1924, the U.S. astronomer Edwin Hubble turned the astronomical world on its ear when he announced that galaxies appeared to be moving away from Earth. What is more, Hubble discovered that the more distant the galaxy, the faster it was receding. The universe appeared to be blowing up, "inflating," like a balloon. The implications were truly astonishing: For the universe to be expanding, a force of incredible magnitude must have set matter on its outward-flowing course. The name astronomers eventually coined for this violent genesis was the Big Bang.

IN THE BEGINNING

Unfortunately, the term "Big Bang" is a misnomer that has led to some confusion. There was no "bang," no explosion in the strictest definition of the word, where one thing erupts into the space of something else. This is because there was no space. Instead, the Big Bang was more an unfolding of space and matter—from a point no larger than the period at the end of this sentence. This happened between 13 billion and 15 billion years ago.

After the bang A fraction of a second after the Big Bang, the

CREATION STORY The universe began with a bang, and in one-millionth of a second became a mass of radiation and particles. These particles formed the first atoms of hydrogen and helium. After several billion years, gravity caused clouds of gas to collapse, forming stars and galaxies.

universe was a hot, seething mass of radiation and exotic particles. This expanded and cooled, and more familiar sorts of particles formed, including the neutrons, electrons, and protons that make up everyday matter.

Matter forms Gradually, elements came into being—mostly hydrogen and helium—and these eventually collapsed under the influence of gravity to create galaxies, stars, and planets.

EVIDENCE FOR THE BIG BANG

The most convincing single piece of evidence for the Big Bang is the cosmic background radiation (CBR), a uniformly distributed all-sky glow. It is thought to be the last vestige of heat from the Big Bang itself. That initial outburst of fiery energy has cooled greatly, to −455°F (−270°C), just barely above absolute zero and some hundred million times cooler than a typical birthday candle.

The Future of the Universe

■ The universe has been expanding since the Big Bang, but will it continue to do so forever? Astronomers have come up with a number of intriguing scenarios, ranging from never-ending expansion to a long return journey that ends with a Big Crunch. In all cases, whether expansion will change at some point in the future depends on the density of the universe, and that depends on the amount of matter it contains.

POSSIBLE FUTURES

If the density of the universe is greater than a certain critical value—that is, the universe contains a sufficient amount of matter—the force of gravity will at some point bring expansion to a halt and the universe will begin to collapse, culminating in a Big Crunch. Such a universe is called "closed." If the density of the universe is less than the critical value—there is not enough matter—expansion will continue indefinitely. This is termed an "open" universe.

A flat universe There is another option. Much observational evidence suggests that the universe is "flat," precisely balanced between open and closed. That means the universe will expand forever, always decelerating, but never quite coming to a halt.

An accelerating universe Yet another possibility is that expansion may actually accelerate. Supernovas observed in distant galaxies in 1998 showed that they are 20 percent fainter than would be expected in a flat or open universe. This indicates that over the past few billion years, the expansion of the universe has sped up and carried the stars to greater distances from Earth.

A LIKELY STORY

Which possible future is most likely? Astronomers are in general agreement that the universe will continue to expand; the evidence does not favor the closed universe scenario. Beyond that, opinions are very much divided. A vigorous debate continues.

BIG CRUNCH The Big Crunch is one possible fate of the universe. At the moment (bottom left sphere), the universe is expanding. If there is enough matter in the universe, the expansion halts and switches into reverse. The end comes with an all-destroying crunch (top right sphere).

INDEFINITE EXPANSION If the universe keeps expanding from the present (bottom left sphere), galaxies will drift farther apart, stars will eventually burn out, and ordinary matter will disintegrate, leaving a boundless "sea" of elementary particles (far right sphere).

STARS

A star is a large sphere of hydrogen and helium, with a smattering of other elements, all in gaseous form. Nuclear fusion reactions in its core create enormous amounts of energy, including light and heat. No two stars are alike—brightness, surface temperature, and mass vary from one to the other.

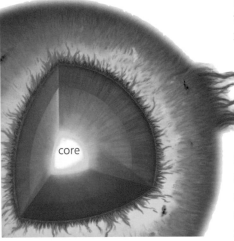

NUCLEAR FURNACE A main-sequence star, such as the Sun, has a nuclear furnace at its core. Nuclear reactions fuse hydrogen into helium and release energy. As each bit of energy reaches the surface, it flies into space—and the star shines.

STAR TYPES

Stars start their lives on what astronomers call the main sequence. These are often called dwarfs, although the term is misleading: some dwarfs are 20 times bigger than the Sun and 20,000 times brighter. Red dwarfs are the most common of all stars.

White dwarfs Smaller than red dwarfs, white dwarfs are typically the size of Earth but the mass of the Sun. They are stars whose nuclear fires have gone out.

Red giants After the main-sequence stars, the most common stars are the red giants. They have the same surface temperature as red dwarfs, but are much brighter and larger.

Supergiants These are the largest stars of all—Betelgeuse, for example, is close to 600 million miles (1 billion km) in diameter. These monsters typically have a mass similar to the Sun's, but, if they traded places with the Sun, their atmospheres would envelop the planets of the inner Solar System.

MULTIPLE STARS

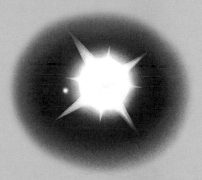

Most stars have at least one companion star: as a singleton, our Sun is in the minority. Double stars probably form when several different parts of the parent cloud of dust and gas begin to collapse at once. Sirius (above), is a double, made up of a brilliant bluish supergiant, the sky's brightest star, plus a faint white dwarf companion.

Stars with two or more companions are known as multiple stars.

COMPARING SIZE The small white ball at right represents a white dwarf star. The Sun, the yellow globe, is huge by comparison, but the red giant behind it is 20 to 40 times larger, and the red supergiant is roughly 800 times larger.

The Life of a Star

■ All stars begin their lives in the same way, by condensing out of clouds of gaseous material. But the details of their lives—and deaths—differ greatly.

TWO PATHS

A star's lifespan depends on its mass. Massive stars form quickly, in, perhaps, hundreds of thousands of years compared with the Sun's tens of millions of years, but have relatively brief lives. A star that is eight times more massive than the Sun will shine for only 40 million years,

A NURSERY IN THE EAGLE Stars are formed inside clouds of gaseous material called nebulas. Light from newborn stars is eroding the gas in these columns, part of a stellar nursery in the Eagle Nebula.

while a star like the Sun can live for 10 or 11 billion years.

Stellar deaths Death, too, depends on mass. After a massive star exhausts its nuclear fuel, it dies in a blaze of glory, as a supernova (see pp. 24–5); the death of a smaller star, such as the Sun, is more subdued, as shown in the diagram below.

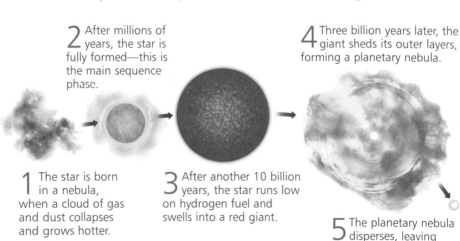

2 After millions of years, the star is fully formed—this is the main sequence phase.

4 Three billion years later, the giant sheds its outer layers, forming a planetary nebula.

1 The star is born in a nebula, when a cloud of gas and dust collapses and grows hotter.

3 After another 10 billion years, the star runs low on hydrogen fuel and swells into a red giant.

5 The planetary nebula disperses, leaving behind a white dwarf, the star's white-hot core.

Supernovas and Novas

■ Novas and supernovas are superficially similar: both involve stars that show unpredictable and significant increases in brightness. In truth, however, they are very different stellar beasts. A nova is a star that suddenly increases in brightness by as much as 10 magnitudes then declines to a value close to its original magnitude. The star is not destroyed and, indeed, may repeat the behavior thousands of years later. A supernova is more final. It is the cataclysmic death of a star.

SUPERNOVAS

Stars that are much more massive than the Sun reach the end of their lives in violent supernova explosions. A supernova is a hundred times more luminous than a nova and can outshine hundreds of billions of stars in its galaxy. These stellar fireballs are instrumental in distributing certain elements, such as iron and nickel, throughout the galaxy.

Binary stars Two types of supernova take place, depending on what kind of star is involved.

The first occurs in a double-star (binary) system. Gas from a moderately massive star accumulates onto a white dwarf, pushing the white dwarf past the point where its internal pressure can counteract gravity. Eventually, the gas causes a nuclear explosion that probably disrupts the entire star system.

Massive stars If a star is particularly massive—about eight times as massive as the Sun—and its nuclear fuel has been expended, it cannot support its own outer layers. The core first collapses then rebounds catastrophically, blowing off the star's outer layers.

Some supernovas are so bright that they can be seen with the unaided eye. The last such naked-eye supernova occurred in 1987 in the Large Magellanic Cloud.

Supernova leftovers No matter how the supernova occurred, the expanding blanket of material which formed the bulk of the star collides with the surrounding interstellar medium to produce an expanding shell of gas. This is known as a supernova remnant.

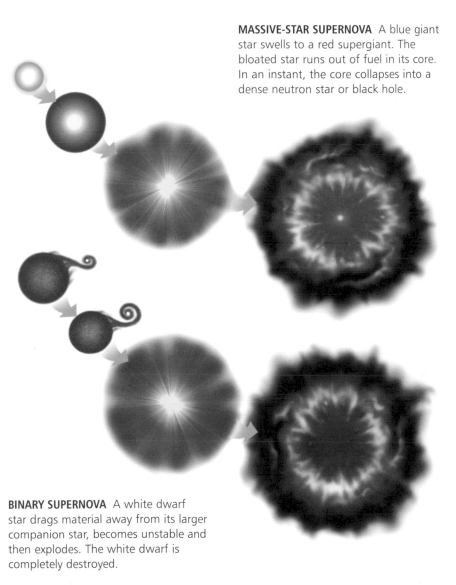

MASSIVE-STAR SUPERNOVA A blue giant star swells to a red supergiant. The bloated star runs out of fuel in its core. In an instant, the core collapses into a dense neutron star or black hole.

BINARY SUPERNOVA A white dwarf star drags material away from its larger companion star, becomes unstable and then explodes. The white dwarf is completely destroyed.

If the collapsed core of a star survives the explosion, it may remain behind in the form of a neutron star. The core becomes extremely dense and is made up entirely of neutrons—tiny particles found in the nucleus of an atom. A neutron star may be visible as a pulsar—a rapidly spinning object that flashes bursts of radio waves.

A black hole forms when an extremely massive star explodes. Too large to be a stable neutron star, the massive star keeps collapsing until it eventually disappears, leaving only a source of gravity so strong that even light waves cannot escape from it.

NOVAS

Novas occur in a binary system in which one star is a white dwarf and the other is an ordinary star. The white dwarf has greater gravity than its companion, and is able to siphon hydrogen-rich gas from it. The gas swirls into a disk around the white dwarf before spiraling down onto the dwarf's surface. When enough gas has

NOVA IN THE MAKING Below: Gas swirls down to a tiny white dwarf from its much larger companion star. The gas may trigger an explosion, causing a nova.

accumulated on the surface, the dwarf erupts in a nuclear explosion, resulting in a nova outburst.

Seen from Earth, the star system brightens by perhaps 10 magnitudes over a few days and remains bright for several days before slowly fading. The explosion may be repeated.

SUPERNOVA REMNANT Right: This is what is left of a star that went supernova 15,000 years ago—streamers of gas called the Veil Nebula or Cygnus Loop.

Black Holes

■ A black hole swallows up anything that comes close to it—even light cannot escape its voracious gravity.

TWO TYPES

A black hole forms when a high-mass star collapses at the end of its life. That produces an object roughly the mass of a star. But black holes can also form when a large number of stars come close together in the dense core of a galaxy. The result is a super-massive black hole. Our own Milky Way is thought to have one of these at its center.

Structure At the heart of a black hole, matter is crushed into a singularity, a point where the laws of physics cease to operate. Surrounding the singularity is an imaginary surface known as the event horizon. Surrounding the black hole itself is an accretion disk, a vast sheet of gas and dust.

LOOKING FOR HOLES

Although black holes themselves cannot be seen, the effects of their gravity can be measured. The black holes' gravity squeezes the accretion disk with great force, heating it to extremely high temperatures. Before matter is sucked into the black hole, it radiates X-rays, radio waves, and large amounts of visible energy.

Hubble's evidence We also have evidence from the Hubble Space Telescope. Photos have shown accretion disks—a telltale sign of a black hole.

DOWN A BLACK HOLE

What would happen if you fell into a black hole? Though time would seem to be passing at a normal rate, anyone watching you would see you slow down until you seemed to be in suspended animation. Space is so warped around a black hole that you would feel a much stronger gravitational pull on your feet than your head (assuming you were going in feet first), and this difference would rip you apart.

Some say that if you could survive the tidal ripping and avoid the crushing force of the singularity at the black hole's heart, you might find yourself in a different universe.

WHIRLPOOL A black hole swallows everything near it. In doing so, it creates an accretion disk, a whirlpool of material made from torn-apart stars and clouds of gas. As this material falls into the hole, it emits copious amounts of energy.

Variable Stars

■ Not all stars shine with a steady light. Many fluctuate in brightness over periods ranging from minutes to years.

CLASSES OF VARIABLES

Astronomers have listed some 30,000 variable stars. There are three broad classes.

Pulsating variables These brighten and fade as their outer layers rhythmically contract and expand. Two common types are Cepheid and Mira variables. Cepheids have very regular periods ranging from one to several days. Mira stars pulsate like Cepheids do, but their cycles are less regular and their periods are longer, ranging from 80 days to five years.

Cataclysmic variables These exhibit sudden and large brightness outbursts. Many are novas, binary systems that erupt once in a cycle that can last thousands of years (see page 26).

Eclipsing variables These are binary systems in which one star eclipses the other during each orbital period. From Earth, we see this as a periodic decrease in light output, followed by a return to normal brightness.

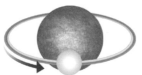

1 Bright white star blocks some light from orange star—medium brightness.

2 White star beside orange star—maximum brightness.

ECLIPSING Some double stars are aligned in such a way that one passes in front of the other, and then behind it, so that the light from the system varies.

3 Orange star blocks all light from white star—minimum brightness.

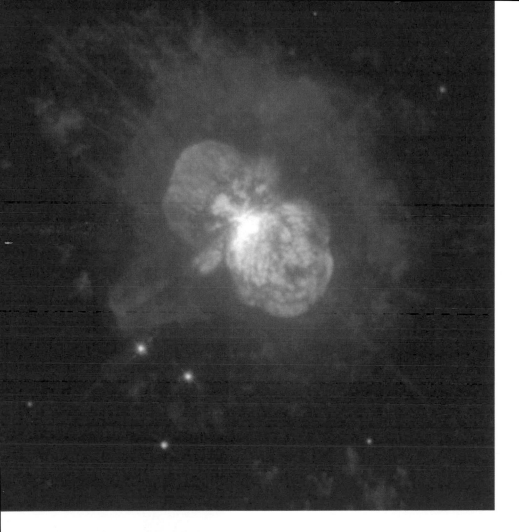

CATACLYSMIC AND PULSATING Light from a cataclysmic variable, such as Eta Carinae (above), varies erratically—there is no predictable pattern. Pulsating variables, by contrast, follow a regular pattern over a definite period of time, from minimum (far left) to maximum (left).

Star Clusters

■ Stars not only come in pairs and multiples, but also in clusters that range in size from tens of stars to more than a million. Mutual gravity holds them together, and they drift through space in the same direction and at the same speed, like a school of fish. Clusters vary in age from a few million to billions of years.

OPEN CLUSTERS

Loose assemblages of stars, containing at most a few thousand members, are called open or galactic clusters. Some 1,200 open clusters are known in the Milky Way Galaxy, and many have been observed in nearby galaxies. The smallest are just a few light-years across; the biggest may be a hundred times larger.

Open clusters are found along the spiral arms of the thin galactic plane. Most of these stars are younger than the Sun, and some are among the youngest stars we can see.

In cosmic terms, open clusters have short lives. Their stars drift apart and scatter in only a few hundred million years.

Some open clusters Examples of this type include the Pleiades in Taurus, the Double Cluster in Perseus, and the Praesepe or Beehive Cluster in Cancer.

GLOBULAR CLUSTERS

Globular clusters are denser and more tightly bound than open clusters. They also contain many more stars—some globulars have more than a million members.

HERCULES The Hercules Cluster (M13) is a globular that contains at least a million stars within a region only 100 light-years across.

Most of the globulars we see are located in a halo surrounding our galaxy, and similar halos of globulars have been observed around other galaxies.

Globulars are ancient. The average age of most of them is about 11.5 billion years—nearly the age of the universe itself.

PLEIADES The Pleiades is probably the best-known open cluster, plainly visible to the naked eye in Taurus. The surrounding dust is revealed clearly only in photos.

Some globular clusters Two fine globulars are Omega Centauri, in Centaurus, and the Hercules Cluster (M13), in Hercules.

NEBULAS

Astronomers originally used the word "nebula" to describe anything that appeared blurry or cloudlike through a telescope. Many of these clouds, it turned out, had distinct spiral or oval shapes and were later recognized to be galaxies. But a large number had no particular shape and appeared to have stars embedded within them. These are true nebulas, complexes of interstellar gas and dust.

TYPES OF NEBULAS

Most nebulas are lit up by light from stars within them. The biggest nebulas do not shine at all—they can be seen only when they block the light of more distant stars.

Emission nebulas In these, atoms are excited, or ionized, by ultra-violet radiation given off by hot stars inside them. This makes these nebulas glow brightly, and shine colorfully in photos. One of the best is the Great Nebula, in the sword of Orion. Emission nebulas are associated with both star formation and star death.

CLOUDS IN SPACE The Great Nebula (above) is lit up by four central stars known as the Trapezium cluster. The Trifid Nebula (right) is a mixture of emission (pink) and reflection (blue) regions.

Reflection nebulas A reflection nebula does not shine on its own power but by the light of adjacent stars scattering off dust grains in the cloud. The tiny dust grains reflect blue light more effectively than red light, so these nebulas often appear blue in color.

Sometimes, both emission and reflection regions exist in the same nebula—the Trifid Nebula in Sagittarius is a good example.

Dark nebulas Dark nebulas are clouds of gas and dust dense enough to block the light from background stars. They show up as dark silhouettes (such as the Horsehead Nebula in Orion) or as "holes" in space (such as the Coal Sack in Crux). Many dark nebulas obscure regions of newly formed stars.

PLANETARY NEBULAS

Quite different to the other clouds of gas and dust are the planetary nebulas. Through a telescope, these often appear as small disks—not unlike a planet, hence the name.

But these expanding rings or shells of gas have nothing to do with planets; nor are they associated with starbirth. They are the final stages in the life of small-mass stars (see pp. 22–3), and they glow because of radiation given off by the hot core of the star, now a white dwarf.

The Ring Nebula in the constellation Lyra and the Dumbbell Nebula in Vulpecula are two of the finest planetary nebulas in the sky.

SUPERNOVA REMNANTS

Like planetary nebulas, supernova remnants are expanding shells of gas—but they are produced by

PLANETARY NEBULA The Cat's Eye Nebula is a planetary nebula, the wreckage of a star that threw off its outer layers—in this case, about a thousand years ago.

massive stars that have exploded in a catastrophic eruption (see pp. 24–5).

Supernova remnants less than a thousand years old are strong sources of radio waves and X-rays. A prominent example is the Crab Nebula in Taurus, first observed as a "guest star" in AD 1054 by Chinese astronomers.

Supernova remnants are usually fainter and less symmetrical than planetary nebulas. As remnants age, they become even less regular in shape, appearing as huge rings, filaments, or arcs of tenuous gas.

Other prominent remnants include the Veil Nebula in Cygnus and the Vela supernova remnant.

DARK HORSE The Horsehead Nebula is a dense black cloud of dust that can be seen only because it blots out the light coming from the glowing streamers of an emission nebula.

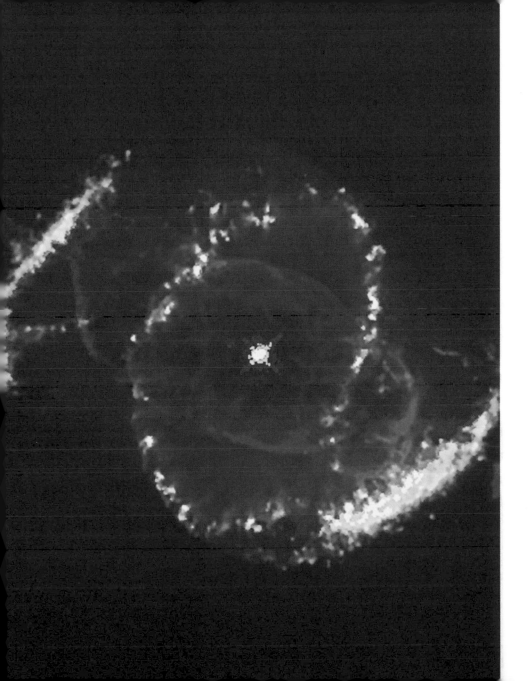

GALAXIES

Stars are not randomly scattered in space. Instead they gather in galaxies, bound together by gravity. There are billions of galaxies in the universe.

A GALAXY OF GALAXIES

Astronomers classify galaxies by shape. Galaxies come in a great variety, from pinwheels and spheres to ellipsoids and shapeless blobs.

Elliptical galaxies These are shaped like spheres, although many appear flattened or lens-shaped. The largest have diameters of 100,000 light-years or more and have a mass 100 trillion times that of the Sun. More common are the dwarf ellipticals, which may have a diameter of only 1,000 light-years or so and have a mass a few million times that of the Sun.

Spiral galaxies Most bright galaxies are spirals. These range in size from 15,000 to 150,000 light-years across and may contain anywhere between 10 billion and 10 trillion times

ELLIPTICAL GALAXY Elliptical galaxies vary in size from dwarfs to giants. M87 is thought to have a mass equivalent to more than a million Suns.

the mass of the Sun. The arms unwind from a bright central region, called the nucleus, and wrap around the disk. A spiral galaxy's hub may be prominent in some cases and almost non-existent in others.

Barred spiral galaxies In this type, the bright stars and hot gas of the inner regions extend for thousands of light-years from either side of the center in a

SPIRAL GALAXY Left: The Whirlpool (M51) is a spectacular spiral galaxy.

IRREGULAR GALAXY Right: Like many other irregular galaxies, the Small Magellanic Cloud is small but contains many bright nebulas and hot, young stars.

BARRED SPIRAL GALAXY Left: The center of a barred spiral, such as the Great Barred Spiral (NGC 1365), is longer than it is wide.

straight "bar" before wrapping back around the galaxy in the form of arms. In obvious cases, each arm looks like a scimitar or scythe blade.

Lenticular galaxies These have shapes that fall between the highly flattened elliptical and spiral categories. They have a central nucleus and are lens-shaped like spiral galaxies but, like the ellipticals, show little or no evidence of a spiral structure.

Irregular galaxies As their name suggests, irregular galaxies have no defined shape. They look patchy and sprawling, although some have conspicuous bars, and others have bars plus a distinctive but faint spiral arm pattern.

ACTIVE GALAXIES

Some galaxies are very turbulent places indeed. Astronomers call these active galaxies, and they are intense sources of infrared, radio, and X-ray energy. The emissions are evidence of violent activity in the galactic cores. Quasars are extremely distant objects believed to be the cores of active galaxies.

COLLIDING GALAXIES

Sometimes two or more galaxies pass very close to one another. When they "collide," few stars are actually hit because they lie too far apart. But the galaxies are pulled out of shape and may eventually merge. Also, the gravitational pull of the collision triggers starbirth.

COLLISION IN PROGRESS The Hubble Space Telescope captured a collision between the galaxies NGC 2207 and IC 2163 (left). They may well merge into a single galaxy billions of years from now.

QUASAR The bright cores of active galaxies that vary in brightness over weeks or days are known as quasars. These objects are incredibly distant— about 1.5 billion light-years from Earth.

Our Galaxy

■ The Milky Way is our home galaxy. Spiral in shape, it contains an estimated 400 billion stars, not to mention dense clouds of dust and gas.

SIZE AND STRUCTURE

The Milky Way is vast—the Sun is no more than a speck in one of its spiral arms. Its disk is 1,500 light-years thick, with spiral arms uncoiling to a distance of 75,000 light-years from the center. Surrounding the disk is a halo of old stars and star clusters that stretches perhaps another 75,000 light-years. Each star and nebula orbits the Galaxy's center more or less independently. Our Sun completes one orbit in about 240 million years.

Spiral arms

Astronomers have traced nearby sections of the Milky Way's spiral arms, but more distant sections are more difficult to make out, because dust gets in the way. For that reason, we are unsure about how many spiral arms there are. There may be as many as five.

The center Astronomers think that an object with a mass about 2.6 million times that of the Sun lies at the center of our Galaxy. They believe it to be a super-massive black hole.

FACE-ON Seen from above, the Milky Way looks like a pinwheel and has at least two spiral arms trailing from the disk.

EDGE-ON Seen edge-on (below), the Milky Way has a fairly thin disk, with a bulge at the center. Surrounding it is a halo of old stars and star clusters.

INSIDE VIEW From Earth, the Milky Way appears like a gossamer band of light or a high, thin cloud. In fact, it is a galaxy—our Galaxy—seen from the inside.

The Local Group

■ Like stars, galaxies tend to congregate into clusters. The Milky Way belongs to a small cluster of galaxies known as the Local Group. Astronomers know of at least 35 Local Group galaxies spread across roughly 8 million light-years of space. All member galaxies are linked to one another by the pull of gravity.

WITHIN THE GROUP

Most of the Local Group's members are dwarf elliptical and irregular galaxies containing only about a million stars each. Two large galaxies dominate—the Milky Way and the Andromeda Galaxy—and each has attracted a collection of smaller galaxies. For example, the Milky Way's satellite

GALACTIC NEIGHBORS The 17 largest members of the Local Group are illustrated here, with the Milky Way, Andromeda, and Pinwheel Galaxies the largest of all. Most of the small galaxies orbit around either the Milky Way or Andromeda.

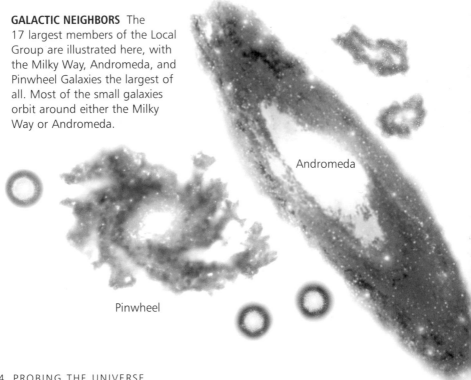

Andromeda

Pinwheel

galaxies are the Large and Small Magellanic Clouds and several dwarf galaxies.

OTHER GROUPINGS

Galaxy surveys have found nearly 3,000 clusters within 4 billion light-years. Compared with some of these, the Local Group is tiny. The Virgo cluster has more than 2,000 members, while the Hercules cluster contains tens of thousands of galaxies.

Superclusters Clusters of galaxies themselves belong to larger groupings called superclusters. With many other clusters, the Local Group and Virgo cluster form the Local Supercluster, some 60 million light-years across.

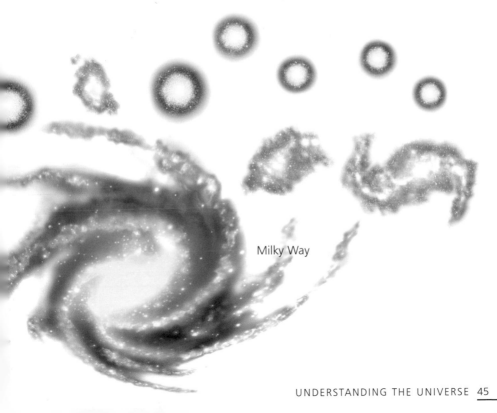

Milky Way

THE BIG PICTURE

On a large scale, the universe is a strange place. Astronomers have found that galaxies are clumped together to form sheets and filaments separated by seemingly empty space. Even stranger, we now think that most of the matter in the universe cannot be seen.

FINDING A PATTERN

Superclusters of galaxies are not distributed evenly in the universe. They form enormous honeycomb-like structures, with vast voids between them. One

ANCIENT GALAXIES This Hubble image shows the oldest galaxies ever seen. Astronomers study these ancient galaxies to see how today's galaxies evolved.

explanation for this pattern looks back 300,000 to 500,000 years after the Big Bang, when some parts of space became denser than others. The denser regions later became galaxies; the other regions became the voids between them.

DARK MATTER

The way galaxies move in clusters and superclusters shows that they are being tugged by something invisible. Most galaxies are probably surrounded by halos of this invisible "dark matter." In fact it could make up some 90 percent of the universe's mass.

Two theories The two main hypothetical candidates for this material are WIMPs (weakly interacting massive particles) and MACHOs (massive compact halo objects). Neither type has yet been directly observed, but the quest continues.

WALLS OF GALAXIES This map of super-clusters shows that on a very large scale, the universe has a structure of "walls" of galaxies separated by dark voids.

Our Solar System

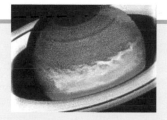

THE SUN AND ITS FAMILY

The Solar System consists of the Sun; nine planets and their dozens of satellites; millions of asteroids, or minor planets; innumerable meteors and comets; and a plane of dust that pervades all of interplanetary space.

THE SOLAR NEBULA

How did all these very different objects come into being? Most astronomers believe that the Solar System formed less than five billion years ago from a cloud of hot hydrogen and helium gas and dust known as the solar nebula.

Formed from a cloud Some 4.6 billion years ago, a large cloud of cold dust and gas was drifting around the center of the Milky Way. The cloud began to collapse, possibly set off by the explosion of a nearby star.

Eventually a forerunner to our Sun was born at its center. The grains of material from the nebula consolidated into solid lumps of material. These collided and coalesced with one another to form larger bodies, which became the planets we see today.

Among the objects that did not become planets or moons are comets, small frozen objects which normally inhabit the Solar System's outer edges; asteroids, most of which orbit within the region between Mars and Jupiter; and meteoroids, fragments of comets and asteroids.

THE NATURE OF THE PLANETS

Because temperature decreases with distance from the Sun, the composition of the planets differs according to where they formed.

Inner planets The inner solar nebula was too hot for such substances as water and methane to exist as solids, so the inner planets formed from materials such as iron and silicates.

Outer planets The cold of the outer solar nebula allowed planets there to hold onto large amounts of water, ice, and other elements easily destroyed by heat. The greater mass of these planets also meant that they could sweep up large quantities of hydrogen and helium, which created voluminous atmospheres.

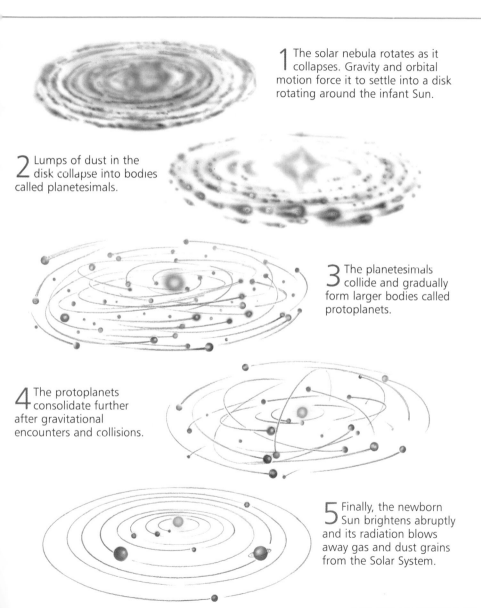

1 The solar nebula rotates as it collapses. Gravity and orbital motion force it to settle into a disk rotating around the infant Sun.

2 Lumps of dust in the disk collapse into bodies called planetesimals.

3 The planetesimals collide and gradually form larger bodies called protoplanets.

4 The protoplanets consolidate further after gravitational encounters and collisions.

5 Finally, the newborn Sun brightens abruptly and its radiation blows away gas and dust grains from the Solar System.

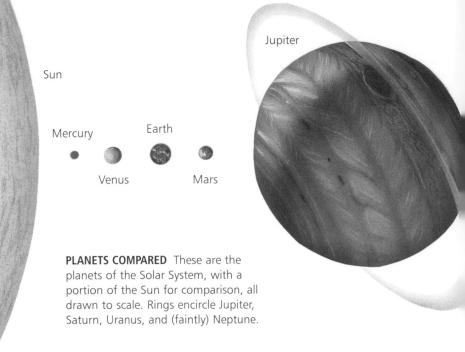

Sun

Mercury

Venus

Earth

Mars

Jupiter

PLANETS COMPARED These are the planets of the Solar System, with a portion of the Sun for comparison, all drawn to scale. Rings encircle Jupiter, Saturn, Uranus, and (faintly) Neptune.

THE SUN AT THE CENTER

All planetary bodies, from Jupiter to the smallest particle of dust, move about the Sun. The orbits are not circular but elliptical. This means that each body goes through two extreme points in its orbit, one nearest the Sun, called perihelion, and one farthest from the Sun, aphelion.

With the exception of comets, all bodies orbit in the same direction as Earth. If you could stand well above Earth's North Pole and look down on the Solar System, you would see the planets moving counterclockwise. Most of the planets also rotate in the same direction as their orbital motion.

The planets go around the Sun nearly in the same plane—that is, on the same "level." Pluto is the odd man out, its orbit taking it a long way above and below the the other planets. Comets are able to approach the Sun from any direction and angle.

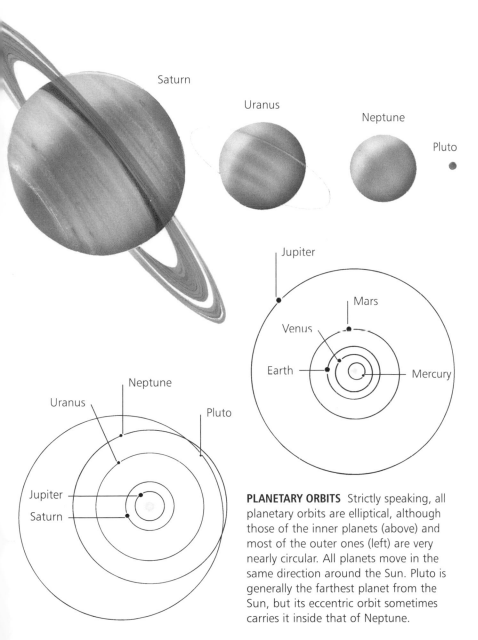

Saturn

Uranus

Neptune

Pluto

Jupiter

Mars

Venus

Earth

Mercury

Neptune

Uranus

Pluto

Jupiter

Saturn

PLANETARY ORBITS Strictly speaking, all planetary orbits are elliptical, although those of the inner planets (above) and most of the outer ones (left) are very nearly circular. All planets move in the same direction around the Sun. Pluto is generally the farthest planet from the Sun, but its eccentric orbit sometimes carries it inside that of Neptune.

Terrestrial and Gas-giant Planets

■ Most planets fall into two groups based on size, density, and chemical makeup. Pluto is neither terrestrial nor jovian, but resembles instead the rock–ice moons of the outer planets.

TERRESTRIALS

Mercury, Venus, Earth, and Mars are the terrestrial planets. These are small bodies made up mainly of rock and metals, with densities three to five times that of water. Terrestrial planets have relatively thin atmospheres.

GAS GIANTS

Jupiter, Saturn, Uranus, and Neptune are the jovian or gas-giant planets. They are all more than a dozen times more massive than Earth. In fact, Jupiter out-weighs our planet by hundreds of times.

Each jovian planet is thought to have a tiny rocky core buried under layers of hydrogen and helium thousands of miles deep. A gas-giant planet has a density near that of water, and Saturn's is actually lighter than ice.

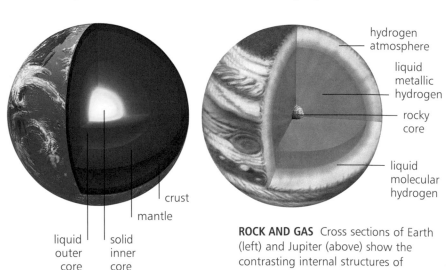

hydrogen atmosphere

liquid metallic hydrogen

rocky core

liquid molecular hydrogen

crust

mantle

liquid outer core

solid inner core

ROCK AND GAS Cross sections of Earth (left) and Jupiter (above) show the contrasting internal structures of terrestrial and gas-giant planets.

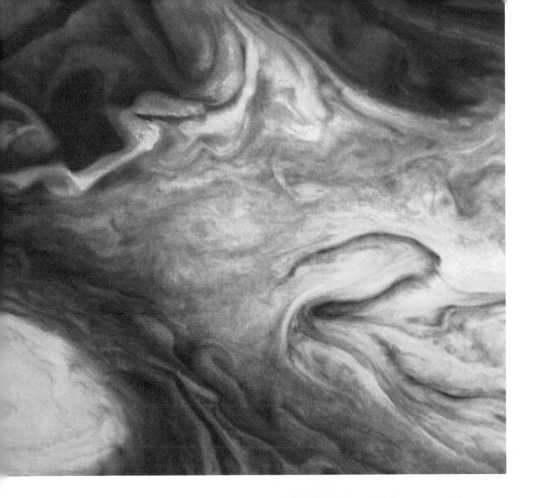

GAS BALL The photo (above) shows a close-up of Jupiter's atmosphere. What you are seeing is merely the outermost layer of a huge, mostly gaseous, ball.

ROCKY WORLD From the Himalayas (here seen from space) to the core, Earth is made up mainly of dense, rocky materials such as basalt, and metals, such as iron.

The Sun

■ To us, the most important object in our sky is the Sun. Its energy powers Earth's climate and supports life. Yet the Sun is an ordinary star like a million others in the Milky Way Galaxy.

OUR STAR

The Sun is a huge ball of hot gas, mostly hydrogen and helium. In its core, high temperatures and pressures fuse hydrogen into helium, releasing energy.

Structure Fusion occurs from the center of the Sun out to perhaps a quarter of its radius. Above this is the radiative zone, in which

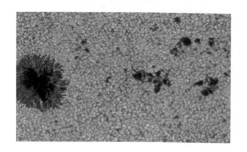

SEEING SPOTS The Sun's best-known features are sunspots, dark regions which are cooler than their surroundings.

radiation carries the energy. On top of this layer the Sun's energy moves in the same way that boiling water does. Heated from below, the gas rises to the surface, radiates energy into space, cools, then sinks again. This convective region forms the Sun's outer third.

The photosphere is the Sun's visible surface, and this is where the dark regions call sunspots form. Above this, the Sun has a complex atmosphere consisting of the chromosphere (a thin, cool layer) and the corona, which is almost as hot as the core. Both are usually only visible during solar eclipses.

FACT FILE

DISTANCE FROM EARTH
93 million miles (150 million km)
SIDEREAL REVOLUTION PERIOD
365.26 days
MASS (EARTH=1) **333,000**
RADIUS AT EQUATOR (EARTH=1)
109
APPARENT SIZE **32 arcminutes**
SIDEREAL ROTATION PERIOD
(AT EQUATOR) **25.4 days**

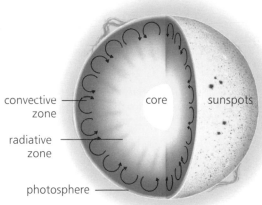

convective zone — core — sunspots

radiative zone —

photosphere —

SOLAR POWERHOUSE The Sun's photosphere—the surface we can see—lies above boiling convection layers, an intermediate radiative zone, and a nuclear powerhouse at the core (left). The corona—the Sun's outer atmosphere—is heated by millions of brilliant arches, called coronal loops (above). These fountains of extremely hot gas may be up to 300,000 miles (480,000 km) high.

Mercury

■ Mercury is a small, rocky, airless world with an extreme climate—roastingly hot during the day, frigidly cold at night. Its pockmarked surface is reminiscent of the Moon's.

CLIMATIC EXTREMES

Mercury's mass is just one-eighteenth that of Earth's, and much too small to retain an atmosphere. With the Sun so close, and lacking the protection from extremes that an atmosphere would give, Mercury has a very uncomfortable climate, to put it mildly. The planet's day side

MARINER 10 Most of what we know about Mercury comes from just one spacecraft, Mariner 10, which made three flybys in 1974–5. It photographed about 45 percent of the surface.

reaches 800°F (430°C) by noon. The heat dissipates into space at night, when temperatures drop dramatically, bottoming out just before dawn at –280°F (–170°C). This is the widest temperature range of any of the planets.

THE SURFACE—AND BELOW

Mercury could almost double as the Moon. The entire planet is pockmarked with impact craters ranging in size from the smallest detectable, ½ mile (1 km) across, to the giant "bull's eye" of the Caloris Basin, some 830 miles (1,340 km) wide. Highlands,

FACT FILE

DISTANCE FROM SUN **0.39 AU**
SIDEREAL REVOLUTION PERIOD (ABOUT SUN) **88.0 days**
MASS (EARTH=1) **0.055**
RADIUS AT EQUATOR (EARTH=1) **0.38**
APPARENT SIZE **5–13 arcseconds**
SIDEREAL ROTATION PERIOD (AT EQUATOR) **58.6 days**
MOONS **none**

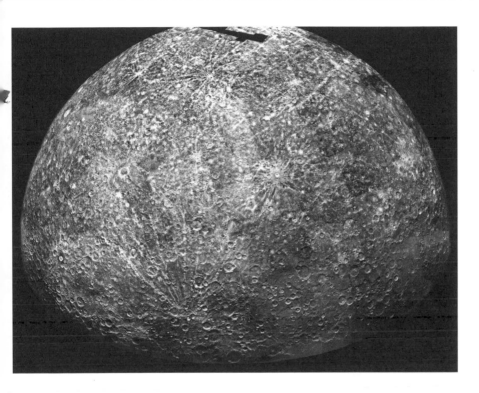

ridges, and lava-flooded basins complete the picture.

Inside Mercury Scientists think that Mercury has a unique internal structure: Like a thick rind on a piece of fruit, a crust and mantle 330 miles (600 km) thick cover a huge metallic iron-nickel core making up 60 percent of the planet's total mass and

CRATERED SURFACE Like the Moon, the surface of Mercury is dominated by impact craters and large basins. Some craters also have prominent ray systems.

filling three-quarters of its radius. The large core may have formed that way, or it may be the result of Mercury losing some of its upper layers in a massive collision.

Venus

■ With its thick shroud of clouds, Venus kept its secrets well hidden until recent times. The Pioneer, Venera, and Magellan spacecraft have found a forbidding yet fascinating world of scorching temperatures, rocky plains, and huge volcanoes.

VENUS'S HELL

Given its greater proximity to the Sun you would expect Venus to be warmer than Earth. In fact, it is an inferno, with a surface temperature of 890°F (470°C)— hot enough to melt lead and zinc.

Greenhouse The explanation for this lies in Venus's atmosphere of carbon dioxide, a layer so dense that the pressure at the surface of the planet is nearly a hundred times that of Earth. This thick blanket traps the Sun's heat at the planet's surface, producing an extreme greenhouse effect. Even at night, the temperature hardly drops at all. Venus can never cool down.

Cloud layers stretch upward from an altitude of 30 miles (48 km) above the surface. These are no ordinary clouds—they consist almost entirely of sulfuric acid droplets.

SURFACE FEATURES

Nearly 85 percent of Venus's surface consists of flat lava plains which resemble the maria, or "seas," of the Moon.

clouds reflect much of the Sun's energy

some solar energy passes through clouds and heats surface

carbon dioxide keeps heat from escaping into space

GREENHOUSE EFFECT Venus suffers from a runaway greenhouse effect. Sunlight filters through the clouds and heats the surface, but the clouds and carbon dioxide in the atmosphere keep the heat from escaping back into space.

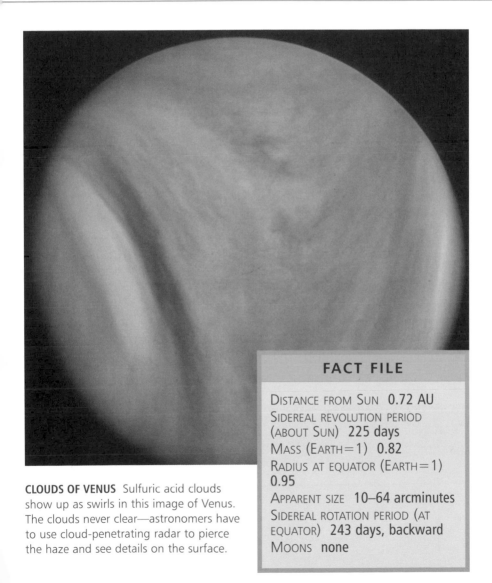

CLOUDS OF VENUS Sulfuric acid clouds show up as swirls in this image of Venus. The clouds never clear—astronomers have to use cloud-penetrating radar to pierce the haze and see details on the surface.

FACT FILE

DISTANCE FROM SUN **0.72 AU**
SIDEREAL REVOLUTION PERIOD (ABOUT SUN) **225 days**
MASS (EARTH=1) **0.82**
RADIUS AT EQUATOR (EARTH=1) **0.95**
APPARENT SIZE **10–64 arcminutes**
SIDEREAL ROTATION PERIOD (AT EQUATOR) **243 days, backward**
MOONS **none**

Volcanoes Above the plains stand mountain ranges—including the Maxwell Mountains, which rise nearly 7.5 miles (12 km)—and thousands of volcanoes. Nearly 500 of these volcanoes are larger than about 12 miles (20 km) in diameter. Venus must once have been extremely volcanically active, but no one knows for sure if any activity occurs today.

"Continents" On a planet without oceans, it may seem odd to talk about "continents." Nevertheless, planetary scientists have identified two such landmasses. They are Aphrodite Terra, which covers a portion of the planet from the equator into the southern hemisphere, and Ishtar Terra, in the high latitudes of the northern hemisphere.

NAMING VENUS

Venus is the name of the Roman goddess of beauty and love. The International Astronomical Union (IAU) has decided that the names given to all features on the planet named after her should (appropriately enough) be female. Thus the Greek goddess Aphrodite's name has been given to a "continent" and a crater carries the name of jazz singer Billie Holiday. There is one exception, though: Scottish physicist James Clerk Maxwell is "the only man on Venus," with Maxwell Montes, the Maxwell Mountains, named after him.

Craters Venus has an estimated 900 impact craters, all bigger than about 2 miles (3 km) in diameter. It seems likely that the dense atmosphere has protected the surface from small asteroids and comets; only large objects survive a fiery descent to find their way to the ground. The craters are fairly young in

MAAT MONS This image from the Magellan spacecraft shows one of Venus's many volcanoes, Maat Mons. It rises 5 miles (8 km) above the plains.

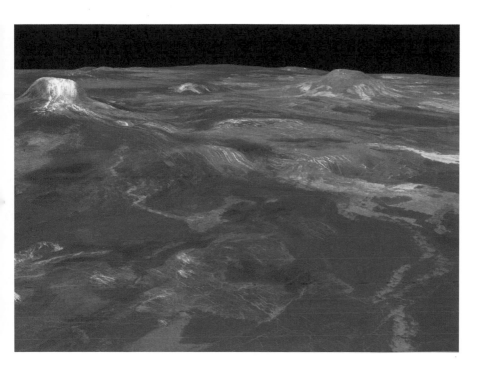

LAVA PLAINS Lava plains cover most of Venus's surface. This Magellan image shows the Eistla region of the planet.

geological terms, at less than 500 million years old. Volcanic activity has probably destroyed signs of earlier impacts.

SLOW AND BACKWARD

Venus rotates very slowly—once every 243 Earth days, 18 days longer than it takes to circle the Sun. And it spins not from west to east, like the other planets, but from east to west.

This slow retrograde motion has a strange effect on the Venusian calendar. If you were on Venus, you would see the Sun rise in the west, cross the sky, and set in the east some 59 Earth days later. Perhaps an early collision between Venus and an asteroid or comet set the planet on its backward course.

Earth

■ Earth is just another planet in the Solar System. True, perhaps, but the more we learn about the other planets, the more we appreciate how special the third rock from the Sun really is.

A LIVING WORLD

Earth is unique—a geologically active world cloaked in water and oxygen, with a diversity of life.
Geological activity Geologically, Earth is very active. Its surface is split into plates, floating on a rocky mantle. Earthquakes, volcanic activity, and mountain-building are concentrated along the boundaries of these plates.
Water Water is found in oceans (which cover 70 percent of Earth's surface), lakes and rivers; below the surface as groundwater; locked up in frozen polar ice caps and glaciers; and as vapor carried in the atmosphere. Earth is the only planet where temperatures allow surface water to exist in solid, liquid, and gaseous states.
Atmosphere Earth's atmosphere is rich in nitrogen and oxygen. It sustains life, protects us from the Sun's higher energy radiation, and drives our weather (by interacting with the Sun's heat).

STORM WARNING Earth's atmosphere creates dramatic weather, such as this severe storm over the Pacific Ocean viewed from space.

FACT FILE	
DISTANCE FROM SUN	**1.00 AU**
SIDEREAL REVOLUTION PERIOD (ABOUT SUN)	**365.26 days**
MASS (EARTH=1)	**1.0**
RADIUS AT EQUATOR (EARTH=1)	**1.0**
SIDEREAL ROTATION PERIOD (AT EQUATOR)	**23.9 hours**
MOONS	**1**

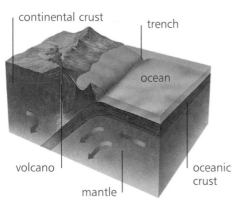

continental crust

trench

ocean

volcano

mantle

oceanic crust

THE VIEW FROM SPACE Swirling white clouds of water vapor make Earth a brilliant beacon in the Solar System.

COLLIDING PLATES Earth's crust and part of the mantle beneath it form a zone that is broken into plates. When a thin oceanic plate collides with a continental plate, the oceanic plate is drawn under and melted.

Earth's Seasons

■ The seasons happen because Earth is tilted—its rotation axis tips 23.5 degrees to its orbit.

THE TILTED EARTH

On one side of our orbit, Earth's Northern Hemisphere tilts toward the Sun. The Sun appears high in the sky, producing long, hot summer days.

Half a year later, Earth has moved to the opposite side of the Sun. Now, that same hemisphere is tilted away from the Sun. Winter days are short and the Sun appears low in the sky. The Sun's energy enters our atmosphere at a shallow angle, spreading the energy over a large surface area and diminishing its warming power.

TURNING POINTS

Four special dates punctuate the calendar. Around June 21, the North Pole is tilted most directly toward the Sun. This is the solstice, and it marks the start of summer in the Northern Hemisphere and winter in the Southern. Around December 21,

REASONS FOR SEASONS Because Earth's axis is tilted, the Sun's rays strike at various angles during the planet's orbit. The varying amounts of solar energy produce the seasonal changes.

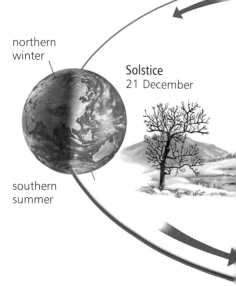

northern winter

Solstice
21 December

southern summer

another solstice occurs when the North Pole is tilted most directly away from the Sun. This marks the start of the northern winter and the southern summer. The equinoxes, in March and September, are times when the Sun is directly over the Equator and day and night are equally long everywhere on Earth.

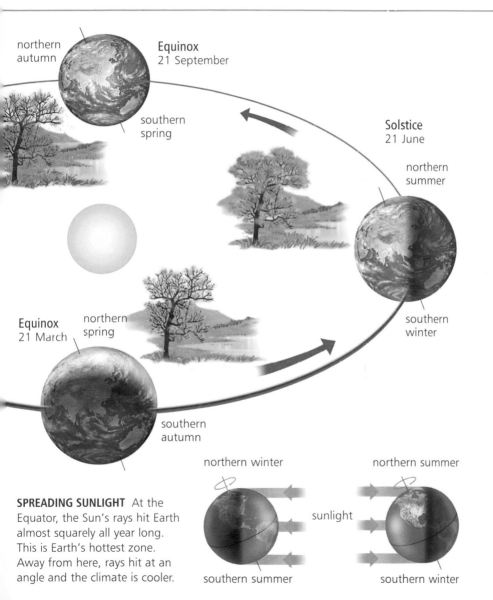

northern
autumn

Equinox
21 September

southern
spring

Solstice
21 June

northern
summer

Equinox
21 March

northern
spring

southern
winter

southern
autumn

northern winter

northern summer

sunlight

SPREADING SUNLIGHT At the
Equator, the Sun's rays hit Earth
almost squarely all year long.
This is Earth's hottest zone.
Away from here, rays hit at an
angle and the climate is cooler.

southern summer

southern winter

The Moon

■ The Moon is the first celestial object most new telescope owners look at—and with good reason. The sight of craters, rays, and mountains is spellbinding.

A VIOLENT PAST

The favored theory as to how the Moon came into being is that about 4.5 billion years ago a huge object struck Earth, melting the object, plus most of Earth, and sending a spray of rock into space. The spray cooled into a ring of rocky debris, which eventually coalesced and solidified into the Moon.

Bombardment For 500 million years after its formation, the Moon was bombarded by asteroids and meteorites. The biggest impacts created basins hundreds of miles across that later flooded with lava. These dark regions are known as maria (singular, mare) or "seas." The remainder of the Moon's surface, unaffected by lava flooding, forms the bright and intensely cratered highlands. Relatively recent impacts are responsible for the bright streaks called rays.

Today, the Moon is quiet, impacts being rare and volcanic activity at least a billion years in the past.

THE FAR SIDE

The Moon completes one orbit around Earth in 27.3 days, which also happens to be how long it takes to complete one rotation on its axis. This means that it keeps one side turned perpetually toward Earth. We cannot see the far side, but images taken by spacecraft show a battered surface similar to the near side.

FACT FILE

DISTANCE FROM EARTH
239,000 miles (384,000 km)
SIDEREAL REVOLUTION PERIOD
(ABOUT EARTH) **27.3 days**
MASS (EARTH=1) **0.012**
RADIUS AT EQUATOR (EARTH=1)
0.272
APPARENT SIZE **31 arcminutes**
SIDEREAL ROTATION PERIOD
(AT EQUATOR) **27.3 days**

FACE OF THE MOON The Moon's main surface features can easily be seen by the unaided eye (above). The dark patches are maria, lava-filled basins mistaken for dried-up seas by early observers. The bright areas are highlands, where most craters are located. Craters range from tiny pits to large bowls with central mountain peaks and walled plains (left).

Phases of the Moon

■ For thousands of years, the changing face of the Moon has fascinated skywatchers. In fact, the earliest known astronomical record may be a 32,000-year-old bone marked with what could be the Moon's phases.

THE LUNAR CYCLE

Earth's rotation on its axis gives us the day; the Moon's motion around Earth gives us the month. The Moon takes 27.3 days to return to the same spot in the stars, a period known as the sidereal month. A more obvious cycle is the time it takes the Moon to go through a complete cycle of phases.

Phases Just like Earth, half the Moon is always illuminated by the Sun and half is always dark. Contrary to widespread belief there is no perpetual "dark side of the Moon" (although the Moon's far side cannot be seen from Earth, see p. 68).

The Moon presents a varying amount of its lit face to us during its monthly orbit, because of the changing relationship between it, the Sun, and Earth. These are known as its phases. At Full Moon, it is opposite the Sun from our point of view, so we see the entire side of it that faces us lit with sunlight. At New phase, the Sun shines on the far side of the Moon; the sunlit face is hidden. At other phases, we see only part of the Moon's sunlit surface. All the time, whether it is lit or not, we are only ever looking at the one face of the Moon.

THE TIDES

Anyone who has visited an ocean beach will be aware of the rise and fall of the tides. The Moon's gravity, and to a lesser extent that of the Sun, causes two high tides on Earth each day—one every 12 hours and 25 minutes. The gravitational pull of the Moon tugs Earth, causing the waters on the side facing it to pile up, accounting for one high tide. The high tide on the other side of Earth arises because the Moon's gravity is such that Earth itself is pulled a little toward the Moon. This results in the waters on the far side being "left behind" and piling up.

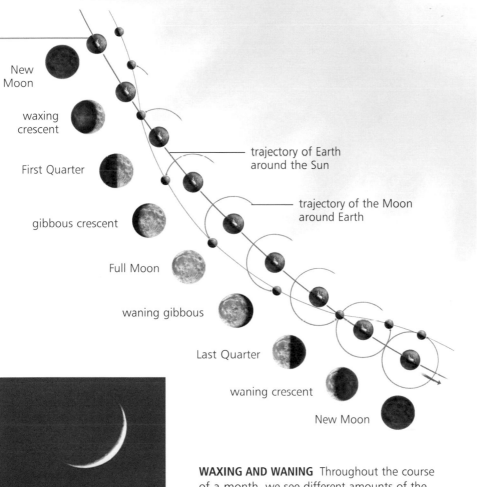

New
Moon

waxing
crescent

First Quarter

gibbous crescent

Full Moon

waning gibbous

Last Quarter

waning crescent

New Moon

trajectory of Earth
around the Sun

trajectory of the Moon
around Earth

CHANGING FACE The Moon's
changing face led many early
peoples to associate it with
myths of creation and rebirth.

WAXING AND WANING Throughout the course
of a month, we see different amounts of the
Moon lit up, depending on where it is in its
orbit around Earth. In the phases between
New and Full, the Moon seems to be growing
larger (waxing) in the sky. Between the Full
Moon and the next New Moon, it seems to
be growing smaller (waning).

Mars

■ Mars is often called the most Earth-like planet. It has basins, plains, and highland regions that are recognized as continents. It has four seasons and its day lasts about the same as ours. Like Earth, Mars has polar ice caps, and it retains an atmosphere.

AN UNEARTHLY WORLD

A close look at the Red Planet shows that these similarities are only skin deep.

Climate The thin Martian atmosphere—95 percent carbon dioxide—offers only a small

MOONS Mars's two moons are tiny, and may be captured asteroids. The larger, Phobos, is 8½ miles (13.5 km) in diameter; Deimos is only 7½ miles (12 km) across.

barrier to escaping heat. Temperatures range from −193°F (−125°C) in the polar winter to 62°F (17°C) in the southern summer. At some places on Mars, it is cold enough for carbon dioxide to freeze out of the atmosphere as dry ice.

Red desert The surface of Mars is dry and desolate, with no ecosystem or oceans. The planet's ruddy color—detectable even by the naked eye—comes from its rusty rocks and dust. A telescope shows an ocher-colored surface with darker markings—vast lava flows and boulder fields. Huge dust storms rack the planet.

VANISHED OCEANS?

Four and a half billion years ago, Mars was a very different planet indeed. It had a thicker atmosphere and, judging from the

---

FACT FILE

DISTANCE FROM SUN **1.52 AU**
SIDEREAL REVOLUTION PERIOD (ABOUT SUN) **687 days**
MASS (EARTH=1) **0.11**
RADIUS AT EQUATOR (EARTH=1) **0.53**
APPARENT SIZE **4–25 arcseconds**
SIDEREAL ROTATION PERIOD (AT EQUATOR) **24.6 hours**
MOONS **2**

many rivulets, channels, and canyons that have been seen by space probes, abundant water. Other spacecraft findings point to thick deposits of sedimentary rocks, possibly laid down in now-vanished lakes or oceans.

Where is the water now? Some water still exists in the planet's

FACE OF MARS From space, Mars is a dry and desolate-looking place. Across its center stretches the Valles Marineris canyon, 2,500 miles (4,000 km) long.

atmosphere and polar caps. There may also be water beneath the ground at depths of 330 to 1,300 feet (100 to 400 m).

VOLCANOES AND CANYONS

Mars is not all rock-strewn plains and channels. It has some spectacular features.

Olympic majesty One of the most prominent is Olympus Mons, perhaps the largest volcano in the Solar System. It rises some 13 miles (21 km) above the surrounding plains on the planet's western hemisphere. Three other large volcanoes lie to the southeast in a region of ancient volcanic activity called the Tharsis bulge, or ridge.

OLYMPUS MONS Olympus Mons is huge: 340 miles (550 km) across and 13 miles (21 km) high. Its eruptions and lava flows must have been massive.

Grandest canyon The Valles Marineris, just south of the equator, is also remarkable. This system of canyons up to 4 miles (7 km) deep forms an immense gash stretching some 2,500 miles (4,000 km) across the planet. Scientists think that activity in the Tharsis bulge broke open the crust in this region and widened the canyon as ice washed out of the canyon walls.

LIFE ON MARS?

Mars is well embedded in the popular imagination as the most likely abode of life outside Earth. We now have evidence of land-forms caused by flowing water. That raises the possibility that life may have existed when Mars's climate was less severe. The 1976 Viking missions, however, found no traces of organic compounds in the soil. Whether life once existed on Mars—or if it still exists—is a question that only extensive exploration will settle.

VIKING The Viking 2 lander reached Mars in 1976, and began looking for traces of life. The results, and those of Viking 1 elsewhere on the planet, were negative.

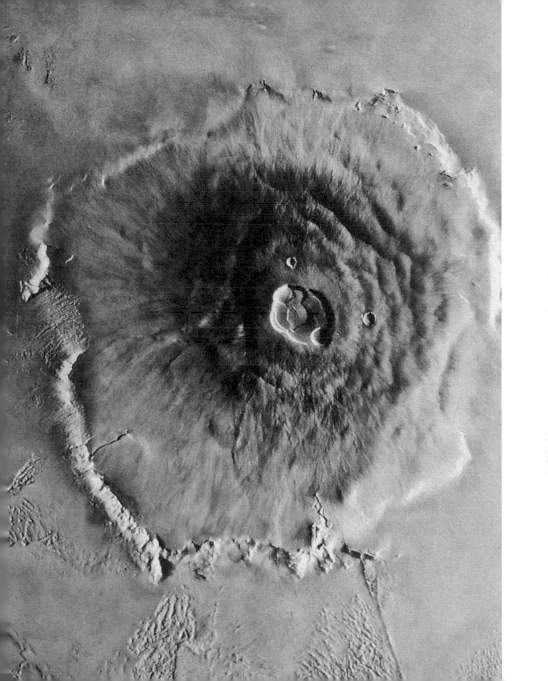

Asteroids

■ Scattered throughout the Solar System are many thousands of bodies called asteroids.

ASTEROID TYPES

Asteroids, also known as the minor planets, are metallic, rocky objects without atmospheres. They consist of material that failed to form a planet-size body when the Solar System was taking shape. More than 35,000 asteroids have well-surveyed orbits, but establishing exactly how many exist is probably impossible.

Main belt asteroids Most asteroids with known orbits occupy a vast doughnut-shaped ring between Mars and Jupiter called the main asteroid belt. Sixteen of these asteroids have diameters of 150 miles (240 km) or greater. Most asteroids in the main belt take between three and six years to complete a full circuit around the Sun.

Trojan asteroids Jupiter has two clutches of asteroids traveling with it in its orbit, one ahead and one behind. They are known as the Trojan asteroids, and are traditionally named after figures from the Trojan Wars.

Near-Earth asteroids Other asteroids have trajectories that take them toward us. An asteroid that comes within 121 million miles (195 million km) of the Sun is known as a near-Earth asteroid (NEA). Some of these have orbits that cross Earth's, with a risk of collision. There are about 500 known NEAs, but astronomers think there may be thousands more that are large enough—¹/₂ mile (1 km) in diameter—to cause devastation if they hit us.

IDA AND DACTYL Ida is a main belt asteroid more than 32 miles (52 km) long. The dot at right in the photo is Ida's tiny moon, Dactyl.

ORBITS AND IMPACTS Most asteroids orbit in the main belt, between Mars and Jupiter (left). Another group, the Trojans, consists of two clusters that lie in the orbit of Jupiter. The elliptical orbits in the diagram belong to some of the near-Earth asteroids—ones that cross Earth's path. Asteroids have struck Earth many times in the past (below), but the most recent large impact was 65 million years ago. This led to such a change in Earth's climate that dinosaurs became extinct.

Meteors and Meteorites

Earth experiences a continuous rain of objects, called meteoroids, which range in size from microscopic particles to small boulders. When they enter the atmosphere—visible as a streak of light, a "shooting star"—they are called meteors. Those that make it to the ground are meteorites.

VISITORS FROM SPACE

Meteoroids are fragments of asteroids or comets. Debris from comets is fragile and burns up high in the atmosphere. But a piece of an asteroid is often larger and tougher; many survive to land as meteorites.

Meteors appear 50 to 75 miles (80 to 120 km) above Earth's surface and move at speeds of between 25,000 and 160,000 miles per hour (11 and 72 km/s).

Composition Stony meteorites consist of silicates—rocky material. Iron meteorites, the second most common type, consist of 90 percent iron and 10 percent nickel with traces of silicates. The rarest meteorites are a stony-iron mixture.

STREAK OF LIGHT A meteor, or shooting star, provides a burst of movement in an otherwise still, starry sky.

METEOR SHOWERS

On most moonless nights, you could expect to see around four or five meteors per hour. Meteor showers offer something much more spectacular.

Comet debris Meteor showers occur at certain times of the year when Earth sweeps through the trail of dust from a comet. Sometimes thousands of "shooting stars" literally light up the sky—in November 1833, people on North America's east coast saw up to 200,000 meteors per hour.

Major showers Meteor showers are named after the constellation or star nearest to the point in the sky from which they appear to come, a region called the radiant. The shower that appears to come from Gemini every 14 December is called the Geminids. Other annual showers include the Perseids of August, the Leonids of November, the Quadrantids of January, and the Lyrids of April.

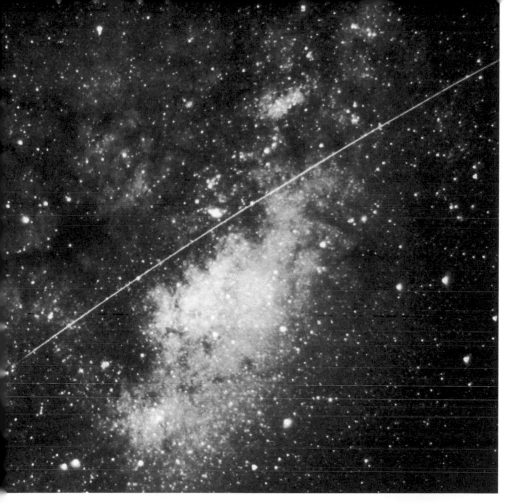

Iron meteorite

Stony-iron meteorite

Stony meteorite

Jupiter

■ Jupiter was named after the chief god in Roman mythology, and rightly so. Its size alone makes it king of the planets: 88,846 miles (142,984 km) across at the equator, about 11 times the figure for Earth. It is also more than 300 times as massive as Earth and twice as massive as all the other planets combined.

INSIDE A GAS GIANT

The colorful clouds of Jupiter's visible surface are just a thin layer masking the bulk of an immense atmosphere thousands of miles deep.

FACT FILE

DISTANCE FROM SUN **5.20 AU**
SIDEREAL REVOLUTION PERIOD (ABOUT SUN) **11.9 years**
MASS (EARTH=1) **318**
RADIUS AT EQUATOR (EARTH=1) **11.2**
APPARENT SIZE **31–48 arcseconds**
SIDEREAL ROTATION PERIOD (AT EQUATOR) **9.9 hours**
MOONS **At least 61**

Clouds Crossing Jupiter's disk are bright and dark clouds, known as zones (the light-colored bands) and belts (the dark ones). Here, wild winds blow at 400 miles per hour (640 km/h).

The Great Red Spot is the best-known cloud formation. It varies in size—and color intensity—and at its largest is 25,000 miles (40,000 km) long and 8,700 miles (14,000 km) wide.

Interior Hydrogen and helium make up most of the atmosphere. Beneath the clouds lies a layer of hydrogen gas. Moving toward the center, this layer turns to a liquid as temperatures and pressures increase. The planet's center is thought to contain a core of rocky material, 10 to 20 times the mass of Earth.

GRAVITY

Jupiter's gravitational attraction is second only to the Sun's. This force directs the fate of many comets, and it can send asteroids racing through the Solar System. It also governs a miniature Solar System of at least 61 moons.

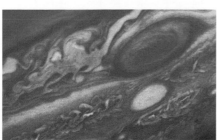

COLORFUL GIANT Jupiter presents a complex and colorful face of dark belts, light zones, and various cloud structures (above). The Jovian day spins the belts and zones into streaks and disturbances, driven by winds that blow in alternating directions parallel with the equator. The Great Red Spot (left) has been observed for more than 300 years.

The Moons of Jupiter

■ At last count, Jupiter had at least 61 moons, most of them fairly small. Several outer satellites are thought to be captured asteroids. The four largest—and the focus of most scientific attention—were discovered in 1610 by Galileo.

GALILEAN SATELLITES

The four largest moons, from Jupiter outward, are Io, Europa, Ganymede, and Callisto.

Io and Europa Io is so affected by Jupiter's tidal forces that it is in turmoil, its surface constantly being repaved by sulfurous

ICY SHELL The surface of Europa is a bright shell of ice crisscrossed by fracture lines (in red) filled with fresh ice.

volcanic eruptions. Europa, in contrast, has an icy surface resembling a planet-wide skating rink. Astronomers suspect that an ocean lies beneath it.

Ganymede and Callisto The Solar System's largest moon, Ganymede has a complex surface and perhaps a subsurface ocean like Europa's. Callisto is densely cratered, with one crater measuring some 900 miles (1,500 km) in diameter.

Io
Io is the most volcanically active body in the Solar System. Eruptions occur constantly.

Europa
Europa's surface is almost pure water-ice. Does it cover an ocean which might harbor life?

Ganymede
Ganymede is bigger than Mercury. Its surface is scarred with craters.

Callisto
This is the Solar System's most heavily cratered moon. It is made of rock and ice.

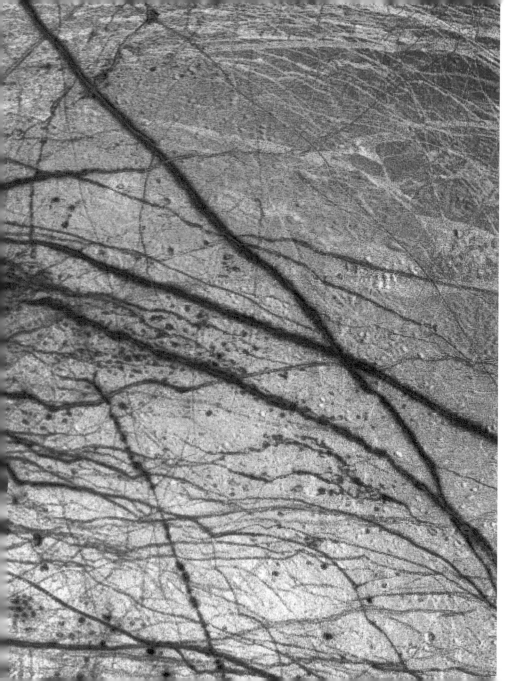

Saturn

■ Saturn is best known for its spectacular rings (see pp. 86–7), but the planet has many other wonders worthy of attention.

ABOUT SATURN

Saturn has a smaller diameter (75,000 miles or 120,660 km) than its fellow gas giant, Jupiter, and it is much lighter, with a mass equal to 95 Earths. Its composition closely parallels that of Jupiter: 74 percent hydrogen, 24 percent helium, and small amounts of methane, ethane, and ammonia. Chemical reactions by the latter three cause Saturn's tan color and faint cloud banding.

Clouds The surface we see is crossed by cloud bands. Since Saturn orbits farther from the Sun than Jupiter, its environment is colder. This means it has less "weather" and so displays fewer features in its cloud tops.

INNER STRUCTURE

Scientists think that Saturn's inner structure resembles that of Jupiter. A layer of clouds covers a thick layer of fluid hydrogen

that grows hotter and denser the farther it is from the surface. This probably becomes metallic about 20,000 miles (30,000 km) down. The core is thought to be a molten rocky ball weighing a dozen or more Earth masses.

FLATTENED PLANET The Voyager 2 spacecraft snapped this close-up of Saturn during its flyby in July 1981. Note the obvious flattening of the planet's disk at the poles—a direct result of Saturn's extremely rapid rotation (just over 10 hours at the equator).

FACT FILE

DISTANCE FROM SUN **9.54 AU**

SIDEREAL REVOLUTION PERIOD (ABOUT SUN) **29.5 years**

MASS (EARTH=1) **95.2**

RADIUS AT EQUATOR (EARTH=1) **9.5**

APPARENT SIZE (PLANET'S DISK) **15–21 arcseconds**

SIDEREAL ROTATION PERIOD (AT EQUATOR) **10.7 hours**

MOONS **At least 31**

The Rings of Saturn

■ Jupiter, Uranus, and Neptune also have rings, but Saturn's are by far the most magnificent. What exactly are the rings and how did they get there?

RING STRUCTURE

The rings span 170,000 miles (270,000 km) and are no more than a few hundred yards thick. **The main rings** From Earth, we can see what look like three rings, A, B, and C. A gap, known as the Cassini division, separates rings A and B. Spacecraft images have revealed four additional rings.

RINGS AND RINGLETS This Voyager 2 image shows numerous bright and dark ringlets within the C ring. Each ringlet contains myriad icy fragments and boulder-size rocks.

Composition The rings are made up of thousands of ringlets, each consisting of ice and rock chunks. Even the empty-looking Cassini division contains many particles.

A REASON FOR THE RINGS

No one is sure why Saturn has rings. The likeliest theory says that the rings are the remains of one or more shattered moons.

ORIGIN OF THE RINGS
Did Saturn gain its rings when a comet collided with one of its moons? The diagrams show a possible scenario.

Cosmic collision
A few hundred million years ago, a large comet or asteroid smashes into an icy moon orbiting Saturn.

Orbiting swarm
The impact shatters the moon into a cloud of icy particles. These then start to orbit Saturn.

Spreading out
Collisions among the particles grind
them into smaller pieces. These
spread out to encircle the planet.

Shepherd moons
The rings assume the shape we see
today. They are gravitationally kept
in place by small "shepherd" moons.

The Moons of Saturn

■ Saturn has at least 31 known satellites, ranging in size from mere rocks a few miles across to Titan, the second-largest moon in the Solar System.

THE MAIN MOONS

From Saturn's extended family, four moons stand out.

Titan At 3,200 miles (5,200 km) across, Titan is bigger than Mercury. It is unique among moons in having a thick atmosphere—mostly nitrogen with trace elements. Exposed to sunlight, the trace elements produce a smog which hides the moon's surface features.

Iapetus The moon Iapetus is known for its peculiar dark and bright hemispheres. The dark material is thought to be carbon-based, but astronomers do not know if it came from within Iapetus or was deposited from space. Iapetus is about 900 miles (1,400 km) in diameter.

Enceladus Enceladus has a diameter of 300 miles (500 km) and consists largely of water-ice. It appears to be the most geologically active of Saturn's moons. Its bright surface is a mixture of old, well-cratered areas and newer terrain that is grooved and fissured.

Mimas Mimas is fairly small, being 240 miles (390 km) across. It is pockmarked by impacts—a particularly large crater is the result of a collision that must have almost torn the moon apart.

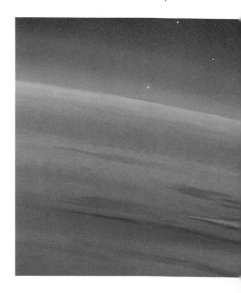

TITAN'S HAZE This artist's impression shows Saturn viewed through the hazy atmosphere of its moon, Titan. No other moon has such a thick atmosphere.

Iapetus

Below: One side of this moon is very light; the other is very dark. No one knows why.

Titan

Right: Saturn's largest moon looks like a billiard ball—its surface is obscured by dense smog.

Mimas

The "bull's eye" on Mimas is the giant Herschel crater.

Enceladus

Much of this moon's surface may have been resurfaced by eruptions.

Uranus

■ Uranus is a blue-green world nearly four times the size of Earth. It was poorly understood until very recently.

BLUE-GREEN GAS GIANT

Most of Uranus is hydrogen and helium, like the Sun. And like the other gas-giant planets, it has no solid surface. In 1986, Voyager 2 saw a featureless, blue-green planet, but scientists using the Hubble Space Telescope are now seeing signs of storms in Uranus's upper atmosphere.

Blue wavelengths The blue-green color of Uranus comes from traces

TWO MOONS Two of Uranus's five major moons are Ariel (below left), 720 miles (1,160 km) in diameter, and Miranda (below right), 300 miles (485 km) across.

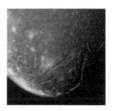 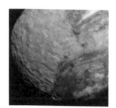

of methane in its atmosphere. The methane reflects the blue wavelengths of sunlight and absorbs the red.

MYSTERIOUS MOON

Many Uranian moons are small and asteroid-like, but five are quite large. One of them, Miranda, has a surface unlike any other moon in the Solar System. Images show a jumble of unusual terrains, including cratered plains and grooved regions. No one knows how it came to look like this.

URANUS'S WORLD This infrared image of Uranus captures a wealth of detail, including the rings, some of the moons, and various cloud features.

FACT FILE

DISTANCE FROM SUN **19.2 AU**
SIDEREAL REVOLUTION PERIOD (ABOUT SUN) **84.0 years**
MASS (EARTH=1) **14.5**
RADIUS AT EQUATOR (EARTH=1) **4.0**
APPARENT SIZE **3–4 arcseconds**
SIDEREAL ROTATION PERIOD (AT EQUATOR) **17.2 hours, backward**
MOONS **At least 24**

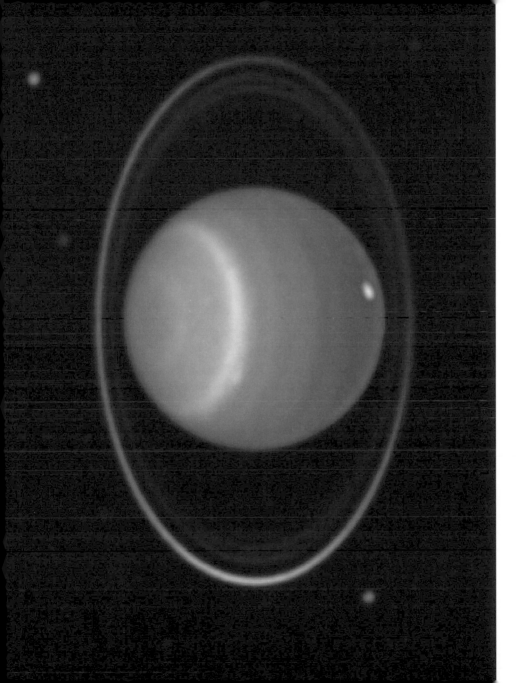

Neptune

■ Neptune is the smallest and most distant of the gas giants. It is also one of the most interesting, with a surprising amount of "weather" and a moon whose vents erupt nitrogen, not lava.

RAGING STORMS

Neptune's atmosphere is mostly hydrogen and helium gas with traces of methane. Temperatures in the upper atmosphere are so low that methane freezes.

Storms and clouds Neptune has raging storms, probably powered by a heat source deep within the planet. In 1989, Voyager 2 photographed a storm called the Great Dark Spot, which was nearly 6,000 miles (10,000 km) in length. It also saw a small white cloud, dubbed Scooter because of its rapid motion. Observations from Earth show that such storms come and go over the years.

RINGS AND MOONS

In 1984 astronomers found that Neptune had rings. Within this faint system are bright clumps, caused perhaps by moons that are yet to be discovered.

TRITON Triton is volcanically active, with geysers shooting nitrogen gas into the sky. With few craters, Triton's surface is covered in frosts of mostly nitrogen and methane.

VOYAGER We knew little about Neptune until the Voyager 2 flyby of 1989. The spacecraft took this shot of the planet's south pole (above), and discovered much about Neptune's moons, including Triton and Nereid (right).

Nereid

Triton

Two Neptunian moons were known before Voyager. Its flyby added six. By far the most fascinating is Triton.

Triton With a diameter of 1,700 miles (2,700 km), Triton is the largest Uranian moon and one of the largest in the Solar System—it is about two-thirds the size of our Moon and a little larger than Pluto. Its surface features range from the run-of-the-mill (impact craters) to the extraordinary (strange dimpled regions). In places, nitrogen gas shoots upward from vents for 5 miles (8 km) into the thin atmosphere of nitrogen vapor, before wafting downwind to form dark plumes on the ground.

Pluto

Pluto

■ Pluto is a maverick. It is tiny and has a markedly eccentric orbit. Definitely not a gas giant, neither is it a terrestrial world. Where does Pluto fit in?

OUT IN THE COLD

Pluto lies in the dark, cold hinterlands of planetary space. It takes 248 years for Pluto to orbit the Sun, 2.8 billion miles (4.5 billion km) away at closest approach. At the moment it is the farthest planet from the Sun, but because Pluto's orbit is so elongated it is sometimes nearer to the Sun than Neptune. Pluto's orbital path is also gently tilted from the plane in which the other planets orbit.

Rock and ice Being so far away, Pluto is the only planet that has not been visited by a spacecraft, so there is much that we do not know about it.

What we do know is that Pluto has a diameter of only 1,430 miles (2,300 km), making it the smallest planet—smaller even than our Moon. Pluto has a mass only one-fifth that of Earth and a rock-ice composition similar to Neptune's moon Triton.

Atmosphere Pluto's atmosphere may contain mostly nitrogen with some carbon monoxide and methane. It is very thin, however, and may exist as a gas only when Pluto is closest to the Sun. The planet's surface temperature varies between about −390° and −346°F (−230° and −210°C).

PLUTO'S ORIGINS

Pluto's unique features have led some astronomers to theorize that it came from the Kuiper Belt, a disk-shaped region lying beyond the zone of the planets. The bodies found there are icy planetesimals—comets without tails. Pluto may be the largest example of this group.

Charon

DOUBLE PLANET Charon, Pluto's moon, is half the size of its planet, making the two almost a double planet. Pluto's surface may look like this (below): rocky with a layer of nitrogen and methane ice.

FACT FILE

DISTANCE FROM SUN **39.5 AU**
SIDEREAL REVOLUTION PERIOD
(ABOUT SUN) **248.0 years**
MASS (EARTH=1) **0.002**
RADIUS AT EQUATOR (EARTH=1)
0.18
APPARENT SIZE **0.04 arcseconds**
SIDEREAL ROTATION PERIOD
(AT EQUATOR) **6.39 days**
MOONS **1**

Comets

■ When a comet is far from the Sun, it is a cold body, perhaps a few miles across, that looks like a large, dirty snowball. Astronomers believe that most reside in an enormous sphere of comets surrounding the Sun, known as the Oort Cloud, well beyond the orbit of the most distant planets.

FROM SNOWBALL TO COMET

Occasionally, one dirty snowball is jolted onto a path inward toward the brilliance of the Sun. As it closes in, the ice begins to boil away, and a head, or coma, of gas and dust develops. The material leaves the comet to form separate gas and dust tails streaming away from the Sun.

Periodic comets Sometimes a comet passes close to a planet, usually Jupiter, and the planet's gravity changes the comet's orbit. Repeated encounters may result in a new orbit that causes the comet to return over and over again to the inner Solar System. With its period of 76 years, Comet Halley is the best-known example of such a periodic comet.

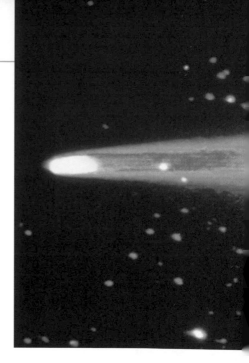

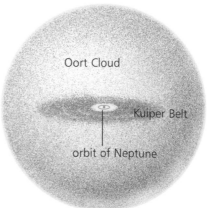

COMET ORIGINS Many comets come from the Oort Cloud, while others arrive from the Kuiper Belt, beyond Neptune.

COMET HALLEY Recorded sightings of Comet Halley go back more than 2,000 years. It last visited Earth's skies in 1986, when this photo was taken.

gas tail

dust tail

coma

nucleus

COMET STRUCTURE A typical comet has a tiny nucleus of ice and dust surrounded by a gaseous coma. Dust and gas stream from the coma in separate tails. The tails of a large comet might be tens of millions of miles long.

OTHER SOLAR SYSTEMS

Throughout history, the only planets that anyone knew about were Earth and its sisters orbiting the Sun. Then came the 1995 discovery of the first planet outside our Solar System. Scientists found a planet about half the mass of Jupiter orbiting a star called 51 Pegasi. Since then, more than 60 planets have been recognized, and there are many more tentative findings.

PLANET-HUNTING

The search is difficult because it is impossible to see these planets directly. Viewed from Earth, the planets appear close to their star, so they are lost in its glare. To find the planets, astronomers use indirect means. They try to detect little "wobbles" in the movement of a star caused by the gravity of an orbiting planet.

Orbiting close A look at the other planetary systems shows that they are built differently from the Sun's. Our Solar System has small-mass planets, such as Earth, orbiting near the Sun, while the largest planets, such as Jupiter, orbit much farther out. But the other solar systems have large planets close to their star. Perhaps, as these solar systems were forming, something happened that moved the large planets inward.

NOTHING LIKE EARTH

So far, astronomers have found only massive planets with strong gravity orbiting fairly close to their star. These are planets about the size of Jupiter.

No one has seen what these planets look like, and nobody has found a planet anything like as small as Earth. But astronomers are hopeful that with improved equipment, Earth-size planets will be discovered too. Planets the size of Earth would be the most likely places to look for evidence of alien life.

ANOTHER SOLAR SYSTEM What would an alien planet system look like? All planets found around other stars are large bodies with masses roughly similar to Jupiter's. Astronomers believe that such planets would probably resemble Jupiter and have cloud belts and swirling storms.

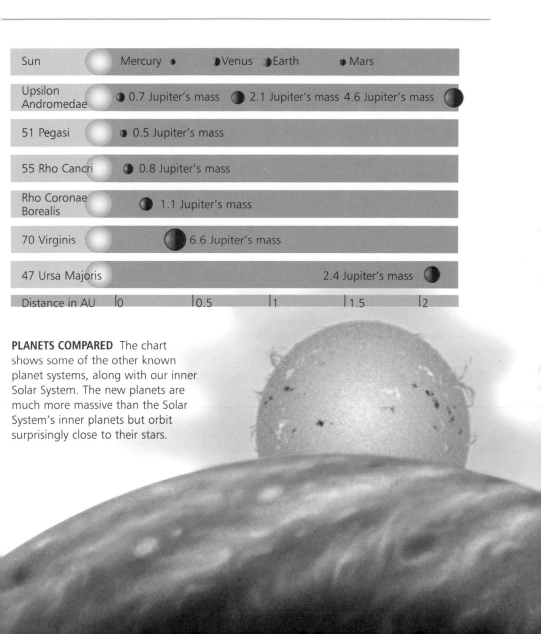

Sun		Mercury •	◗Venus	◍Earth	• Mars	
Upsilon Andromedae		◑ 0.7 Jupiter's mass	● 2.1 Jupiter's mass	4.6 Jupiter's mass		◐
51 Pegasi		◑ 0.5 Jupiter's mass				
55 Rho Cancri		◑ 0.8 Jupiter's mass				
Rho Coronae Borealis		◐ 1.1 Jupiter's mass				
70 Virginis		◐ 6.6 Jupiter's mass				
47 Ursa Majoris				2.4 Jupiter's mass	●	
Distance in AU	⌐0	⌐0.5	⌐1	⌐1.5	⌐2	

PLANETS COMPARED The chart shows some of the other known planet systems, along with our inner Solar System. The new planets are much more massive than the Solar System's inner planets but orbit surprisingly close to their stars.

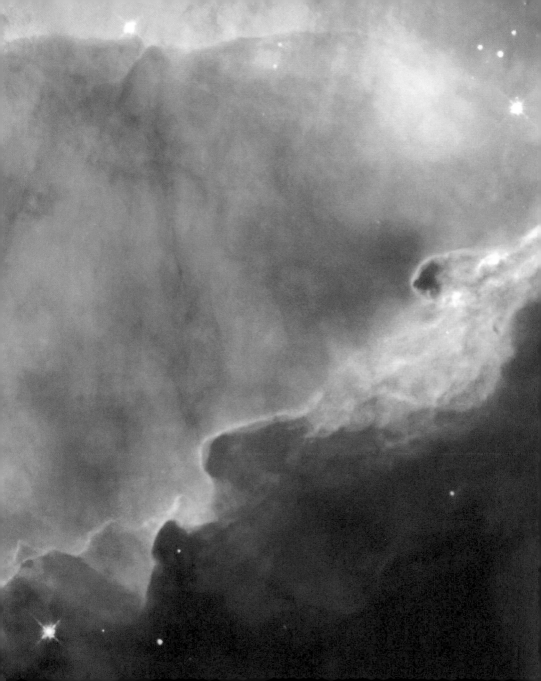

Reaching into the Universe

LARGE TELESCOPES

The telescope has come a long way from its origins in the early 17th century. Galileo's first telescope was cruder than even a cheap pair of binoculars today, but it opened a new world.

EVER BIGGER Larger and larger telescopes followed William Herschel's 18th-century reflector (right). Its 48 inch (1.2 m) size compares with the 200 inch (5 m) built in the 1940s by George Hale (above).

TELESCOPE BUILDERS

The age of the giant telescope dawned in England in the 18th century. More powerful telescopes led to further discoveries.

First steps William Herschel discovered Uranus in 1781, and went on to build large telescopes that showed faint star clusters and nebulas. The Earl of Rosse built a 72 inch (1.8 m) reflector in 1845, and used it to discover the spiral structure of the galaxy M51.

Hale's giants The early 1900s saw an explosive growth in the size of telescopes and in their light grasp,

much of it due to George Hale, a U.S. astronomer. Hale built four "glass giants," culminating in the 200 inch (5 m) telescope on Mount Palomar, California, completed in 1948. It now bears Hale's name to honor a lifetime's contribution to astronomy.

EVEN BIGGER TELESCOPES

Cosmologists today use even larger telescopes to map the universe in ever greater detail. The world's largest are the two 400 inch (10 m) Keck telescopes

LIGHT GATHERERS Astronomy's need for more light—and bigger telescopes— is inescapable because that is all the universe sends us.

on Mauna Kea, Hawaii. Bigger telescopes are being planned.

Computers now run observatories: They aim the telescopes, operate the instruments, calibrate the data, and keep the optics in line. And computer-controlled adaptive optics cancel out much atmospheric distortion and produce sharper images.

THE FULL SPECTRUM

The universe produces radiation over a wide spectrum. This radiation travels in waves of various lengths—from long radio waves, through infrared and optical waves, and on into shorter ultraviolet rays, X-rays, and gamma rays. Only a tiny part of the spectrum is visible.

VISIBLE LIGHT

The light we see is made up of a rainbow spectrum, each color representing a wavelength.

DOPPLER The principle of the Doppler shift allows astronomers to measure the direction of movement of stars and galaxies in relation to Earth.

A spectroscope breaks light from a star into a spectrum crossed by dark and bright spectral lines. By studying such lines, astronomers can determine many of the star's properties, including its composition and temperature.

The spectroscope also lets astronomers measure the speed of a star toward or away from us by noting a change in the wavelength of the lines. This is the Doppler shift (see diagram below).

LONGER WAVES

The low-frequency, low-energy part of the spectrum is the domain of infrared, millimeter, and radio radiation.

1 No shift in the spectral lines: The galaxy is at rest.

2 A shift toward the red: The galaxy is moving away.

3 A shift toward the blue: The galaxy is approaching Earth.

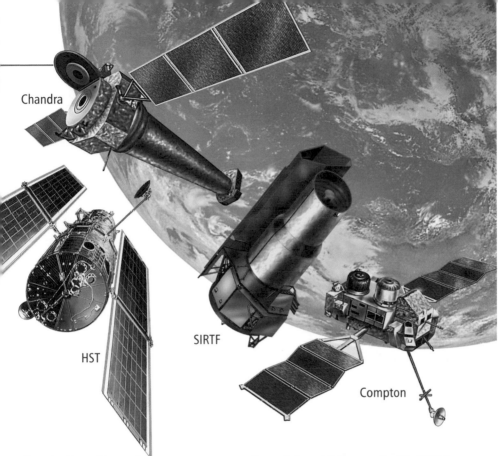

Chandra

HST

SIRTF

Compton

Chandra X-ray Observatory
The Chandra Observatory was launched in 1999, and is surveying the entire sky. It is looking for X-rays from objects such as distant exploding stars and merging clusters of galaxies.

Hubble Space Telescope (HST)
Instruments aboard the Hubble Space Telescope study the universe mainly in visual light. HST does, however, have the ability to capture images in near-infrared and ultraviolet wavelengths.

Space Infrared Telescope Facility (SIRTF)
This satellite observatory, due for launch in 2002, will study places where stars and planets are born. Such places give off radiation that falls mostly in the infrared region of the spectrum.

Compton Gamma-ray Observatory
This satellite mapped gamma-ray bursts until it was brought down from orbit in 2000 when systems began to fail. It will be replaced by the Gamma-ray Large Space Telescope, due for launch in 2005.

Infrared Infrared rays are the radiation we feel as heat. Most infrared sources radiate at temperatures between −430° and 1800°F (−260° and 1000°C). Infrared observations can pierce dense dust clouds to reveal young stars that are invisible at optical wavelengths, accentuate dusty disks around stars, and even pinpoint remote dusty galaxies.

Millimeter The millimeter window is ideal for observing giant molecular clouds in which stars are likely to form.

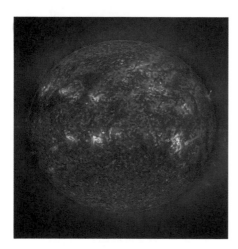

ULTRAVIOLET Observing the Sun at ultraviolet wavelengths highlights many details of the high-temperature solar corona, including sunspots and solar flares.

X-RAYS Purple and red colors indicate regions of high X-ray intensity in this Chandra X-ray Observatory image of NGC 3603, where stars are forming.

Radio Radio astronomy emerged as the first non-optical branch of astronomy. For more information, see pages 108–109.

SHORTER WAVES

At the high-frequency, high-energy end of the spectrum, ultraviolet, X-ray, and gamma-ray radiation unveil the physical and chemical properties of objects that are incredibly hot and energetic.

Ultraviolet light Observing at ultraviolet wavelengths allows astronomers to investigate objects such as gas around ordinary stars and hot stars whose evolution is running faster than the Sun's.

X-rays X-rays allow astronomers to study violent and extremely energetic objects and processes, such as supernova explosions.

Gamma rays Gamma rays provide a look at the oddest, most exotic objects in the universe, such as black holes, the swirling centers of active galaxies, and the Sun's hottest regions.

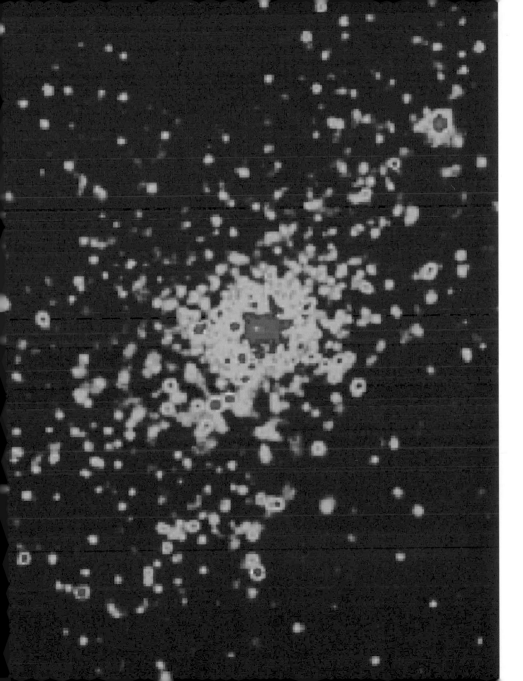

Radio Astronomy

■ Radio is a form of light with wavelengths longer than infrared. Radio astronomers tune in to these wavelengths to study some of the most important objects in the universe.

RADIO TELESCOPES

Most radio telescopes are large metal parabolic dishes, which focus the faint signals they receive from space. Big radio telescopes include the 250 foot (76 m) one at Jodrell Bank, England, and the 1,000 foot (300 m) antenna at Arecibo, Puerto Rico.

Interferometers To gain sharper views, astronomers link a number of large radio telescopes together, creating, in effect, one giant-size telescope. Examples of these interferometers include the Very Large Array in New Mexico (27 antennas spread across many miles) and the Very Long Baseline Array, with 10 antennas from Hawaii to Puerto Rico.

DISCOVERIES

Radio astronomers discovered both pulsars, the spinning remnants of dying stars, and quasars, compact objects thought to be the active cores of very distant galaxies.

One of the most important discoveries came in 1965, when Arno Penzias and Robert Wilson of Bell Laboratories found an intriguing source of static. This was none other than the cosmic background radiation, the fading glow of the Big Bang.

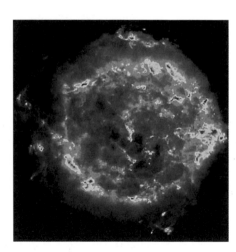

CASSIOPEIA A A radio image shows Cassiopeia A, an expanding shell of gas from a star that exploded as a supernova nearly 10,000 years ago.

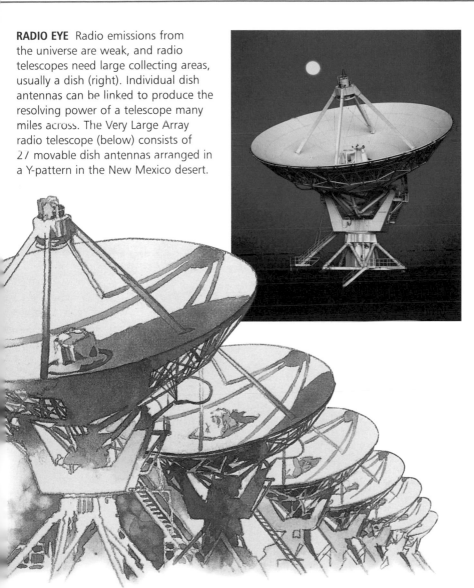

RADIO EYE Radio emissions from the universe are weak, and radio telescopes need large collecting areas, usually a dish (right). Individual dish antennas can be linked to produce the resolving power of a telescope many miles across. The Very Large Array radio telescope (below) consists of 27 movable dish antennas arranged in a Y-pattern in the New Mexico desert.

HUBBLE SPACE TELESCOPE

I n much the same way that
water distorts sunlight, Earth's
atmosphere distorts and filters the
cosmic radiation passing through
it. To overcome this problem,
astronomers some years ago
began lifting telescopes above
the atmosphere by placing them
in rockets and satellites. The
most famous of these orbiting
observatories is the Hubble
Space Telescope (HST).

ASTRONOMY FROM ORBIT

Launched in 1990, the Hubble
Space Telescope has provided
spectacular observations in
visual, near-infrared, and ultraviolet wavelengths, as well

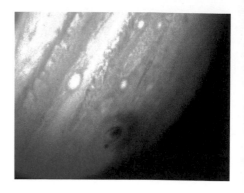

COMET IMPACT In July 1994, more than
20 fragments of Comet Shoemaker-Levy
struck Jupiter. HST's image of the planet
shows one of the smudgy impact areas.

as spectroscopic studies of stars,
the thin interstellar gas, and
galaxies. It consists of a 95 inch
(2.4 m) mirror and a suite of
sensitive scientific instruments.
All-seeing eyes The Wide Field/
Planetary Camera II, the most
often used of HST's instruments,
can detect objects as faint as 28th
magnitude (about a billion times
fainter than can be seen with the

ORION'S PLUME HST zoomed in on part
of the Orion Nebula and snapped this
shot of a gas plume. Gas is condensing
into new stars within the nebula.

naked eye). The Faint Object Camera can also record 28th-magnitude objects, but it offers higher resolution and a wider choice of viewing angles.

Other instruments Two other instruments are the Near Infrared Camera and Multi-Object Spectrometer (NICMOS), and the Space Telescope Imaging

PRECIOUS CARGO The Hubble Space Telescope is prepared for deployment from the space shuttle in April 1990. HST orbits 380 miles (600 km) above Earth.

Spectrograph (STIS). NICMOS handles both imaging and spectroscopic observations of objects at near-infrared wavelengths. It aims to tells us much about the birth of stars in dense, dusty globules, the infrared emission produced by the active centers of distant galaxies, and the nature of a class of galaxies as bright as quasars at infrared wavelengths.

The STIS covers a broad range of wavelengths and can also block out the light of distant stars to search for black holes.

THE UNIVERSE IN CLOSE-UP

HST has looked at well over 14,000 objects and made more than 330,000 exposures. Out of these observations have come significant scientific insights. For example, astronomers now know more about how stars and stellar disks form, and that black holes exist at the centers of galaxies and quasars. HST has also increased our knowledge of the size and age of the universe, and detected galaxies that formed only a billion years after the Big Bang. Its high-resolution images of Mars, Jupiter, Saturn, and Neptune are surpassed only by space-probe photographs. **Detailed view** The detail of HST's observations is so great that astronomers can now see,

STELLAR VIEWS Stars are forming in this gas cloud in the galaxy NGC 6822 (above). A planetary nebula (NGC 6751) (right) in Aquila marks a stellar death.

for instance, great chunks of matter swirling around super-massive black holes at the centers of galaxies and quasars, as well as structural details in the spiral arms of nearby galaxies.

THE NEXT GENERATION

HST is now more than halfway through its planned lifetime. Scientists are planning its replacement, the Next Generation Space Telescope. This orbiting giant will have a mirror 26 feet (7.9 m) across and a light grasp more than 10 times that of HST.

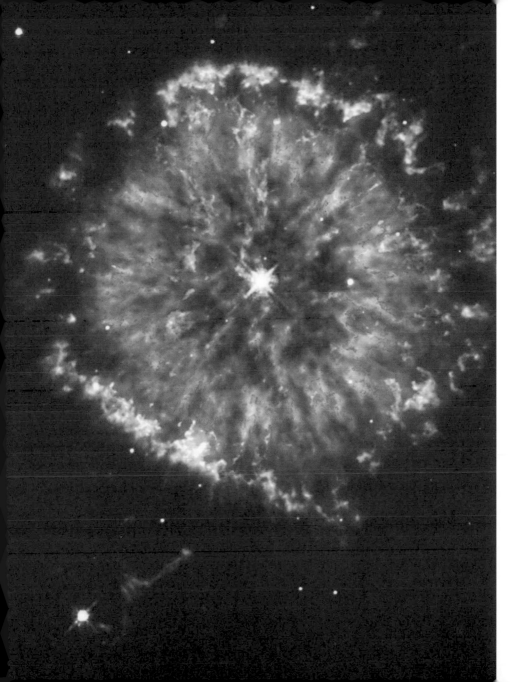

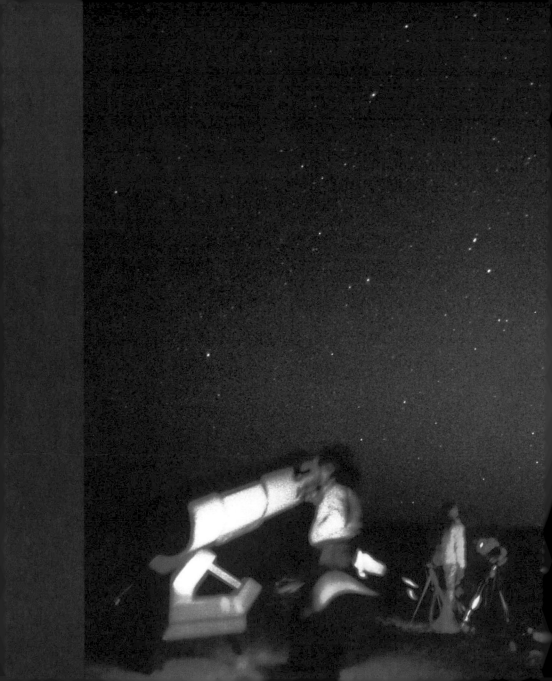

OBSERVING THE SKY

*Down-to-earth advice on
tools and techniques for every
backyard astronomer.*

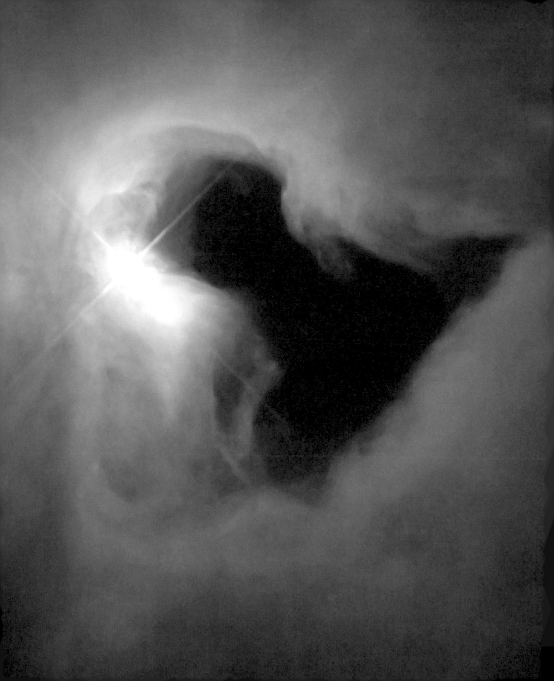

Becoming a Stargazer

How to Start Observing

To become a professional astronomer takes long training in physics and mathematics; to be a backyard skywatcher you simply go outdoors and look up.

Pursuing the Hobby

Astronomy can be pursued on a number of levels. Your curiosity determines how deep you will go. **Naked eye** With no more than an astronomy guidebook, you can enjoy skywatching from any location. A beautiful grouping of the Moon and planets, or the progress of constellations through the year—these are the simple pleasures of naked-eye astronomy.

Binoculars A pair of binoculars opens up exciting new vistas— from the Milky Way resolved into many thousands of stars, to the shuttling moons of Jupiter.

Telescopes If you do not yet own a telescope, wait until you know your way around the sky. When you are ready to buy one, consult the guidelines on pages 126–31. If you already have some equipment, the advice in this and other chapters will help you to make the most of it.

Join the Club

Whether you become a serious observer or not, you will be able to share your interest in the sky with other amateur astronomers. Astronomy clubs are found in most cities and towns. Their meetings provide opportunities to meet fellow skywatchers, see a variety of telescopes in action, and get advice about what pieces of equipment to buy.

WHAT YOU CAN'T SEE

While bigger telescopes can show you more, be warned: no telescope will show nebulas and galaxies with the vivid colors depicted in long-exposure and computer-enhanced photographs. The human eye is simply not sensitive enough to see much color in faint deep-space objects, even through the lens of a large telescope.

Also, do not expect to see the flags or footprints on the Moon left behind by the Apollo astronauts. No telescope on Earth is powerful enough to show these.

EYEPIECE VIEWS The three illustrations below give an idea of what you will see in the eyepiece of a telescope.

The Moon
The Moon fills the eyepiece with its craters, hills, rays, and dark "seas."

Saturn
Saturn's rings are obvious in even a small telescope.

Trifid Nebula
Dark dust lanes run through this nebula's light-colored lobes of gas.

ON TARGET Telescopes range from simple ones such as this, suitable for beginners, to more complicated, computerized types.

Dark Skies and Good Seeing

■ Your observing site will have a greater effect on your skywatching than any piece of equipment.

CHOOSING A SITE

Unshielded street lighting paints a glaring skyglow above every city and town. A dark site, away from urban lights, is ideal.

Urban skies Fortunately for city-bound stargazers, the Moon and planets remain unaffected by light pollution and provide wonderful targets. Even so, try to find a site that is shadowed from street and yard lights.

Head for the hills For the best views of the Milky Way, its star clusters and nebulas, and of faint galaxies beyond, plan to travel away from city lights, perhaps to a park or conservation area. Haze-free and moonless nights (around New Moon) are best—moonlight can wash out faint objects as effectively as can streetlight.

CLEAR SKIES, GOOD SEEING

If the sky is clear, the Milky Way may be seen even from suburban locations, and you are more likely to find some faint objects such as nebulas. Moisture degrades the transparency of the sky.

However, memorable nights of viewing come with many kinds of weather. For the Moon and planets, humid nights with some haze or thin fog can actually bring the sharpest views. Even though little else is visible in the sky, planet disks appear absolutely steady, revealing astonishing detail. This is known as good seeing—it happens when the layers of Earth's atmosphere are calm and stable, and not mixed up by winds at different altitudes. Under turbulent conditions, the poor seeing turns the disks of planets into boiling blobs with, at best, some fleeting moments of sharp views.

Mix and match At most sites, nights of good seeing are often the least transparent, and vice versa. Backyard astronomers soon learn to adapt their observing priorities to the conditions of the night, perhaps pursuing a galaxy hunt on a clear night, and planet studies on nights of good seeing.

LIGHT POLLUTION Modern civilization, with its glow of artificial lighting, puts barriers in the way of appreciating the sky. The scale of the problem can be clearly seen in this satellite image of the night lights of the eastern United States (above). In the most densely populated regions, few locations can be said to be truly dark. The true beauty of the night sky only becomes apparent at a dark site (right).

BINOCULARS

craters. A bright comet is often best seen with binoculars, as are solar and lunar eclipses, and close gatherings of the Moon and planets at twilight.

FINDING THE RIGHT TYPE

Binoculars are identified by a figure such as 7 x 50. The first number refers to the magnification, the second to aperture.

Magnification In the example above, the magnification is 7 power (7x). Note that binoculars with high magnification (16 or 20 power) have a narrow field of view, making it difficult to find objects. They are also hard to hold steady.

The low power, wide field of view, and upright images of binoculars make it a snap to find celestial targets. Spend a year exploring the sky with binoculars and you will be better prepared to find objects with a telescope later.

WHAT YOU WILL SEE

From a dark-sky site, binoculars let you see bright star clusters, many nebulas, several galaxies (including the beautiful Andromeda Galaxy), and many star-packed regions along the Milky Way. Binoculars can also reveal the moons of Jupiter and the largest Moon

THE RIGHT TYPE The most popular binoculars for astronomy have front lenses 50 mm across (top). Make sure they are comfortable to hold (below).

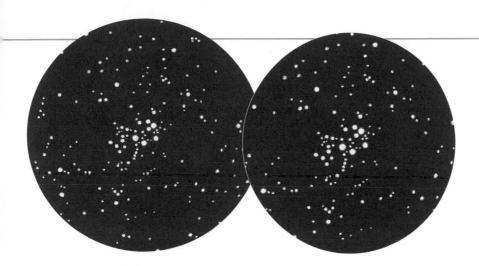

Aperture The second number gives the aperture, in millimeters, of each of the twin front lenses. Compared with 35 mm or 42 mm models, binoculars with 50 mm lenses gather more light and provide brighter images, important for tracking down faint objects in the night sky. Models with larger lenses are heavy and hard to hold. **Recommended models** The best choice is either a 7 x 50 or a 10 x 50 pair. Each offers a good balance of power, image brightness, and light weight. Avoid fixed-focus or zoom binoculars, which provide inadequate image quality for viewing sharp, pinpoint stars.

DIFFERING VIEWS These two views of the Pleiades show the relationship between field of view and magnification. Most 7x binoculars show about 7 degrees of sky (above left). Higher-power 10x models magnify the image more, but usually show only 5 degrees of sky (above right).

FIELD OF VIEW

Most 7-power binoculars provide a field of view of 7 degrees, enough to take in the Pointer Stars of the Big Dipper's bowl, or all of Crux, the Southern Cross. Higher power 10x models usually have a smaller field of view, perhaps 5 degrees, still sufficient to provide impressive sky views.

Some binoculars offer wide-angle eyepieces that provide a

BINOCULAR TARGET The Large Magellanic Cloud is an excellent binocular target. Of course, this photo shows much more detail than binoculars can.

larger field of view than normal, perhaps 7 to 8 degrees on a 10x model. However, image quality often suffers in such models.

HOLD STEADY!

Holding binoculars as steady as possible improves the view, allowing you to see the stars as steady points of light, rather than as a bunch of flitting fireflies. One way to ensure steadiness is to lie

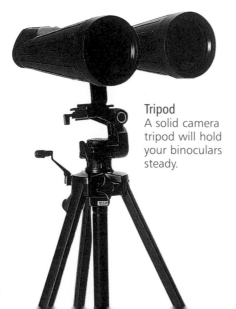

Tripod
A solid camera tripod will hold your binoculars steady.

on a reclining deck chair and prop your arms and binoculars on the chair's arms. You could also simply lean against a wall or fence. As an alternative, many binoculars can be attached to a

camera tripod, but make sure the tripod is a sturdy one. **Cantilever arms** Tripods help with steadiness, but are not much good for scanning directly overhead. For comfortable views of objects high in the sky, consider purchasing a stand with cantilever arms. The arms swing the binoculars away from the tripod allowing you to stand beneath the binoculars.

TELESCOPES

A telescope can show you craters on the Moon as small as 1/2 mile (about 1 km) across, Jupiter's clouds, Saturn's rings, as well as star clusters, nebulas, and galaxies that are too small and faint to show up in binoculars.

TELESCOPE SAVVY

A telescope's most important specification is its aperture—the diameter of its main lens or mirror. The larger the aperture, the brighter and sharper the images. A 6 inch (150 mm) telescope will provide images twice as sharp and four times brighter than will a 3 inch (75 mm) telescope.

Magnification The least important specification is magnification. By changing eyepieces, any telescope can be made to magnify any amount.

TYPES OF TELESCOPE

There are three basic kinds of telescope: refractor, reflector, and catadioptric.

Refractors Refractors with an aperture of more than 4 inches (100 mm) are large, heavy, and expensive, so this type of telescope is most popular in the entry-level 2.4 inch (60 mm) to 3.5 inch (90 mm) aperture sizes. These models produce sharp images of the Moon and planets, but their small apertures limit their use for hunting faint, deep-sky targets.

Reflector Reflectors lack the expensive lenses of refractors, allowing a 4.5 inch (110 mm) or 6 inch (150 mm) reflector to sell for the same price as a smaller refractor. Because of their greater aperture, reflectors are a good choice for viewing nebulas and galaxies from a dark-sky site.

Catadioptric Catadioptric telescopes offer fine optics and generous light-gathering power in compact tubes much shorter than most refractors and reflectors.

MOUNTS

Make sure that the telescope is well mounted. A wobbly stand will produce images that never stop bouncing, making for frustrating viewing.

Refractor
This uses a lens at one end to gather light, which is focused to an eyepiece at the other end.

Reflector
A mirror collects light, which is reflected back up the tube to the eyepiece.

Catadioptric
Light travels back and forth between a mirror and a lens before entering the eyepiece.

Types Mounts come in several varieties. Altazimuth types are easy to set up but cannot follow the stars with one simple motion. Dobsonian mounts, a variation on the altazimuth design, need only gentle nudges to keep objects centered. The more sophisticated equatorial mounts permit motorized tracking of the stars. Fork mounts are standard on many catadioptric telescopes.

WHAT TO BUY

A 6 inch (150 mm) or 8 inch (200 mm) reflector teamed with a Dobsonian mount is one of the best buys for the serious stargazer. You get generous aperture on a rock-steady mount that is simple to set up.

At a similar cost, 4.5 inch (110 mm) reflectors on equatorial mounts have long been popular as starter telescopes. The mounts are

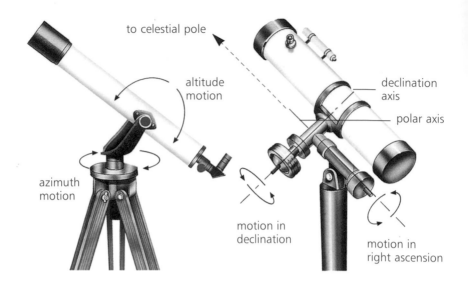

to celestial pole

altitude
motion

azimuth
motion

declination
axis

polar axis

motion in
declination

motion in
right ascension

KNOW YOUR MOUNT The altazimuth mount (left) is widely used on small refractors and is also found on many reflectors. The equatorial mount (right) is used on many small reflectors.

more complex to set up (they must be aligned to the celestial pole to track properly), but do make it easier to follow objects. Look for models with "heavy-duty" or premium-grade mounts.

Some people prefer to select a refractor because it needs less maintenance than a reflector. A 2.7 inch (70 mm) to 3.5 inch (90 mm) refractor, provided it

has a solid altazimuth or equatorial mount, offers sharp optics in a rugged package that rarely needs upkeep. Avoid 2.4 inch (60 mm) refractors, as few models in this size offer good-quality mounts and fittings.

If portability is very important to you, then a catadioptric makes a good, though more costly, choice. Popular models include 3.5 inch (90 mm) and 5 inch (127 mm) Maksutov-Cassegrain and Schmidt-Cassegrain telescopes. The 8 inch (200 mm) Schmidt-Cassegrain models have long been a top-selling

Good choice
A good choice is this reflector on an equatorial mount.

Computer-controlled
At the touch of a button, a computer-controlled telescope locates even the most obscure of galaxies.

Solid mount
The solid, high-quality mount offers rock-steady viewing.

choice of amateur astronomers looking for sizable aperture in a compact telescope.

EYEPIECES

You change magnifications by changing eyepieces. A basic set of three eyepieces might include a 25 mm (for low-power views of deep-sky objects), an 18 to 12 mm (for medium-power views of the Moon and star clusters), and a 10 to 7 mm (for high-power views of planets and double stars). Invest in quality eyepieces, such as Kellners and Modified Achromats. A step up takes you to Plössl eyepieces.

An alternative to high-power eyepieces is to add a Barlow lens. One of these will double or triple the power of any eyepiece inserted into it, while retaining the comfortable eye relief inherent in all low-power eyepieces.

TELESCOPE TARGET Through a medium to large telescope, the Ring Nebula resembles a ghostly smoke ring. A larger instrument can pick out the central star.

Accessories

Accessories include eyepieces (back), colored filters, a Barlow lens (lower left), and a camera adaptor (right), which couples a camera to a telescope.

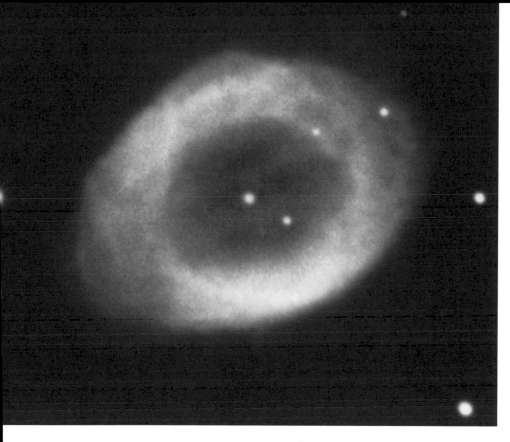

EYEPIECES

A telescope's main lens or mirror gathers the incoming light and focuses it into an image, but it is the eyepiece that magnifies the image. To change magnifications, you need to change eyepieces.

SOLAR SAFETY

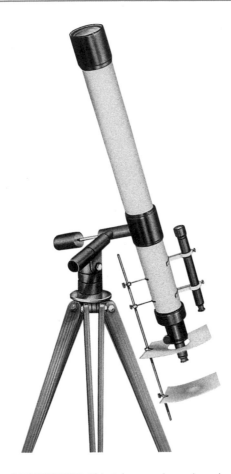

SAFE VIEWING This telescope is equipped with a Sun projection screen. The Sun's image is focused onto the lower screen, while the upper screen shields the image from other sunlight. An advantage of using this method is that it enables a group of people to view the Sun safely.

The Sun is a source of endless fascination, but looking directly at its disk can cause blindness. A few precautions will ensure safe viewing.

TWO METHODS

In the past, many entry-level telescopes came with "sun filters" that screwed into an eyepiece. These are very dangerous and should never be used. Instead, try one of these two methods.

Solar filter The easiest way to view the Sun safely is to use a solar filter that fits over the telescope's aperture. Cover the finderscope to prevent scorching someone by accident.

Sun screen Alternatively, use a Sun projection screen. First cap the finderscope, then position the telescope by moving it until its shadow is at a minimum. The Sun should be shining through the telescope and out through the eyepiece to the ground. Then project the Sun's image onto a piece of paper, shielding this screen from direct sunlight. Focus until the image is sharp.

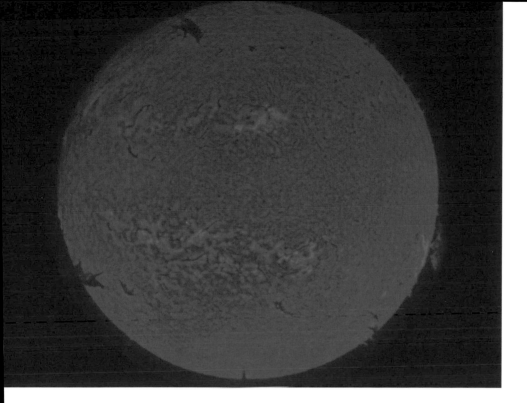

SUN'S SURFACE At high magnification, the Sun's surface, the photosphere, has a granular appearance, like oatmeal.

Solar filter
The large solar filter dwarfs the colored filters, which are used for viewing planets.

ASTROPHOTOGRAPHY

Hardly anyone who has a camera and an interest in photography can resist taking photos of the sky. And capturing the stars does not necessarily mean investing in expensive cameras and films or using difficult techniques.

CAMERAS AND FILMS

For casual sky-shooting, almost any design of camera will do, but it must have a B (for Bulb) setting for the shutter. This is used with a locking cable release to hold the shutter open—most night-sky photos require long exposures.

AIMING AT THE SKY
Cameras with simple mechanical shutters work more reliably than electronic models whose batteries can die during long exposures.

Night shots need the extra light-gathering ability of fast film to bring down exposure times. Use at least an ISO 400 film.

TECHNIQUES

There are two main techniques. One uses a camera on a tripod; a more sophisticated method uses an equatorial mount to track the stars during an exposure.

Camera-on-tripod Load a camera with fast ISO 400 to 800 film, place it on a tripod, and focus the lens to infinity. Set the lens aperture to f/2.8, then frame a constellation. Use a cable release to hold the shutter open for 20 to 40 seconds and you will record as many stars as your eyes can see.

Tracking shots Recording more stars or faint nebulosity requires a dark site and bolting the camera to a motor-driven equatorial mount that can accurately track the stars during a 5- to 15-minute exposure. Your telescope may already have an attachment bolt, or you can buy a bracket. The results of this "piggyback" technique can be spectacular.

STAR TRAILS From a dark site, locking the shutter open for 10 to 60 minutes creates star trail portraits as Earth's motion causes the stars to make streaks on the film.

PIN-POINT SKY Using the piggyback method, stars will record as points, even in 10- to 30-minute exposures. But the telescope must be aligned as closely as possible to the celestial pole.

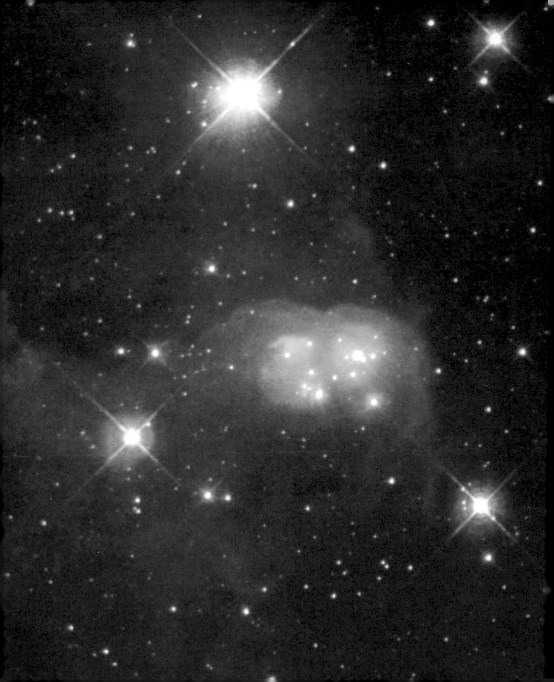

Understanding the Sky

Measuring the Sky

Though we know Earth does the moving, it can still be convenient to picture the sky as the ancients did, as a crystalline sphere turning above our heads with the sky's contents "pasted" to its interior surface.

The celestial sphere

The celestial sphere has an equator and two poles, like Earth. Coordinates similar to latitude and longitude allow astronomers to locate the positions of heavenly bodies accurately.

Declination As latitude measures distance north or south of Earth's equator, declination measures angular distance from the celestial equator. It runs from 0 degrees at the equator to 90 degrees (north and south) at the poles. One degree (°) of declination contains 60 arcminutes ('), and each arcminute contains 60 arcseconds (").

Right ascension The celestial equivalent of longitude is right ascension, or RA. It measures how far east or west a star is. The sky is divided up into 24 hours (h) of RA, each hour containing 60 minutes (m) of time. The equivalent of Earth's 0-degree Greenwich meridian is the point on the celestial equator where the Sun stands each year on the date of the March equinox. The line of right ascension that intersects the celestial equator at this point is defined as 0 hours RA.

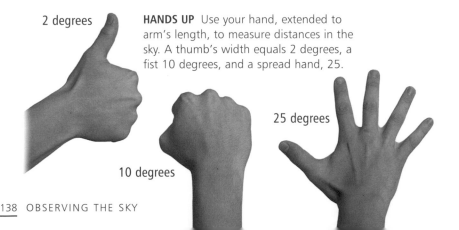

2 degrees

HANDS UP Use your hand, extended to arm's length, to measure distances in the sky. A thumb's width equals 2 degrees, a fist 10 degrees, and a spread hand, 25.

25 degrees

10 degrees

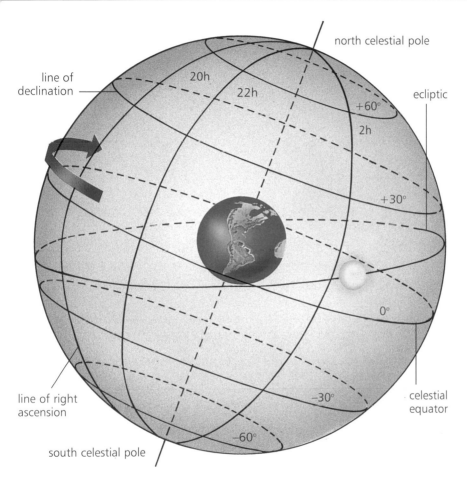

line of declination

north celestial pole

20h

22h

ecliptic

+60°

2h

+30°

0°

line of right ascension

south celestial pole

−30°

−60°

celestial equator

CELESTIAL SPHERE The positions of stars are described by coordinates on an imaginary sphere. The ecliptic is the Sun's apparent path across the background of the celestial sphere. The red arrow indicates the sphere's apparent daily movement westward.

The Motion of the Stars

■ At first glance, the stars seem to be fixed in place in the night sky, immovable. But a little observation over just a few hours will show that this is not so.

THE CHANGING SCENE

As the world turns, stars rise above the eastern horizon and set below the western horizon. On a December evening, for example, you might see Orion rising in the east. But by midnight Orion stands high in the sky. By dawn, it is setting in the west.

As Earth revolves around the Sun, the night side of the planet looks out toward a changing array of constellations. In June, we look toward Sagittarius. Orion lies in the opposite direction, near the Sun in the daytime sky. Six months later in December, the night side of Earth looks toward Orion while the Sun appears to be in Sagittarius.

CHANGES WITH LATITUDE

As Earth spins, the sky appears to rotate around its two celestial poles. Just how the stars move in relation to your horizon depends on where on Earth you live (see diagrams, below).

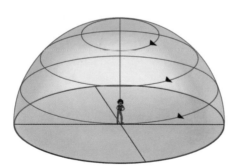

At the North Pole (90°N)
The north celestial pole is directly overhead. Only stars in the northern half of the celestial sphere are visible.

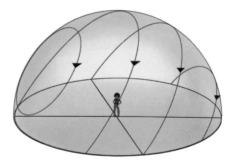

At northern middle latitudes
Part of the sky is always invisible, and stars turn in circles centered on the celestial pole, lying due north.

SLOW MOVEMENT Earth's rotation makes the sky appear to move from east to west. The illustration shows Orion as seen looking south.

GRADUAL CHANGE Two weeks later, at the same place and same time of night, you can see how Orion has moved slightly to the west.

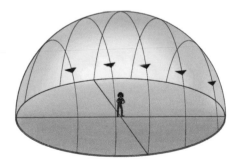

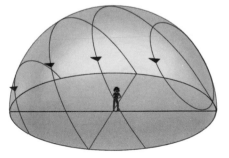

At the Equator (0°)
The celestial equator is directly overhead. The stars rise straight up and sink straight down again below the horizon.

At southern middle latitudes
Part of the sky is always invisible, and stars turn in circles centered on the celestial pole, lying due south.

STAR BRIGHTNESS

The first thing you notice on looking skyward is that stars vary in brightness. They do so for two reasons: some are closer to us than others, and some really are brighter than others.

TWO MAGNITUDES

The concepts of absolute and apparent magnitude allow us to describe star brightness precisely.

Apparent magnitude This indicates how bright a star appears to the naked eye—the lower the magnitude, the brighter the star. For example, the brightest star in the sky, Sirius, shines at about −1.5 magnitude, while the faintest stars visible to the naked eye in a dark sky are about magnitude 6. A difference of five magnitudes equals a difference of a hundred times in brightness.

Absolute magnitude The nearer the star is to Earth, the brighter it will appear, and since stars also shine with different luminosities, apparent magnitude does not measure the true brightness of a star. In order to describe intrinsic brightness, astronomers define absolute magnitude as the apparent magnitude a star would have if it were 10 parsecs or 32.6 light-years from us.

For example, the Sun's apparent magnitude is −26.8, but its absolute magnitude is 4.8. Sirius is intrinsically much brighter than the Sun: it has an absolute magnitude of 1.4.

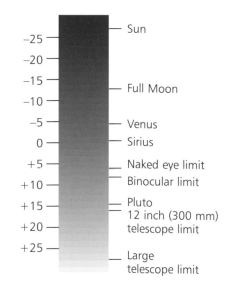

APPARENT MAGNITUDE SCALE The apparent magnitude scale describes how objects *appear* in our sky. It does not describe the objects' true brightness.

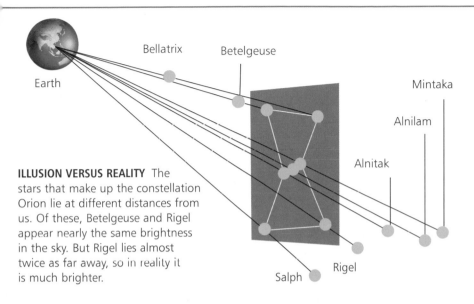

ILLUSION VERSUS REALITY The stars that make up the constellation Orion lie at different distances from us. Of these, Betelgeuse and Rigel appear nearly the same brightness in the sky. But Rigel lies almost twice as far away, so in reality it is much brighter.

The 10 Brightest Stars		
COMMON NAME	CONSTELLATION NAME	APPARENT MAGNITUDE
Sirius	α Canis Majoris	−1.46
Canopus	α Carinae	0.72
Alpha Centauri	α Centauri	0.01
Arcturus	α Boötis	0.04
Vega	α Lyrae	0.03
Capella	α Aurigae	0.08
Rigel	β Orionis	0.12
Procyon	α Canis Minoris	0.8
Achernar	α Eridani	0.46
Hadar	β Centauri	0.66

NAMES IN THE SKY

The night sky is divided into constellations and known stars are given names or numbers.

CONSTELLATIONS

Constellations are just join-the-dot patterns in the sky invented by skywatchers through the ages. There are 88 of them, their borders defined by astronomers in 1930. The boundaries may be modern, but many constellations are ancient. Taurus dates from the 3rd millennium BC. Others, such as Tucana, are inventions of 17th- and 18th-century astronomers.

WHAT'S IN A NAME? Many stars and deep-sky objects have more than one name. The Great Nebula is also known as the Orion Nebula, M42, and NGC 1976.

HOW STARS ARE NAMED

The names we use for stars come mainly from early Greek and Arab astronomers. But several other naming systems are also used.

Bayer letters Greek letters are applied to stars in a constellation, so that the brightest star is generally called alpha (α), the

Tucana

The Greek Alphabet

SYMBOL	NAME	SYMBOL	NAME	SYMBOL	NAME
α	alpha	ι	iota	ρ	rho
β	beta	κ	kappa	σ	sigma
γ	gamma	λ	lambda	τ	tau
δ	delta	μ	mu	ν	upsilon
ε	epsilon	ϑ	nu	φ	phi
ζ	zeta	ξ	xi	χ	chi
η	eta	ο	omicron	ψ	psi
θ	theta	π	pi	ω	omega

next brightest beta (β), and so on. Betelgeuse in Orion is therefore also called Alpha (α) Orionis, Orionis being the genitive form of the constellation name.

Flamsteed numbers Stars are numbered west to east across a constellation, so Betelgeuse is also 58 Orionis.

M objects These are star clusters, nebulas, and galaxies in the Messier list, compiled by the 18th-century French comet-hunter Charles Messier.

NGC objects These are star clusters, nebulas, and galaxies

Taurus

listed in the New General Catalogue of J. E. L. Dreyer, published in the late 1880s. The NGC, along with its two index catalogs (IC), lists more than 13,000 objects.

FINDING YOUR WAY AROUND

Finding your way around the sky can seem daunting for a novice, but it is really no harder than reading a road map. The first step when observing is to get oriented. To make sense of star charts you need to know which way is north and south. And for telescopes with equatorial mounts to track properly they must be aligned to the celestial pole in your hemisphere.

FINDING NORTH
Northern Hemisphere dwellers are fortunate in that the sky provides a bright star close to the north celestial pole. This is Polaris, the pole star.

There is also a convenient way to find it. Just locate the Big Dipper (in Ursa Major), mentally draw a line joining the two stars at the end of the bowl, extend it five times, and you have arrived at Polaris.

FINDING SOUTH
For Southern Hemisphere sky-watchers, finding south is not quite so easy. But although the south celestial pole is not marked by a bright star, there are several ways to find the pole.

The easiest method involves first locating Crux, the Southern Cross. Its long axis points to the south celestial pole, a blank area marked by the dim star Sigma Octantis. The pole lies halfway between Crux and the bright star Achernar and forms a right-angle triangle with brighter Canopus. A line perpendicular to a line joining Alpha and Beta Centauri also points to the pole.

BRIGHT CONSTELLATIONS
In finding your way around the sky, it rapidly becomes apparent that a few constellations are bright and easy to find. These can be used as jumping-off points on your journeys from star to star.

For example, Orion is prominent in the sky from most locations in the first few months of the year. More or less opposite Orion in the sky is Scorpius, which is prominent in the northern summer (southern winter) sky. Another bright

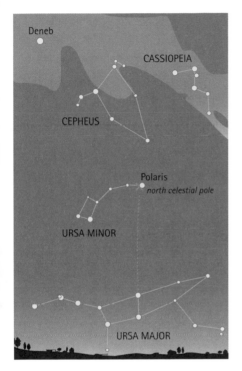

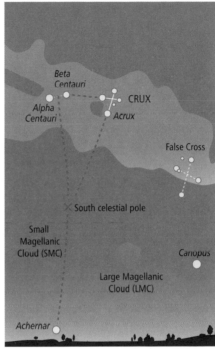

FINDING NORTH Draw a line through the two stars at the end of the Big Dipper's bowl, then extend it to Polaris.

FINDING SOUTH With no bright "south star" to mark due south, use Crux to point to the sky's southern pole.

constellation, familiar to most southern observers, is Crux, the Southern Cross.

Other landmarks Some prominent groupings of stars are not complete constellations. These are called asterisms. Examples include the Big Dipper in Ursa Major, the W shape of Cassiopeia, the "teapot" of Sagittarius, the Great Square of Pegasus, and the sickle of Leo.

OBSERVING TIPS

The Moon's craters; a dust storm on Mars; Jupiter's Great Red Spot; a galaxy's spiral arms—the night sky offers all this and more to those who know how and where to look.

SOME GENERAL TIPS

Whether you use binoculars or a telescope, make sure the optics are mounted steadily. Telescopes that shimmy and shake cannot show anything clearly.

Seeing The quality of atmospheric seeing determines how much you can see on a given night, so do not observe over rooftops or parking lots, where rising warm air disturbs the view.

Dark-adapted eyes At the beginning of an observing session, take 15 minutes or so to adapt your eyes to the dark. The pupils of your eyes will gradually open to allow in more light from the stars. Use red-filtered flashlights to keep the eyes dark-adapted.

OBSERVING THE MOON

The best time to look for details on the Moon is when sunlight strikes its surface at a shallow

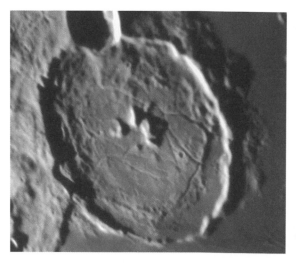

FIRST QUARTER Dark "seas" occupy much of the First Quarter moon. Craters (see close-up at right) are clustered in the south.

angle, and the line between lunar night and day throws craters, domes, and hills into starkest relief. This happens twice a month for about a week at a time, centered on the dates of the First and Last Quarter phases. The Full Moon does have its attractions, however. Its flat lighting is best

FULL MOON At Full Moon, light from the Sun flattens all perspective, leaving only variations of light and dark caused by differences in age and composition.

for tracing the bright rays and for examining varied shades that mark different lava flows in the dark "seas," or maria.

Moon-roving Start with the lowest magnification eyepiece your telescope has. Then slowly increase the power as one feature or another catches your eye. If views become unsteady, reduce the magnification until details sharpen again. (Viewing the entire Full Moon is almost painful, so bright is its disk, and some telescopic observers use gray filters to reduce the glare.)

If you have a Moon map, you can start to work your way systematically over the lunar surface. Identify any large maria you can see, and use them as a guide to take you farther.

OBSERVING PLANETS

Planets move slowly among the stars, following patterns that repeat over months or years.

Two inner planets (Mercury and Venus) orbit closer to the Sun than Earth, while six outer planets (Mars through Pluto) orbit farther out than Earth. This difference determines how each planet moves during its apparition, or period of visibility. It also determines how and where you need to look for a planet.

Inner planets Mercury (or Venus) first appears low in the western sky after sunset. It climbs higher day by day, becoming most visible at greatest eastern elongation. It then passes between Earth and the Sun (called inferior conjunction) and moves into the morning sky for best visibility at greatest western elongation. It then moves onward to round the far side of the Sun. This is superior conjunction, the start of a new cycle.

IN THE EYEPIECE
What can you expect to see of the planets? An ice cap on Mars (left) and Jupiter's clouds and Galilean moons (far left) are just some of the features visible in a telescope's eyepiece.

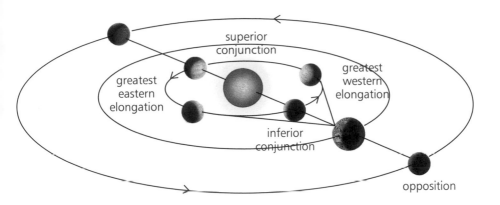

superior
conjunction

greatest
eastern
elongation

greatest
western
elongation

inferior
conjunction

opposition

Outer planets An outer planet's apparition begins as it becomes visible low in the east just before sunrise. Each day the planet rises earlier. Eventually it rises at sunset, a point called opposition which marks best visibility. The planet then starts setting sooner and sooner after the Sun, and finally disappears into the solar glare. The process restarts when the planet emerges at dawn again.

Planet-hunting To find a planet, consult astronomy magazines, almanacs, or computer software. Telescopes for planet-watching need sturdy mountings and high-quality optics. Most observers use powers of 200x or less, due to unsettled seeing. Also useful are colored filters, which accentuate specific features on the planets.

INTERIOR–EXTERIOR Interior planets, such as Venus, reach best visibility at the points of greatest elongation, while exterior planets, such as Mars, are best seen around the time of opposition.

Keep in mind that looking through a telescope is an acquired skill. It may take a few months of viewing before your eyes become trained to see the finest details on the small disks of planets.

OBSERVING DEEP-SKY OBJECTS When we look past the brightest stars, some of the specks of light we see are star clusters, nebulas, and galaxies. Many of these can be seen using binoculars and small to medium telescopes. But no matter what instrument you use, dark, clear skies are essential for deep-sky astronomy. Some galaxies are only slightly brighter than the background skyglow, so you need all the contrast you can muster from your instrument and your eyes. Here are a few tools and techniques that can improve your view of these distant objects.

Filters If you live in and around the city, you can effectively boost the contrast by using light pollution reduction (LPR) filters on your telescope. They work by blocking the wavelengths from artificial lighting, and are especially useful for nebulas, many of which are normally invisible from cities.

Averted vision To see faint nebulas and galaxies, try looking off to one side to place the image on the more light-sensitive outer portion of your eye's retina. This technique, called averted vision, will often reveal otherwise invisible deep-sky denizens.

For especially low-contrast objects, use averted vision and the "jiggle" method. Simply give the telescope tube a light tap when you think a nebula is in the field. The eye can detect contrast differences more easily if the image moves slightly.

Magnification What magnification you should use depends on the brightness and size of the object. Objects that have large diameters and faint magnitudes—as many galaxies do—require low magnification and an alertness to low-contrast details, while objects with small diameters and bright magnitudes—such as planetary nebulas—demand greater magnification and accurate positioning of the telescope's field of view.

Filters
LPR filters provide clearer images of some deep-sky objects.

GALAXY CHALLENGE Although bright at magnitude 5.7, the Pinwheel Galaxy is difficult to see because it is spread out over a large patch of sky.

FILTERED VIEW A light-polluted view of the Veil Nebula (above) shows a dramatic improvement when a light pollution filter (LPR) is used (left).

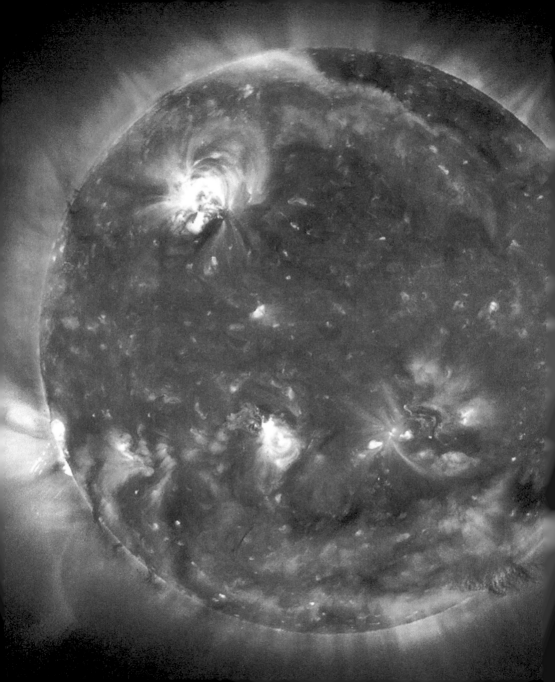

Observing the Moon and Sun

OBSERVING THE MOON

- Visibility: most surface detail seen at local lunar sunrise or sunset

- Apparent size: about 32 arcminutes

- Apparent magnitude: −12.7 (Full Moon); −10.5 (Quarter Moon)

- Diameter: 2,160 miles (3,476 km)

- Surface shaped by impacts and volcanism

The best time to look for details with binoculars or telescopes is around local sunrise or sunset on the Moon. This is when sunlight falls at a shallow angle on the ground, and the line between lunar night and day throws craters, domes, and hills into starkest relief. The flat lighting of Full Moon is best for tracing the bright rays and for examining varied shades that mark different lava flows in the dark "seas." (Early astronomers mistook these for dried-up ocean beds and called them *maria*, from the Latin word for sea.)

Whether you use binoculars or a telescope, make sure the optics are mounted steadily. Telescopes that shimmy and shake cannot show anything clearly. The quality of atmospheric seeing determines how much you can see on a given night, so do not observe over rooftops or parking lots, where rising warm air disturbs the view.

It is best to start with the lowest magnification eyepiece your telescope has. Then, slowly increase the power as one feature or another catches your eye. If

FULL MOON'S GLARE At Full Moon, the light from the Sun flattens all perspective, leaving only variations of light and dark, which are caused by differences in age and composition.

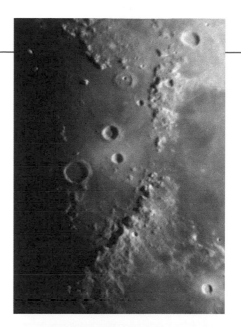

LUNAR PORTRAIT Photographs taken with even small telescopes show an amazing amount of surface detail.

views become unsteady, reduce the magnification until details sharpen again.

Viewing the entire Full Moon is almost painful, because of the brightness of the reflected light from the Sun. As a result, some telescopic observers use gray filters to reduce the glare.

The maps on pp. 159 and 161 have north at the top, showing the Moon as observers in the Northern Hemisphere would see it with the naked eye or binoculars. Astronomical telescopes generally invert this view, putting south at the top. Southern observers will find that the maps are likely to match their telescopic views.

VIEWING TIMES The best times to observe the Moon are when sunlight strikes it at a shallow angle, throwing its subtle features into sharp relief. This happens during the First and Last Quarter Phases.

First Quarter Moon

- Visibility: visible in late afternoon and evening

- Contains sites of first and last lunar landings

- Has best example of an impact basin: Mare Nectaris

- Has best example of a wrinkle ridge: Serpentine Ridge

- Has largest expanse of ancient terrain: the highlands in the south

■ The eastern hemisphere of the Moon contains several lava-filled impact basins. Among them is Mare Nectaris, which was flooded only partly and which still shows portions of its upthrown basin rim, the Altai Scarp or Rupes Altai. Notice how features touched by the lava appear softened and melted. Mare Nectaris, 540 miles (860 km) across, lies on the edge of the highlands, an ancient terrain that covers most of the Moon's far side. The highlands are so heavily battered that any new impact would destroy existing craters.

Mare Serenitatis, 570 miles (920 km) across, is another impact basin, but is completely filled with lava. Across it snakes the Serpentine Ridge, the Moon's largest wrinkle ridge. Some 300 to 600 feet (100 to 200 m) high, it formed as the weight of the lava buckled the basin floor. The lava filling Serenitatis has different colors, showing that it came from separate eruptions. The light streak across the mare is a ray from the crater Tycho, hundreds of miles to the southwest.

Mare Crisium, 460 miles (740 km) across, appears to be elongated north–south thanks to perspective, but it actually extends east–west. This impact basin appears full of lava, while traces of a broken outer rim show that the Crisium basin, when fresh, was twice its current size.

The first Moon landing (Apollo 11 in 1969) was in Mare Tranquillitatis, and the last (Apollo 17 in 1972) was in the Taurus Mountains (Montes Taurus) on the southeast shore of Serenitatis. Unfortunately, the Apollo landers, flags, and footprints are too small to be seen from Earth.

Lunar features

1 Albateginus
2 Aristoteles
3 Atlas
4 Endymion
5 Hercules
6 Hipparchus
7 Langrenus
8 Mare Crisium
9 Mare Fecunditatis
10 Mare Frigoris
11 Mare Nectaris
12 Mare Serenitatis
13 Mare Smythii
14 Mare Tranquillitatis
15 Mare Vaporum
16 Maurolycus
17 Montes Caucasus
18 Montes Taurus
19 Posidonius
20 Rupes Altai
21 Serpentine Ridge
22 Theophilus
23 Werner

24 Apollo 11 site
25 Apollo 16 site
26 Apollo 17 site

SEA VIEWS Five "seas" occupy much of the First Quarter Moon: Mare Crisium, Serenitatis, Tranquillitatis, Fecunditatis, and Nectaris. Highlands dominate the south.

Last Quarter Moon

- Visibility: visible from after midnight until after sunrise

- Has Moon's most spectacular crater: Copernicus

- Shows best ray pattern: Tycho

- Has Moon's most dramatic mountain range: Montes Apenninus

- Has the largest amount of lava coverage

■ The western hemisphere of the Moon contains Oceanus Procellarum, a vast lava flow connecting several lunar "seas." Nearby, the Copernicus crater is the Moon's most outstanding impact crater. It is 58 miles (93 km) in diameter, with gullies on its outer walls, collapsed terraces inside, and multiple central peaks made from material dredged up from deep within the Moon. Surrounding the Copernicus crater is a splash of rays made from rock that shattered when the crater was formed approximately 800 million years ago.

North of Copernicus lies Mare Imbrium, some 720 miles (1,160 km) across. The impact that created the Imbrium basin scarred much of the Moon's face, 3.84 billion years ago. The lavas filling the basin are hundreds of millions of years younger. The impressive Apennine Mountains line part of Mare Imbrium with peaks over 16,000 feet (5,000 m) high. Apollo 15 landed at their foot in 1971.

Montes Alpes, the Alps, cut through by the Alpine Valley, contain the crater Plato, which is 63 miles (101 km) in diameter. The crater's interior was then flooded by lava. To its west lies Sinus Iridum, a 160 mile (260 km) impact crater that lost part of its rim when lava filled the Imbrium basin.

Mare Humorum partly resembles Mare Nectaris, with partially destroyed craters. It is 260 miles (425 km) in diameter. Its best feature is a ruined crater, Gassendi, 68 miles (110 km) across. Gassendi was invaded by lava, and broken faults scar its floor. In the highlands to the southeast lies Tycho, 53 miles (85 km) in diameter, hub of the Moon's grandest ray system.

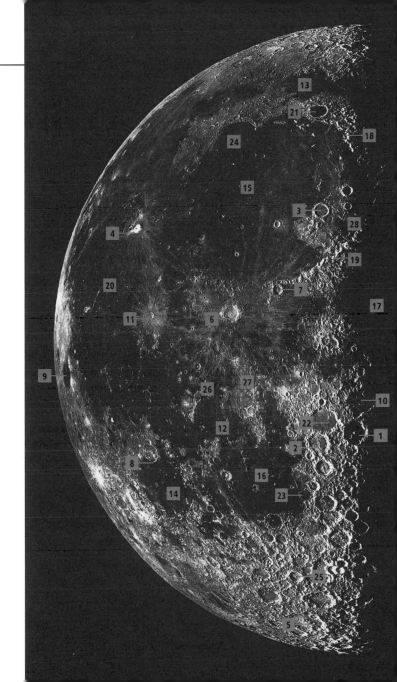

Lunar features

1 Albateginus
2 Alphonsus
3 Archimedes
4 Aristarchus
5 Clavius
6 Copernicus
7 Eratosthenes
8 Gassendi
9 Grimaldi
10 Hipparchus
11 Kepler
12 Mare Cognitum
13 Mare Frigoris
14 Mare Humorum
15 Mare Imbrium
16 Mare Nubium
17 Mare Vaporum
18 Montes Alpes
19 Montes Apenninus
20 Oceanus Procellarum
21 Plato
22 Ptolemaeus
23 Rupes Recta
24 Sinus Iridium
25 Tycho

26 Apollo 12 site
27 Apollo 14 site
28 Apollo 15 site

CRATER SHOWPIECE

The Last Quarter Moon's
showpiece is the crater
Copernicus, at the center
of a system of rays.

Observing Lunar Eclipses

- Visibility: visible over wide areas; no travel needed
- Optical equipment helpful but not necessary
- Occur twice a year on average
- Total phase of eclipse lasts over an hour
- Easy to see and photograph

■ A lunar eclipse happens when the Moon passes through Earth's shadow, which can occur only at Full Moon. The shadow extends behind Earth like a cone of darkness pointing at the stars. Lunar eclipses are either total or partial, depending on whether the Moon goes completely into the shadow. But not every Full Moon sees a lunar eclipse because the Moon's orbit tilts a few degrees relative to Earth's orbit around the Sun. This means that at most Full Moons, the Moon misses Earth's shadow, passing above or below it.

During a total eclipse, the Moon turns reddish-copper in color as it is lit by sunlight filtering into Earth's shadow.

Depending on how dusty the Earth's atmosphere is, the eclipsed Moon may be bright or dark. Lunar eclipses are widely visible (unlike total solar ones): everyone on the night side of Earth while the eclipse is underway can enjoy it, if the skies are clear.

Viewing by naked eye is easy, and observers with telescopes and binoculars often watch the moving edge of shadow darken craters. Others put a camera on a tripod and shoot scenes with an eerie, reddish Moon in the sky. Some photographers attach the camera to a telescope tracking the stars and make a multiple exposure. This captures the Moon as it moves through the eclipse.

Alternatively, you can frame the Moon in the sky with a foreground tree or building, and then take a series of exposures on the same frame 5 or 10 minutes apart exactly. ISO 400 film captures partial phases with a 1/125th second at f/8; during totality use 1 second at f/4. Adjust other film speeds appropriately.

RUDDY MOON

In a total eclipse, sunlight refracting through Earth's atmosphere stains the gray lunar dust with the reddish hues of sunrise and sunset.

TIME LAPSE

The photographer of this image placed the partially eclipsed Moon at the upper left of the frame and snapped a short exposure. Then, without changing the camera's aim or advancing the film, the photographer took an exposure every few minutes as the Moon slipped into total eclipse and then emerged.

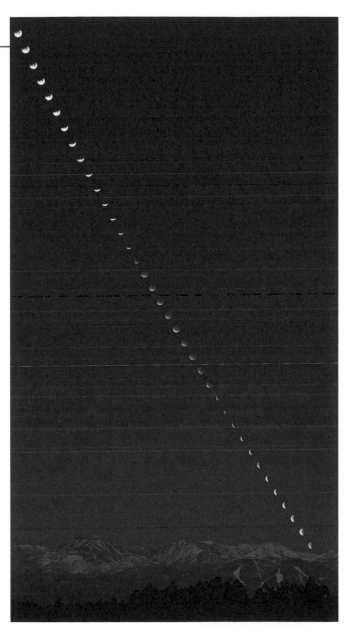

OBSERVING THE SUN

- Never look at the Sun through binoculars or an unfiltered telescope
- Visibility: sunspots are seen best at maximum solar activity
- Apparent magnitude: −26.7
- Apparent size: about 31 arcminutes
- Diameter: 865,000 miles (1,392,000 km)

Always look at the Sun with proper protection—you could be blinded by even a split second of unfiltered light. To view the Sun safely, use a solar filter that fits over the telescope's aperture (solar filters that fit over the telescope's eyepiece are not safe and should be avoided). Cover the finderscope to prevent scorching someone or something by accident.

An alternative to using a proper solar filter is to set up your telescope with a Sun projection screen (see the illustration and caption, right).

The Sun's surface—the photosphere—shows many telescopic features. At high magnification it has a granular

appearance, like oatmeal. The granules are cells of hot rising gas, with the smallest spanning 700 miles (1,100 km). Large, irregular bright patches called faculae show up best near the Sun's edge, which looks slightly darker in photographs.

The main features, however, are sunspots. These are places where the Sun's magnetic field becomes twisted enough to block

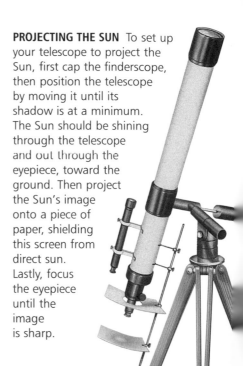

PROJECTING THE SUN To set up your telescope to project the Sun, first cap the finderscope, then position the telescope by moving it until its shadow is at a minimum. The Sun should be shining through the telescope and out through the eyepiece, toward the ground. Then project the Sun's image onto a piece of paper, shielding this screen from direct sun. Lastly, focus the eyepiece until the image is sharp.

the normal outflow of heat. Therefore sunspots are cooler places, and thus appear to be darker. On rare occasions a sunspot may become big enough to see by eye (look through a solar filter only). Sunspots are intensely magnetic, and wax and wane over an 11-year cycle. The last sunspot maximum occurred in 2000–2001.

Sometimes magnetic activity erupts as flares, which shoot charged particles into space. The most powerful flares—white light flares—can disturb Earth's ionosphere and cause magnetic storms and auroras.

An ordinary solar filter shows the "white-light," everyday Sun. To see more solar activity, some observers buy special filters that isolate a narrow wavelength, usually hydrogen-alpha (6563 Å). These can reveal prominences and other surface details. For example, most flares are invisible without an H-alpha filter.

The corona, the Sun's outer atmosphere, has a temperature of millions of degrees but can be seen only during a total eclipse.

SPOTS ON THE SUN The Sun almost always displays a few sunspots. Observations of sunspots show the Sun rotates about once a month.

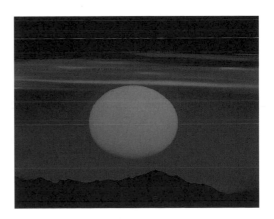

DARKNESS DESCENDS Sunset ends another day's solar observations. Many people find that solar-viewing fits more easily into their daily lives than night-time astronomy.

Observing Solar Eclipses

- Partial solar eclipses each year (on average): 3

- Total solar eclipses each year (on average): 1

- Maximum length of total eclipse: 7 minutes 40 seconds

- Total eclipses visible only along a narrow path

- Total eclipses offer best chance to see the solar corona

■ Solar eclipses can be total, partial, or annular. In a total solar eclipse the Moon covers the disk of the Sun, leaving only its corona and a few prominences uneclipsed. A partial eclipse leaves some of the Sun's surface uncovered, while an annular eclipse is a dramatic type of partial eclipse. In it, the Moon passes directly over the Sun, but appears too small to eclipse it entirely. Thus the Moon is encircled by a bright ring—an annulus—of uneclipsed Sun.

Observing a solar eclipse is much like ordinary solar observing. During a partial eclipse (or during all partial phases of a total eclipse), use a Sun filter or a projection screen (see p. 164) to protect your eyes and telescope. This allows you to watch the lunar edge crawl across the Sun, engulfing sunspots. As sunlight diminishes, do not be tempted to look at the Sun with the naked eye. If an eclipse is total, once the Sun is completely eclipsed, you can remove the filter and

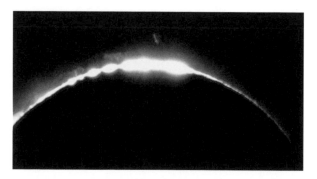

BAILY'S BEADS Just before totality comes the shimmering Baily's beads phenomenon, in which sunlight sparkles through the valleys of the Moon.

safely view the amazing spectacle without it.

As the total phase begins, the last rays of sunlight stream through valleys on the Moon's edge, a phenomenon called Baily's beads. A soft halo of pearly light surrounds the black disk of the Moon. This is the corona, the Sun's extremely hot outer atmosphere. It is too dim to see except during an eclipse. A telescope may also show solar prominences reaching up from behind the Moon. Totality ends in a burst of light, so keep the solar filter ready.

ANNULAR ECLIPSE In an annular solar eclipse, the Moon does not cover the Sun completely, and a ring of the Sun's uneclipsed surface surrounds the silhouetted lunar disk.

GRAND EVENT A total solar eclipse is one of Nature's grandest spectacles, and is something everyone should try to see at least once in their life.

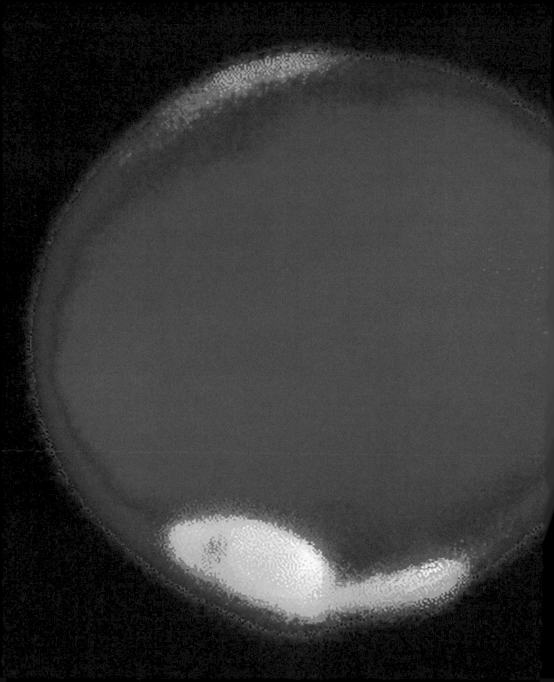

Observing the Solar System

OBSERVING PLANETS

- Visibility: generally visible every night in the year, although not all can be seen at once or on any given date

- Consult astronomy magazines, almanacs, or software for planet positions

- Inner planets: Mercury and Venus

- Outer planets: Mars, Jupiter, Saturn, Uranus, Neptune, and Pluto

Planets move slowly among the stars, following patterns that repeat over months or years. Two inner planets (Mercury and Venus) orbit closer to the Sun than Earth, while six outer planets (Mars through Pluto) orbit farther out than Earth. This difference determines

how each planet moves during its apparition, or period of visibility.

An inner planet first appears low in the western sky after sunset. Day by day it climbs higher, becoming most visible at greatest eastern elongation. It then passes between Earth and the Sun (called inferior conjunction) and moves into the morning sky for best visibility at greatest western elongation. It then moves onward to round

INTERIOR–EXTERIOR Interior planets such as Venus reach best visibility at the points of greatest elongation, while exterior planets such as Mars are best seen at opposition. All planets disappear into the Sun's glare at conjunction.

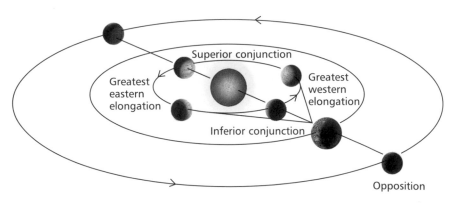

Superior conjunction

Greatest eastern elongation

Greatest western elongation

Inferior conjunction

Opposition

SKY LIGHTS The two brightest objects in the night sky are the Moon and Venus.

the far side of the Sun. This is superior conjunction, the start of a new cycle.

An outer planet's apparition begins as it becomes visible low in the east just before sunrise. Each day the planet rises earlier. Eventually it rises at sunset, a point called opposition, which marks best visibility. The planet then starts setting sooner and sooner after the Sun, and finally disappears into the solar glare. The process restarts when the planet emerges at dawn again.

Telescopes for planet watching need sturdy mountings and high-quality optics. Most observers use powers of 200x or less, due to

FOUR-PLANET LINE-UP Four of the five naked-eye planets lined up to get their picture taken in early March 1999. From the horizon upward, they are Mercury, Jupiter, Venus (the brightest), and Saturn. Such gatherings in the dawn or dusk are rare.

unsettled seeing. Also useful are colored filters, which accentuate specific features on the planets.

OBSERVING MERCURY

- Visibility: seen only in twilight, soon after sunset, or before sunrise
- Apparent magnitude: +3 to –2
- Apparent size: 5 to 13 arcseconds
- Diameter: 3,029 miles (4,875 km)
- Heavily cratered, lunar-like surface

Mercury is little seen. As the Solar System's innermost planet, its orbit keeps close to the Sun, so the planet is visible only shortly before sunrise or briefly after sunset. The best viewing times for Northern Hemisphere observers are evening apparitions in March–April and morning ones in September–October. (In the Southern Hemisphere, the best evening apparitions are in September–October, and morning ones in March–April.) During times of best visibility, Mercury stands low in the twilight for about three weeks. It looks like a warm-white star, and binoculars often help you spot it.

In a telescope Mercury's apparent size (and brightness) vary according to its distance from Earth and place in orbit, with the planet showing phases like our Moon. The phases can be hard to discern because Mercury's disk never appears large, and poor seeing near the horizon seldom leaves it steady. At moments of quiet seeing, however, the planet presents a grayish disk, like a tiny Moon with no features. When seen near elongation, it appears half-lit, and close to the time of inferior conjunction, it shows a crescent.

On rare occasions, Mercury passes directly between Earth and the Sun. These events are known as transits. The next two transits occur on May 7, 2003 and November 8, 2006; each lasts about four hours. Prepare your telescope for solar viewing (see p. 164) and locate the tiny black dot moving slowly across the face of the Sun.

Mariner 10, the only spacecraft to visit Mercury, radioed back images of an airless, rocky surface covered with many craters and showing several giant impact basins. Unfortunately, none of this detail is visible to Earthbound telescopes.

MERCURY OCCULTED The Moon occasionally covers, or occults, a planet or star. Consult astronomy magazines, almanacs, or sky-charting software programs to find out when occultations are going to happen, and whether they will be visible from your location. Here, Mercury is emerging from occultation behind the crescent Moon.

SPOTTING MERCURY Because it stays near the Sun, spotting Mercury means searching twilight skies for a dot of light. Binoculars often help. Here, Mercury is the "star" closest to the horizon, just below Jupiter. At such times, telescopic views are usually disappointing because of poor seeing.

OBSERVING VENUS

- Visibility: best seen not long after sunset and before sunrise

- Apparent magnitude: –4.0 to –4.6

- Apparent size: 10 to 64 arcseconds

- Diameter: 7,521 miles (12,104 km)

- Lava plains and "continents" hidden under white clouds

Even novice stargazers will have no difficulty finding brilliant Venus, often called the morning or evening star. Venus appears bright enough to look like an airplane with landing lights on (or a UFO), and can even cast a faint shadow under the right conditions.

Venus shines brightly because its thick white clouds reflect 76 percent of the sunlight falling on them. Its cycle of appearances resembles Mercury's (see p. 172), but lasts longer and is easier to follow. Over eight years, Venus makes five apparitions. Its best visibility runs from before elongation in the evening sky, through inferior conjunction, until after morning elongation. This period lasts about 25 weeks. When Venus is near greatest elongation, its size in a telescope is about 25 arcseconds and its phase appears half-lit. Near inferior conjunction, Venus spans more than 60 arcseconds (1 arcminute) and shows a thin crescent phase.

Venus' brightness is dazzling against a dark sky. Therefore

VENUS OCCULTED Venus is occulted by a crescent Moon. An occultation is basically a form of eclipse.

experienced observers view it in twilight, or even in daylight. They track the planet as dawn becomes day, or offset the telescope from the Sun.

In a telescope, Venus' opaque clouds usually appear featureless. Sometimes, however, observers are able to make out faint, darkish patches on the white disk—probably cloud features. When the planet shows a crescent phase, some observers have reported seeing a faint glow on the dark hemisphere. Called the "ashen light," the glow is probably an optical illusion.

Venus occasionally passes across the Sun's face at inferior conjunction. Such events are called transits and they occur in pairs eight years apart. The next pair of transits will occur on June 8, 2004 and June 6, 2012. In 2004, Venus crosses the Sun's southern part and in 2012, the northern part.

EVENING STAR Venus can outshine everything in our view except the Sun and Moon. Even twilight glow and city lights do little to dull the planet's light.

Observing Mars

- Visibility: best seen six weeks before and after opposition

- Apparent magnitude: +2 to −2

- Apparent size: 4 to 25 arcseconds

- Diameter: 4,213 miles (6,780 km)

- Cold, cratered desert, very thin atmosphere, polar caps

Mars reaches opposition and best visibility every 780 days on average, about two years, seven weeks. At opposition its distance from Earth can vary from 35 to 63 million miles (56 to 101 million km), which produces nearly a twofold change in apparent size.

On first viewing Mars by telescope, beginners are often startled by its smallness. Even at its closest approach, Mars appears no larger than a small lunar crater. From Earth, the best telescopic views resemble naked-eye views of the Moon. Typical first looks show an amber disk, some faint markings, and maybe a whitish polar cap, depending upon the time of year and the viewing conditions.

Mars is a planet with delicate, elusive features. To see it best, use at least a 5 inch (125 mm) refractor, a 6 inch (150 mm) reflector, or an 8 inch (250 mm) catadioptric scope. Filters held over the eyepiece also help: blue (Kodak Wratten 44a) and green (58) filters reveal clouds and other atmospheric features, while orange (21 or 23a) and red (25) ones enhance surface markings.

Mars' four seasons each last about twice ours. The season on Mars at opposition is one season ahead of Earth's at that

POLAR CAPS When the view is calm and steady, and using high power, Mars' ice caps appear as whitish patches. You may be able to see one of the caps grow or shrink as a Martian season progresses. The southern cap is shown here.

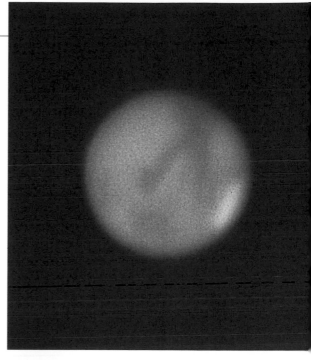

time. The polar caps grow and shrink, while dark markings, once believed to be vegetation, are vast lava flows. Their visibility changes as winds blow dust across them. Sometimes no markings appear for days or weeks, thanks to planet-wide dust storms.

ON THE MOVE Mars can appear at any place in the sky on the ecliptic, rather than always staying near the Sun, like Mercury and Venus. Here it is, glowing dull orange, in Scorpius (this page, on right) and in Taurus (facing page).

OBSERVING JUPITER

- Visibility: easy to spot, apparitions last about a year

- Apparent magnitude: −1.2 to −2.5

- Apparent size: 33 to 50 arcseconds

- Diameter: 88,730 miles (142,796 km)

- No solid surface, deep atmosphere with cloud belts

To the naked eye, Jupiter is a bright white "star" that slowly moves along the ecliptic, taking 12 years to circle the sky once. It is the largest of the gas giants and the most changeable planet visible in a telescope, displaying a constantly varying cloudscape as it rotates in less than 10 hours. Like Mars, Jupiter rewards patient observing.

Jupiter is mostly hydrogen and its "surface" is the cloudy top of a deep atmosphere, roiled by internal heat. Compounds of sulfur and phosphorus may produce the colors in the bands, which are visible with a telescope. Jupiter's rapid rotation smears cloud features into east–west stripes paralleling the equator and also gives it a pronounced oval shape. The light-colored zones you see are high, cool clouds in regions of updrafts, while the darker belts mark warmer areas of downdrafts.

The north and south equatorial belts are the least variable, but all belts change in strength and position. They show subtle colors as well—browns, tans, yellows, oranges, and shades of blue-gray—which can be made to appear more pronounced with filters such as light blue (Kodak Wratten 80A or 82A) and yellow or orange (12 or 21).

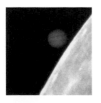 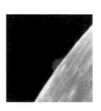

JUPITER OCCULTED
Occultations of Jupiter tend to be more dramatic than those of other planets because Jupiter looms relatively large in the telescope's field of view.

CHANGING VIEWS Jupiter's disk offers the backyard astronomer a wealth of ever-changing detail that can be seen in almost any telescope. Bright zones and dark belts vary in strength and change their position slightly. The Great Red Spot fluctuates in size and intensity of color.

Jupiter's most famous single feature is the Great Red Spot, a vast and turbulent eddy located just below the south equatorial belt that has been observed for at least 300 years. Its color and size change, perhaps in response to solar activity, being redder at solar maximum. When the Great Red Spot has faded, look for the Red Spot Hollow, an indentation that surrounds it.

Jupiter makes a good subject to draw. Before you begin, look at the planet for a few minutes to note the belts and zones. Using a 2B pencil, try to draw the major features in about 10 minutes, as Jupiter's rotation carries features along quickly. You can then fill in the details later.

LORD OF THE ECLIPTIC As Jupiter makes its way slowly along the ecliptic, it passes various clusters, nebulas, and bright stars. Here it lies near the Beehive Cluster in Cancer, creating a beautiful sight for binoculars.

Observing Jupiter's Moons

- Visibility: four brightest are visible in binoculars

- Apparent magnitude: Io +5.0, Europa +5.3, Ganymede +4.6, Callisto +5.7

- Actual diameter: Io 2,263 miles (3,643 km), Europa 1,939 miles (3,120 km), Ganymede 3,273 miles (5,268 km), Callisto 2,983 miles (4,800 km)

- Biggest four discovered in 1610 by Galileo

■ Like a miniature version of the Sun and the planets, Jupiter controls a solar system of at least 61 moons. The four biggest and brightest moons are Io, Europa, Ganymede, and Callisto, in order from Jupiter outward. They were discovered in January 1610 by Galileo Galilei, in one of his first telescopic discoveries, and they are collectively named for him.

You can duplicate Galileo's feat with a pair of ordinary binoculars. Observe Jupiter at the same time each night. On a piece of paper plot a big dot for Jupiter and put smaller dots on either side to represent the minute points of light that flank it. In a week or so, the pattern of the moons' movements will emerge.

In a telescope, these moons are 5th and 6th magnitude in brightness, and resemble nothing more than points of light, even at high power. However, the plane of their orbits lies in Jupiter's equator and is close to our line of sight to the planet. Thus at times you can see one or more slowly cross Jupiter's disk over several

MINI-SOLAR SYSTEM
A telescope or binoculars lets you experience what Galileo saw when he discovered Jupiter's four largest moons—a solar system in miniature.

hours. The moon may be hard to spot, but its dark shadow shows clearly.

On the far side of their orbits, the moons go behind Jupiter with an odd three-dimensional effect. Before Jupiter reaches opposition, moons enter the planet's shadow before going behind the planet, thus they seem to vanish into space. After opposition, the shadow lies differently, and the moons reappear equally abruptly as they leave Jupiter's shadow.

Each satellite is distinctive. Io is fiercely volcanic, repaving itself with lava every few million years. Europa hides an ocean of water under a bright icy crust. Ganymede may also harbor water under a rock-and-ice surface, and it has a magnetic field. Callisto bears an ancient, heavily cratered crust.

SHUTTLING MOONS This series of photos, taken over four successive nights, follows the Galilean moons as they shuttle around their home planet. On one night, all four moons are visible; on another you may see only three, with a fourth in front of or behind Jupiter.

OBSERVING SATURN

- Visibility: resembles a fairly bright star; telescopes show three rings
- Apparent magnitude: +3 to –2
- Apparent size: 15 to 21 arcseconds
- Diameter: 74,900 miles (120,500 km)
- Biggest and brightest ring system of any known planet

To the naked eye, Saturn is just a brightish "star" creeping along the ecliptic, taking 30 years to circle the sky. But when someone sees Saturn for the first time through a telescope, they almost always exclaim with delight—thanks to the rings.

Being a gas-giant planet like Jupiter, Saturn's "surface" is a cloud deck at the top of a deep atmosphere of hydrogen and helium. It displays fewer features than Jupiter, but slightly darker equatorial bands are visible in medium-size telescopes. On rare occasions, a large white cloud appears near the equator.

To see Saturn's low-contrast cloud features better, try using a Kodak Wratten 80A or 82A blue filter or view in mid-twilight.

Almost any small telescope will show Titan, Saturn's largest moon, and at least three other moons will be apparent in a 6 inch (150 mm) telescope. Jupiter's Galilean moons always seem to be in a line, but Saturn's moons (see pp. 184–5) can be above or below the planet, as, like Earth, the planet is tilted slightly away from the plane of the Solar System.

WHEN TO LOOK Viewing Saturn in twilight can help to reveal the planet's banded cloud features. In full darkness, try a filter.

MEMORABLE SIGHT
Saturn is probably the most memorable sight in a telescope you can have. Visible in this photo are the dark Cassini Division, separating rings A and B, and faint cloud markings.

For many, however, the rings are the main attraction. Because Saturn's axis tilts 27 degrees to its orbit, our view of the rings is constantly changing as the planet moves around the Sun. At times the rings are tipped toward us; at others they are seen edge-on. In 2009, they will disappear from view for about a week, being too thin to see.

As seen from Earth, the rings have three bands. The outermost is the A ring. The dark Cassini Division separates it from the B ring, which is the widest and brightest. The gauzy C (or crepe) ring lies on the B ring's inner edge, and is hard to see except when the rings are tipped open.

CHANGING ASPECTS As Saturn orbits the Sun once every 30 years, we see its rings slowly change appearance. When the rings are seen edge-on, which happens twice each Saturnian year, they briefly disappear from sight in small telescopes. These changes confused Galileo, the first person to view Saturn by telescope. His instrument was not powerful enough to show the rings' true appearance, and he came to the conclusion that the planet had handles that came and went.

Observing Saturn's Moons

- Visibility: four brightest are visible through telescopes

- Apparent magnitude: Titan +8.0, Rhea +9.9, Dione +10.6, Tethys +10.4

- Actual diameter: Titan 3,200 miles (5,200 km), Iapetus 900 miles (1,400 km)

- First four moons discovered by Giovanni Cassini from 1671 on

■ Saturn has at least 31 moons, many being mixtures of ice and rock. Most, however, lie beyond the reach of amateur telescopes. The largest is 8th magnitude Titan, visible even in a 3-inch (75-mm) scope.

Giovanni Domenico Cassini (1625–1712), who is famous for discovering the gap between the A and B rings of Saturn, was the first to discover Saturn's moons. In 1671, he discovered the first of four moons, Iapetus. The following year he found Rhea, and on one night in 1684 he discovered two more moons: Dione and Tethys.

Titan is the second-largest moon in the Solar System, after Jupiter's Ganymede, and is bigger than Mercury. It circles Saturn every 16 days, and when lying due east or west of Saturn, is about 4.5 ring-diameters away from the planet's center. Titan is a very strange world indeed. At almost 3,200 miles (5,100 km) across, it is bigger than the planet Mercury. An opaque, smoggy atmosphere of nitrogen and methane blankets its surface, which may feature lakes of hydrocarbons. Some of the questions about Titan will be answered when the Cassini

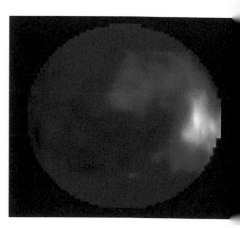

TITAN A near-infrared Hubble image of Titan shows light and dark features across the moon's surface.

mission arrives at Saturn in 2004 and launches the Huygens probe.

Inside Titan's orbit, other moons to look for are Rhea, Dione, and Tethys. Careful observation may also catch the magnitude 11.9 Enceladus.

Be sure not to overlook the oddball Iapetus. Because its leading side is coated with dark dust, Iapetus is more than twice as bright when it lies west of Saturn than when it lies east of it—ranging from 10th down to 12th magnitude. Iapetus circles

SATURN AND ITS MOONS Saturn's moons have an astonishing variety of features, ranging from the thick, smoglike atmosphere of Titan to the enormous "bull's-eye" crater on Mimas. The composite image of photos taken by Voyager 1 shows Saturn with six of its satellites, clockwise from left: Dione (in foreground, left), Rhea, Titan, Mimas, Tethys, and Enceladus.

outside the orbit of Titan every 79 days at a distance of about 13 ring-diameters.

Observing Meteors

- Visibility: best seen by naked eye; the greatest number of meteors is visible in the after-midnight hours
- Few meteors last more than a second or two
- Some major showers: the Perseids (August), the Leonids (November), the Geminids (December)

Meteors or "shooting stars" are bright trails of light caused by bits of interplanetary debris entering Earth's atmosphere at speeds up to dozens of miles per second. Friction with air molecules makes them glow, then vaporize. Some meteors leave a train lingering a few seconds to a minute. Meteors as bright as Venus are called fireballs. Those that appear to break up are called bolides (pronounced "*bo*-lydes").

Observing requires little except warm clothing and a lawn chair, although binoculars can help reveal fainter meteors. You can see four or five meteors an hour on any moonless night. Such random meteors are called sporadics. They are more

METEOR SHOWERS Bright streaks against a starry background are part of the 1998 Leonid meteor shower (left). Because of perspective, the meteors appear to radiate from one point in the sky. Most showers are named for the constellation in which this point (the radiant) lies. For the Leonids, the radiant is in Leo; for the Geminids (right), it lies in Gemini.

plentiful after midnight, when your viewing site turns onto the leading hemisphere of Earth as it travels in its orbit.

At certain times of year, Earth passes near a stream of cometary debris and a meteor shower then occurs. This greatly increases the number of meteors. The comet debris is orbiting the Sun in parallel paths, so the meteors appear to come from one point in the sky, the radiant. Meteor showers are named for the constellation or star nearest the radiant. Several dozen major and minor showers occur each year.

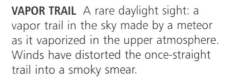

VAPOR TRAIL A rare daylight sight: a vapor trail in the sky made by a meteor as it vaporized in the upper atmosphere. Winds have distorted the once-straight trail into a smoky smear.

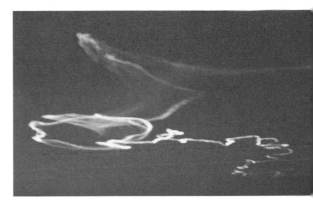

Set yourself up with a chair and a warm blanket, and roughly face the constellation the meteors are named after. (If you are not sure where that is, then turn to the Monthly Star Charts on pp. 212–67.) As your chosen constellation rises higher in the sky, you will be able to see an increasing number of meteors— unless the night is bright with moonlight. This washes out most dim meteors, leaving only the brightest.

OBSERVING COMETS

- Visibility: naked eye to telescopic, apparitions last weeks to months

- Apparent size: a few arcminutes to many degrees

- Apparent brightess: barely visible to very conspicuous

- Diameter: nucleus only a few miles across; tail may be hundreds of millions of miles in length

Unlike with planets and moons, the visibility of comets is unpredictable. Bright ones like Comet Hale-Bopp in 1997 and Comet Hyakutake a year earlier arrive unheralded, appearing out of the night to glide slowly across the heavens for a few magical weeks. When the next such "great comet" will arrive is unknown—we must simply wait and watch.

Comets are wonderful sights— by unaided eye, in binoculars, or through a telescope. The naked-eye view shows the entire comet, and observers frequently note that they display two distinct tails, a bluish one of ionized gas and a whitish one of dust. These tails sometimes point in slightly different directions. A pair of

binoculars takes you closer in on the head and tail, and lets you see more details. These may include streamers or knots in the gas tail.

A telescope lets you study the comet's head far more closely. Many comets show a bright starlike point in the center of the head. But this is not the actual nucleus—the comet's icy core— which is too small to see from Earth. Instead, the bright center is the active cloud of gas and dust that surrounds the real nucleus and hides it from view. As you examine the comet's head closely, look for bright shells and streamers of light—these are produced by gas eruptions on the nucleus. As the icy nucleus spins, it shoots jets of gas that curve like the water from a whirling lawn sprinkler.

According to a tradition going back more than 200 years, new comets are named after their discoverers. Until the discovery of the comet becomes official, up to three independent observers can earn the credit for finding it.

DECADE OF THE COMETS

The 1990s will long be remembered as the comet decade. Comet Levy led the way in 1990, then came Comet Shoemaker-Levy four years later. More impressive was Comet Hyakutake (above), which reached a maximum magnitude of −1 in March 1996. But the show-stopper was Comet Hale-Bopp (right), in March–April 1997. Its brightness (magnitude −1.5) and distinctive forked tail made it the comet of the decade and one of the great comets of the 20th century.

Solar System Challenges

- Visibility: visible in binoculars, better seen in a telescope

- Uranus: blue-green, 6th magnitude, 3 or 4 arcsecond disk

- Neptune: blue-gray, 8th magnitude, 2 or 3 arcsecond disk

- Pluto: white, 14th magnitude, 0.1 arcsecond disk

- Asteroids: white, 8th magnitude and fainter, no visible disk

The Moon, Mars, and Jupiter look grand in any telescope. But the two outer gas-giant planets, Uranus and Neptune, and the enigmatic last planet, Pluto, pose tougher challenges. And the same holds for the fragmentary micro-worlds orbiting between Mars and Jupiter in the asteroid belt.

Uranus was discovered in 1781 by the English amateur astronomer William Herschel, using only a 6 inch (150 mm) telescope. The 6th-magnitude planet appears small, at 3 or 4 arcseconds across. To find it, check an astronomy magazine or software for its position. In the eyepiece it looks distinctly non-starlike and has a vivid blue-green color, thanks to the large amounts of methane contained in its deep gaseous atmosphere.

Neptune was discovered in 1846, and looks like a dimmer, blue-gray echo of Uranus. It appears 8th magnitude and is only 2 to 3 arcseconds across.

It took an intense photographic search to find Pluto (in 1930). This planet, which is smaller than our own Moon, is 14th magnitude and cannot be recognized as a disk in backyard telescopes. Finding it requires accurate position information and a telescope of at least 10 inches (250 mm) aperture.

Asteroids orbit much closer to the Sun, but most are only a few miles across and faint. Several hundred of the larger ones lie within reach of a 3 inch (75 mm) telescope, however. Their positions are available using the appropriate software or the Internet. Locate the right field, plot all the stars you see, and recheck a day or two later. The "star" that has moved is the asteroid.

TWO FAINT WORLDS For beginners, finding Uranus (circled on left) and Neptune (right) against a background of stars is no mean feat. Using a higher magnification, the planets will show up as tiny disks, although no Jupiter-like surface features will be visible.

ASTEROID HUNT To hunt down an asteroid, you will need a telescope, position information, star charts—and patience. The short streak at the center of this photo is an asteroid.

Observing Galaxies

M81

- Constellation: Ursa Major
- Visibility: Northern Hemisphere and north of 15°S
- Magnitude: 6.8
- Apparent size: 16 x 10 arcminutes
- Distance: 11 million light-years

Located 10 degrees northeast of the cup of the Big Dipper, M81 is one of the finest examples of a symmetrical spiral galaxy in the sky. At magnitude 7, it is conspicuous in jet-black skies and can also be seen in 7 x 50 binoculars.

M81 is oriented nearly 45 degrees from being face-on, and appears as a distinct oval disk with a bright, dense core. In dark, lucid skies an 8 inch (200 mm) telescope at a magnification of 40x even shows traces of two tenuous arms spiraling outward from the bright portion of the disk. The spiral arm

extensions that trail farthest from the disk, however, are beyond the light-gathering power of even large telescopes.

The apparent dimensions of M81 are 16 x 10 arcminutes, with the long axis of the oval oriented north to south. Detailed images reveal an even larger disk, some 26 arcminutes long, nearly the apparent size of the Full Moon.

OUTSIDE VIEW
Astronomers say that M81 is probably a fair representation of how the Milky Way Galaxy would look from the outside.

Just half a degree north of M81, and in the same low-power field of view, is the unusual galaxy M82, which is seen edge-on. Try sweeping across both galaxies to compare their shapes.

M82 is classified as a bright starburst galaxy and is about 12 million light-years away from Earth. Some 600 million years ago, M81 and M82 passed very near each other in a "collision" that lasted around 100 million years. The gravitational inter-action greatly affected both systems, spawning new stars in the central region of M81 and a burst of star formation in M82.

Together, M81 and M82 form the nucleus of a small group of galaxies that is one of the nearest to our Local Group.

CLASSIC SPIRAL M81 is one of the most symmetrical spiral galaxies in the heavens. The large, bright core contains most of the galaxy's 250 billion stars. In 1993, a supernova occurred in M81 and was discovered by an amateur Spanish astronomer. The supernova is the righthand star in the triangle of stars directly beneath the core of M81.

M100

- Constellation: Coma Berenices
- Visibility: Northern Hemisphere and north of 68°S
- Magnitude: 9.4
- Apparent size: 7 x 6 arcminutes
- Distance: 56 million light-years

With a diameter of more than 120,000 light-years, M100 is one of the largest spiral galaxies in the Virgo cluster of galaxies. Unfortunately, its colossal size does not make it easy to observe. Located in the constellation Coma Berenices, the galaxy can be seen through a small telescope, but aside from its bright core, it is almost feature-less in anything smaller than an 8 inch (200 mm) telescope.

M100, with its estimated hundred billion Suns, lies about 56 million light-years away, a distance astronomers determined by measuring the luminosity of a number of the galaxy's Cepheid variables. It is known as a grand-design galaxy because of its majestic spiral form. Images and photographs of M100 reveal two prominent spiral arms, as well as an array of secondary ones and dust lanes that can be traced back toward the galaxy's nucleus. The arms are festooned with bright star-forming regions, some of which have spawned supernovas.

To find M100, look 8 degrees east of Denebola, the magnitude 2 star that forms the tail of Leo. The nucleus is oriented not quite face-on from southeast to north-west. Larger telescopes (above 8 inches (200 mm) easily show

LARGEST IN THE CLUSTER
At 7 arcminutes across, M100 presents the largest apparent size of any galaxy in the Virgo cluster.

the galaxy's magnitude 9 nucleus. To detect hints of spiral structure, however, you need very dark skies, low magnification, and a little ingenuity. Once the galaxy is centered, use averted vision (see p. 152) and then very gently tap the telescope tube. The slight jiggling "turns on" the eye's motion sensors, enabling you to detect the tenuous spiral arms just beyond the bright nucleus.

SEEING SPIRAL STRUCTURE M100 is a large face-on spiral galaxy glowing at magnitude 9.4. Its brilliant, star-like core makes it an easy object to locate, but do not expect to see a distinct spiral structure, as in photos such as this. In 8 inch (200 mm) telescopes or smaller, it can resemble a dim globular cluster. Ghostly arms emerge with the use of a larger scope under dark skies.

M87

- Constellation: Virgo
- Visibility: Northern Hemisphere and north of −71°S
- Magnitude: 9
- Apparent size: 7 arcminutes
- Distance: 50 million light-years

A GIANT IN VIRGO Some 1,000 systems make up the Virgo cluster of galaxies. M87 (at top right) is one of the largest.

Located off the hindquarters of Leo near the center of the Virgo galaxy cluster, M87 is one of the largest galaxies in proximity to us. It is also a prodigious source of radio energy as well as a powerful X-ray source. If our eyes were sensitive to these wavelengths, this galaxy would light up the sky like the bright Full Moon.

Unlike spiral galaxies, in which the observer can coax out some tenuous spiral structure, M87 is a giant elliptical galaxy, like the bulge of a spiral galaxy but without the arms. Its 7 arcminute disk, however, is quite bright at magnitude 9, appearing as an oval-shaped, cometlike object in 11 x 80 binoculars and a bright, diffuse sphere in a small telescope.

The source of this galaxy's intense energy is a supermassive black hole churning away at its core. The black hole occupies an area not much larger than our Solar System, but it is packed with the mass of 2.6 billion Suns.

During M87's existence, it has swallowed and assimilated other galaxies, making it one of the galactic heavyweights of the known universe. A powerful beam of radio, X-ray, and visible light energy gushes from the galaxy's core at extraordinary velocities. In large telescopes, in fact, this 4,000 light-year-long jet of plasma can be seen pointing outward like the hour hand of a clock.

To find M87, scan the region roughly between the stars Denebola in Leo and Epsilon (ε) Virginis, into the heart of the Virgo cluster. Do not be confused by the bright pair of galaxies M84 and M86. M87 stands on its own a little over a degree east of these two.

M87'S RETINUE
M87 is surrounded by a collection of over 4,000 globular star clusters, which appear here as fuzzy "stars." Two companion galaxies are visible.

COSMIC JET Long-exposure photos, such as the main image, reveal many details of M87 and its surrounds, but tend to "burn out" the center of the galaxy. A short exposure (inset) shows something very different—a jet of gas emanating from the nucleus. About 4,000 light-years long, the jet is thought to be a high-speed beam of particles, probably associated with a central black hole.

THE BLACKEYE GALAXY

- Constellation: Coma Berenices
- Visibility: Northern Hemisphere and north of 62°S
- Magnitude: 8.5
- Apparent size: 9 x 5 arcminutes
- Distance: 12 million light-years

Lying within the faint L-shaped Coma Berenices constellation is a unique galaxy with a unique name: the Blackeye Galaxy (M64). The nickname arises from an unusually broad band of obscuring dust crossing the galaxy's midsection on its north-eastern flank, giving it the appearance of a closed human eye with the proverbial shiner. The Blackeye Galaxy is located 10 degrees north of Epsilon (ε) Virginis, or 5 degrees north-west of 4th-magnitude Diadem (Alpha [α] Comae Berenices). Zooming in on this field, look for 5th-magnitude 35 Comae Berenices. The galaxy lies 1 degree to the east-northeast.

At magnifications of between 20x and 25x, a 6 inch (150 mm) telescope brings out a shade of the galaxy's signature dust lane, silhouetted, as it were, against the oval disk, which is oriented northwest to southeast. Some observers claim to be able to see it in a 4 inch (100 mm) telescope, but dark, clear skies are required. In the case of M64, higher magnifications may be substituted for lower power since this will increase the contrast between the sky background, the brighter galaxy, and the dust lane.

Even without the distinctive dust lane, the Blackeye Galaxy would be considered unusual. Long-exposure photographs

LOOKING FOR A BLACKEYE A small telescope picks up a suggestion of the Blackeye Galaxy's dust lane.

and digital images show tightly wound, softly textured arms that are nearly circular in shape. Even large ground-based telescopes are unable to resolve the smooth arms into knots of stars. Another fainter dust lane can be seen in images on the inner edge of the luminous arm on the north side of the galaxy.

The Blackeye's rotation is also out of the ordinary. Recent observations appear to indicate that the galaxy's center rotates in the opposite direction to its outer disk. Astronomers suspect a collision between M64 and two other galaxies may have set up the unusual internal motions.

ALL WRAPPED UP The Kitt Peak National Observatory's 150 inch (4 m) reflector captured this image of the Blackeye. Note the galaxy's arms, wrapped tightly around a smooth-looking core.

THE WHIRLPOOL GALAXY

- Constellation: Canes Venatici
- Visibility: Northern Hemisphere and north of 36°S
- Magnitude: 8.1
- Apparent size: 11 x 8 arcminutes
- Distance: 23 million light-years

The lovely face-on spiral M51, the Whirlpool Galaxy, lies just a little over 3 degrees south-southwest of Alkaid (Eta [η] Ursae Majoris), the magnitude 2 star marking the end of the Big Dipper's handle. In a 7 x 50 pair of binoculars, M51 is a small blot of light, similar to a slightly out-of-focus star. Binoculars in the 10 x 50 and 20 x 80 range resolve this into a pearl-shaped object.

An 8 inch (200 mm) telescope at medium magnification reveals the galaxy's true nature—it is, in fact, a binary system. The main disk has a distinct bright round core set within a surrounding film of glaucous light that exhibits a hint of spiral structure. Just off the main disk to the north, we see a diffuse stellar point with flared regions of light on either side. This is NGC 5195, a more distant companion galaxy. Some 400 million years ago, these two galaxies passed very near each other. The resulting gravitational tug-of-war pulled one of M51's spiral arms out of round, as well as disturbing the structure of the companion.

Images made with the Hubble Space Telescope indicate that the galaxy's massive center is about 80 light-years across, with a mass 40 million times that of the Sun. The density of stars in this region is about 5,000 times higher than in the Sun's neighborhood. The very core of M51 contains about one million times the mass of the Sun in a region less than 5 light-years across. This, together with the pattern of crisscrossed dust lanes over the nucleus, suggest the presence of a huge black hole.

TWO-IN-ONE The Whirlpool Galaxy (top) and its companion galaxy NGC 5195 are linked by a bridge of gas created by gravitational attraction. Hot, young stars color the spiral arms blue; stars are being born in the pinkish areas. This binary system is estimated to be more than 65,000 light-years across.

THE ANDROMEDA GALAXY

- Constellation: Andromeda
- Visibility: Northern Hemisphere and north of 42°S
- Magnitude: 3.4
- Apparent size: 2 x 1 degrees
- Distance: 2.9 million light-years

The Andromeda Galaxy (M31) is far and away the brightest and largest galaxy visible from the Northern Hemisphere. At magnitude 3.4, it can be seen on dark evenings with the naked eye alone, some 3 degrees northwest of the middle of the Y-shaped constellation Andromeda. Here the eye catches upon a soft, "barely there" glow, like a piece of detached Milky Way. Closer inspection with 7 x 50 binoculars reveals a decidedly oval disk of

frosty light nearly 2 degrees in length—four times the apparent diameter of the Full Moon. At the center of the oval lies a brilliant starlike nucleus around which the light falls off smoothly toward the edge.

In dark skies, 11 x 80 or 20 x 80 binoculars show how bright and huge M31 is. If you use a telescope of any size, use the lowest power you have if you want to fit as much of it in the field of view as possible. In a 6 or 8 inch (150 or 200 mm) telescope, look carefully north and northwest of the galaxy's hub for hints of a curved dark lane.

NAKED-EYE SIGHT The Andromeda Galaxy is bright enough to be clearly visible to the unaided eye, given a dark enough sky. Here, it glows as a patch of fuzz (top right) near the constellation Andromeda, including the bright star Mirach (center). You are looking across 2.9 million light-years of space.

Just south of the galaxy's bright center lies a separate oval patch of light visible as a magnitude 9 fuzzy point in binoculars. This is the satellite galaxy M32, an elliptical type of galaxy and therefore smooth and featureless. On the opposite side of the disk, farther away, is the fainter galaxy M110. This is another elliptical companion galaxy.

The Andromeda Galaxy is the nearest large galaxy to our own, and one of the few that happens to be approaching rather than receding. Still, even though

GALACTIC COMPANIONS Andromeda is attended by two companion galaxies: M110 (at right) and M32, the starlike blob below Andromeda's center. The photo's field of view approximates that of binoculars or a telescope fitted with a low-power, wide-field eyepiece, but keep in mind that more detail is shown here.

it is considered nearby in astronomical terms, light from the Andromeda Galaxy still takes 2.4 million years to reach Earth, making it one of the most distant objects visible to the unaided human eye.

The Pinwheel Galaxy

- Constellation: Triangulum
- Visibility: Northern Hemisphere and north of 53°S
- Magnitude: 5.7
- Apparent size: 67 x 41 arcminutes
- Distance: 2.9 million light-years

Fourteen degrees southeast of the Andromeda Galaxy lies another huge island universe: M33, known as the Pinwheel. This face-on galaxy covers an area of 67 x 41 arcminutes, larger than the Full Moon's apparent diameter. Being so spread out in the sky, it has a correspondingly low surface brightness, and is therefore often difficult to locate.

M33 is visible, just barely, in binoculars in a dark, clear sky. Nevertheless, many observers claim to be able to see this object with their unaided eyes, while others say they can barely discern it in the telescope. In any event, these conflicting reports should serve to alert novice observers that the Pinwheel Galaxy is probably going to be one of the more challenging objects they will pursue. Once located, however, there are some fascinating visual aspects to this galaxy. In an 8 inch (200 mm) telescope at magnifications of 30x, the galaxy's nucleus is bright and globular—even less starlike

PINK SPOT Apart from its white nucleus, the Pinwheel's most conspicuous feature is a pinkish spot of nebulosity, NGC 604, at outer left in this photo.

than the Andromeda Galaxy (see p. 204)—and surrounded by an attenuated patchy haze that gradually diminishes the farther you look from the center. In very dark skies, 6 and 8 inch (150 and 200 mm) telescopes can pick out some hint of spiral structure in the contrasting sections in the disk, particularly on the north and west edges. Be sure to use averted vision (see p. 152).

The keen observer's eye may also fall upon an enhancement in the disk some 12 arcminutes northeast of the galaxy's hub. This is the star-forming region NGC 604. It is one of the largest stellar associations known, measuring over 1,000 light-years across. Its spectrum reveals that it is similar in composition to the Great Nebula (see pp. 437–8), but over 30 times larger.

A GALACTIC CHALLENGE Although bright, at magnitude 5.7, the delicate Pinwheel Galaxy is hard to see because it appears face-on and is spread over a large patch of sky.

THE LARGE MAGELLANIC CLOUD

- Constellation: Dorado
- Visibility: Southern Hemisphere and south of 10°N
- Magnitude: 1
- Apparent size: 7 x 7 degrees
- Distance: 160,000 light-years

Just 15 degrees and 36 degrees southwest of Canopus lie two bar-shaped patches of light that, to the naked eye, look for all appearances like broken-off pieces of the Milky Way. These clouds are not fragments of our Galaxy, however, but separate, nearby companion galaxies known as the Large and Small Magellanic Clouds (LMC and SMC).

Because of their proximity to the south celestial pole, the Magellanic Clouds can be seen only from the Southern Hemisphere (though in late December and early January they may be found near the southern horizon after sunset from latitude 10°N).

Both clouds belong to a class of galaxies called irregulars, because they exhibit no definite shape. The LMC is 33,000 light-years in diameter and lies about 160,000 light-years away. It is

TARANTULA IN THE LMC
The Tarantula Nebula (left) is the largest of the numerous nebulas in the Large Magellanic Cloud (right). These pinkish regions are sites of active star formation.

rich in young, hot stars, star clusters, and bright nebulas. To view it, there is no need for large instruments, filters, high-power eyepieces, or special observing "tricks"—a pair of 7 x 50 binoculars or a small telescope at low magnification is all you need to enjoy this celestial treasure trove.

The most striking feature in the LMC is the Tarantula Nebula (NGC 2070), which is located at the southeastern end of the cloud. The nebula contains a group of about a dozen very hot, massive stars packed into a region less than 1 light-year across. This concentrated stellar bonfire lies at the center of the spiderlike tendrils of hot gas that give the nebula its name. In 1987, a star exploded on the extreme western end of the Tarantula Nebula. Supernova 1987A was the first supernova seen with the naked eye since 1604.

CLOUDS OF MAGELLAN The LMC (left, and above left) is roughly twice the size of its companion, the SMC (above right), and contains about 10 times its mass.

STAR
CHARTS

*Road maps to guide you through
the night sky, season by season,
constellation by constellation.*

Monthly
Star Charts

■ Using the Charts *214*

USING THE CHARTS

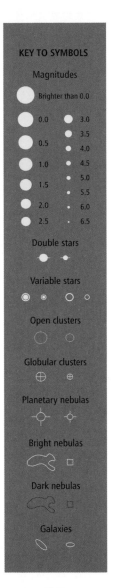

KEY TO SYMBOLS

Magnitudes

- Brighter than 0.0
- 0.0
- 3.0
- 0.5
- 3.5
- 4.0
- 1.0
- 4.5
- 1.5
- 5.0
- 5.5
- 2.0
- 6.0
- 2.5
- 6.5

Double stars

Variable stars

Open clusters

Globular clusters

Planetary nebulas

Bright nebulas

Dark nebulas

Galaxies

These month-by-month charts of the night sky are the essential outdoor guides for identifying the bright stars and the constellations.

The monthly sky maps chart the entire night sky visible through the year. The charts come in two sets: one for the Northern Hemisphere and one for the Southern.

The Northern Hemisphere charts (pp. 218–41) are for the latitudes of the United States, Canada, Europe, and Japan. While they show the sky from a latitude of 40°N, the charts are usable for latitudes 10 to 15 degrees north or south of this.

The Southern Hemisphere charts (pp. 244–67) depict the sky from a latitude of 35°S. These are for use in the South Pacific, Australia, New Zealand, South America, and southern Africa.

Each month's sky is divided into two halves— showing the sky as you would see it facing north and facing south.

Select the hemisphere you live in, then the current month. Each pair of maps for that month depicts the night sky you will see as you face north or south. ■

■ Refer to the description for highlights of what to look for in that month's night sky.

STAR MAGNITUDES

- –1
- 0
- 1
- 2
- 3
- 4
- 5

The dimmest stars shown on each chart are magnitude 5, the faintest visible from locations near city lights.

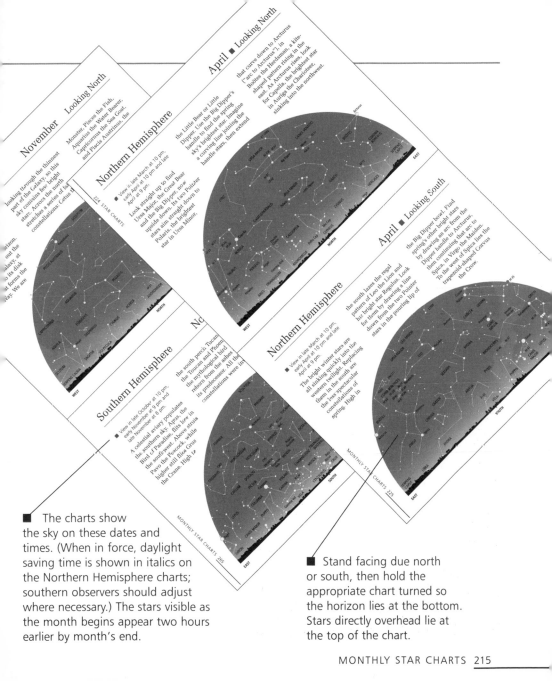

■ The charts show the sky on these dates and times. (When in force, daylight saving time is shown in italics on the Northern Hemisphere charts; southern observers should adjust where necessary.) The stars visible as the month begins appear two hours earlier by month's end.

■ Stand facing due north or south, then hold the appropriate chart turned so the horizon lies at the bottom. Stars directly overhead lie at the top of the chart.

Highlights of the Northern Skies

The northern skies have many fascinating features that are justly famous and worth seeking out with your telescope.

Albireo, in the constellation of Cygnus, is the finest double star in the sky, looking blue and gold through a telescope.

Algol, in Perseus, is the finest example of an eclipsing variable star. A close double, its components orbit each other every 2.87 days and the brightness of the star changes from 2nd magnitude to a dim 3rd and then recovers within a few hours, all visible to the naked eye.

Betelguese is over 1,000 times larger than our Sun. If it was placed at the center of our Solar System it would extend past the orbit of Jupiter. Betelgeuse is also known as Alpha Orionis, in the constellation of Orion.

Antares is a huge red supergiant, about 700 times the size of our sun and 10,000 times brighter. It is the brightest star in the constellation of Scorpius and is surrounded by a nebula of gas. Radiation from its blue stellar companion star causes this nebula gas to glow.

Pleiades (M45) The famous Pleiades is without doubt the best open cluster in the sky. Although known as the Seven Sisters, there are over 3,000 very young, brilliant blue stars in this group. On a dark night you should be able to spot at least six of the stars that give the cluster its name.

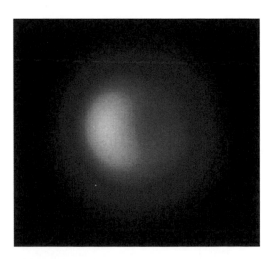

BETELGEUSE This is the only star, other than the Sun, for which we have produced an image of the star's surface, using techniques from radio astronomy. It is over 600 light-years away.

THE GREAT NEBULA The great nebula (M42) is one of the most impressive sights in the sky. Here it is shown with its companion M43 beneath it.

Hercules Cluster (M13) is the most spectacular globular cluster in the northern sky, with over 1 million stars.

Double Cluster (NGC 869 and 884) This pair of bright star clusters is in the Perseus spiral arm of our galaxy.

The Ring Nebula (M57) is one of the best-known planetary nebulas. A white dwarf resides at its heart.

The Crab Nebula (M1) is a supernova remnant that marks the spot where a massive star exploded, an event witnessed by Chinese astronomers in 1054.

The Great (Orion) Nebula (M42), is one of the northern sky's most famous objects. Although a diffuse nebula, it is clearly visible to the naked eye.

The Andromeda Galaxy (M31), our nearest large galaxy, is bigger than the Milky Way and appears as a smudge to the naked eye.

The Whirlpool Galaxy (M51) is a famous spiral galaxy with a hurricane-like appearance, and was the first galaxy in which spiral arms were identified. Satellite galaxies, M32 and M110 are visible on either side.

Bode's Galaxy (M81) is a bright spiral galaxy easily visible in binoculars, and has even been seen with the naked eye. Its neighboring galaxy, M82, part of the M81 group of galaxies, has been deformed by a previous collision with M81.

The Sombrero Galaxy (M104) is a spiral galaxy, seen edge-on. A dark lane of dust, girdling the galaxy's equator, cuts the image in two and, from Earth, gives it the appearance of a Mexican hat.

Northern Hemisphere

January ■ Looking North

■ View in late December at 9 pm, early January at 8 pm and late January at 7 pm.

The Big Dipper, the well-known pattern of stars within Ursa Major, the Great Bear, stands on its handle low on the northeast horizon. Meanwhile, the Little Dipper hangs by its handle from Polaris, the North Star. Cassiopeia the Queen clings to her throne as she hangs upside down high in the north. As you face north, Cassiopeia's familiar "W" of five stars now looks more like a celestial letter M. The twin stars of Castor and Pollux in Gemini the Twins are rising in the eastern sky while Capella, in Auriga the Charioteer, shines down from high in the northeast.

GEMINI · Pollux · Castor · HYDRA · CANCER · LEO · AURIGA · LYNX · LEO MINOR · M 37 · M 36 · M 38 · Capella · URSA MAJOR · 47 UMa · PERSEUS · CAMELOPARDALIS · M 82 · M 81 · Big Dipper · Algol · Double Cluster · Mizar · Alcor · Gamma And · 457 · Polaris · URSA MINOR · Little Dipper · DRACO · M 31 · 7789 · CASSIOPEIA · CEPHEUS · ANDROMEDA · Delta Cep · Mu Cep · HERCULES · LACERTA · North America Nebula · Deneb · CYGNUS · Epsilon Lyr · Vega · LYRA · PEGASUS · Veil Nebula · VULPECULA · DELPHINUS · EQUULEUS · Beehive

EAST · NORTH · WEST

Northern Hemisphere   January ■ Looking South

■ View in late December at 9 pm, early January at 8 pm and late January at 7 pm.

Pegasus the Flying Horse sinks into the west, followed by an arc of stars that marks Andromeda, Cassiopeia's daughter. Her hero, Perseus, swings high overhead. Dim, "watery"

constellations—Aquarius the Water Carrier, Pisces the Fish, Cetus the Sea Monster, Eridanus the River—sprawl in the southwest. By contrast, bright stars surround Orion the Hunter climbing into the east. Aldebaran in Taurus the Bull appears yellow-orange, while above sparkles the Pleiades star cluster. Sirius in Canis Major, the Great Dog, sparkles in the southeast, while blue-white Procyon shines nearby.

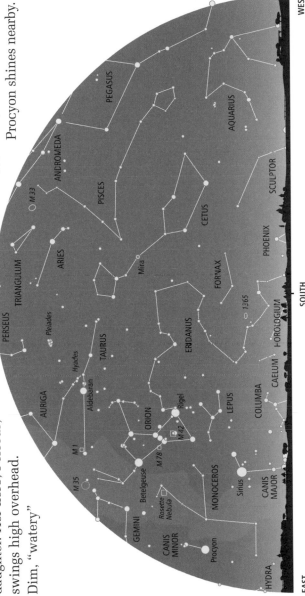

Northern Hemisphere

February ■ Looking North

■ View in late January at 9 pm, early February at 8 pm and late February at 7 pm.

Ursa Major, the Great Bear, climbs up the northeastern sky as he endlessly circles the pole. Within Ursa Major, the Big Dipper rises bowl-first in the northeast.

A line from the Dipper's two Pointer stars extended left parallel to the horizon aims straight at Polaris, the North Star. On the side of Polaris opposite the Big Dipper lies

the bright "W" of Queen Cassiopeia, while between Cassiopeia and Polaris hides the faint house-shaped pattern of Cassiopeia's consort, Cepheus the King. Directly overhead lies the brightest star of Auriga the Charioteer: Capella.

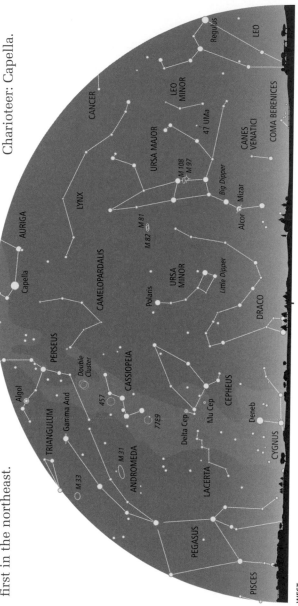

Northern Hemisphere

February ■ Looking South

■ View in late January at 9 pm, early February at 8 pm and late February at 7 pm.

More bright stars adorn the sky now than in any other season. Due south, Orion the Hunter contains Betelgeuse and Rigel. Orion's three Belt stars form a pointer to

other bright stars: the Belt points down to Sirius in Canis Major, the Great Dog, the brightest star in the night sky, and points up toward Aldebaran, the reddish eye

of Taurus the Bull. High in the eastern sky shine two stars of equal brightness—Castor and Pollux in Gemini the Twins. Between them and Sirius sparkles isolated Procyon, in Canis Minor, the Little Dog.

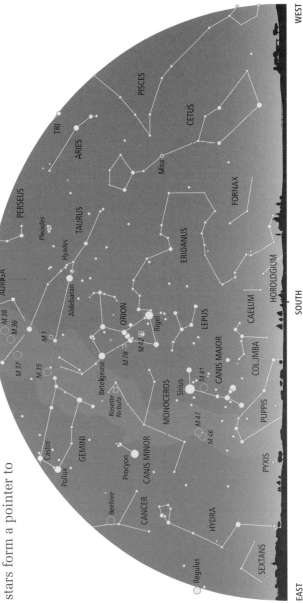

Northern Hemisphere

March ■ Looking North

■ View in late February at 10 pm, early March at 9 pm and late March at 8 pm.

Ursa Major, the Great Bear, now walks upside down high in the north. The brightest seven stars within the Bear form the familiar Big Dipper pattern. The Dipper's two Pointer stars in its Bowl aim down to Polaris, the North Star. Swinging off to the right, or east, of Polaris six other stars form the Little Dipper, also called the Little Bear or Ursa Minor. While well known, the Little Dipper is faint and hard to pick out of urban skies. Only Polaris and the two stars forming the pouring lip of the Little Dipper—the "Guardian" stars—are bright enough to see in the city.

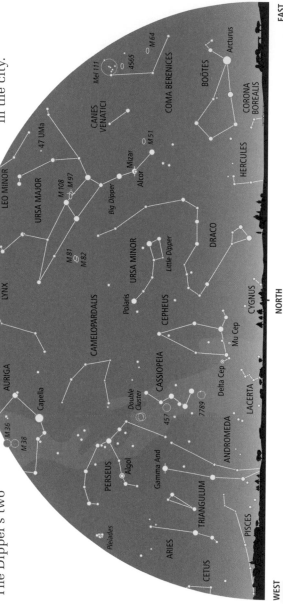

Northern Hemisphere

March ■ Looking South

■ View in late February at 10 pm, early March at 9 pm and late March at 8 pm.

Orion the Hunter and his stellar companions are creeping into the southwest, gradually leaving the winter evening sky. Sirius, the night sky's brightest star, is now at its most obvious, twinkling as high as it gets for the year above the southern horizon. Find Sirius by drawing a line down from the Belt of Orion. Above Sirius stands another bright blue-white star, Procyon. Continue up the sky and you arrive at twin stars almost overhead. These are Pollux and Castor in Gemini the Twins. To the east, rise Regulus and the stars of Leo the Lion.

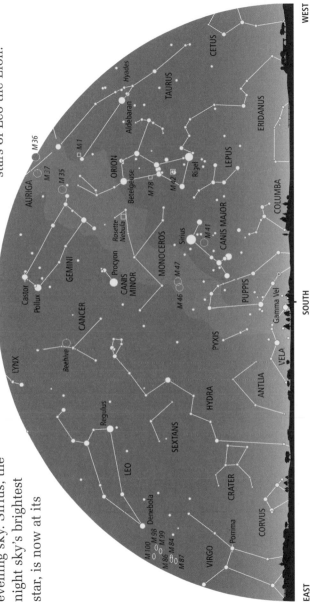

Northern Hemisphere

April ■ Looking North

■ View in late March at 10 pm, early April at 10 pm and late April at 9 pm.

Look straight up to find Ursa Major, the Great Bear, and the Big Dipper, now upside down. Its two Pointer stars aim straight down to Polaris, the brightest star in Ursa Minor,

the Little Bear or Little Dipper. Use the Big Dipper's handle to find the spring sky's brightest star. Imagine a curving line joining the handle stars, then extend

that curve down to Arcturus ("arc to Arcturus"), in Boötes the Herdsman, a kite-shaped pattern rising in the east. As Arcturus rises, look for Capella, the brightest star in Auriga the Charioteer, sinking into the northwest.

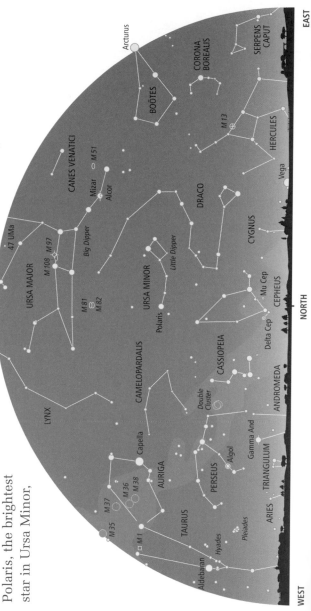

Northern Hemisphere

April ■ Looking South

■ View in late March at 10 pm, early April at 10 pm and late April at 9 pm.

The bright winter stars are all sinking quickly into the western twilight. Replacing them in the south are the less spectacular constellations of spring. High in the south lazes the regal pattern of Leo the Lion and his bright star Regulus. Look for them by drawing a line down from the two Pointer stars in the pouring lip of the Big Dipper bowl. Find spring's other bright stars by drawing an arc from the Dipper handle to Arcturus, then continuing that arc to Spica, in Virgo the Maiden. To the west of Spica lies the trapezoid-shaped Corvus the Crow.

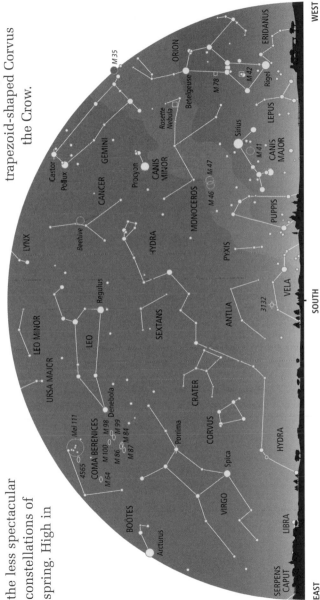

Northern Hemisphere

May ■ Looking North

■ View in late April at midnight, early May at 11 pm and late May at 10 pm.

Capella, a bright star of winter, swings close to the northwestern horizon in the early evening hours, sparkling like a jewel low in the sky. Also skimming the

northern horizon, but due north, lies the stellar "W" of Cassiopeia the Queen. Meanwhile, Deneb and Vega, stars of summer, are beginning to climb into the

northeast. The Big Dipper lies upside down high overhead, its two Pointer stars aiming at Polaris and the Little Dipper. From a rural site you may also be able to trace Draco the Dragon's faint stars winding between the Dippers.

Northern Hemisphere

May ■ Looking South

■ View in late April at midnight, early May at 11 pm and late May at 10 pm.

In spring, you look straight out of the plane of the Milky Way Galaxy which now surrounds you on the horizon. High overhead lies the north pole of our Galaxy, home to hundreds of other galaxies suitable for telescopic exploration. The Realm of the Galaxies lies between Leo the Lion and Boötes the Herdsman.

Find Leo by drawing a line through the Dipper's Pointer stars south to Leo's brightest star: Regulus. The Dipper's curving handle points to Arcturus in Boötes. Extend that arc and you arrive at Spica in Virgo the Maiden.

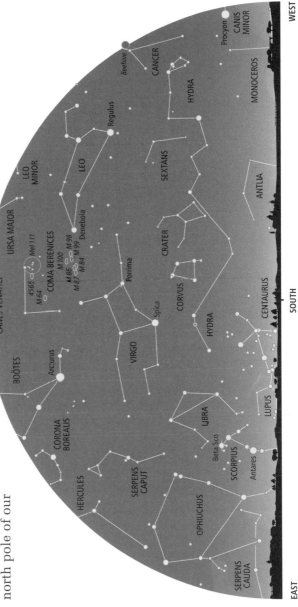

Northern Hemisphere

June ■ Looking North

■ View in late May at midnight, early June at 11 pm and late June at 10 pm.

Ursa Major, the Great Bear, and the Big Dipper lie high in the northwest, to the left of Polaris as you face north, while the Little Dipper swings above Polaris.

If the skies are dark, you may be able to trace out a winding chain of stars that marks the wriggling form of Draco the Dragon, between the two Dippers. His head

lies in a box of four stars near Vega, the bright blue-white star now dominating the eastern sky. Below Vega, look for Deneb in Cygnus the Swan, while the "W" of Cassiopeia the Queen skims low across the northern sky.

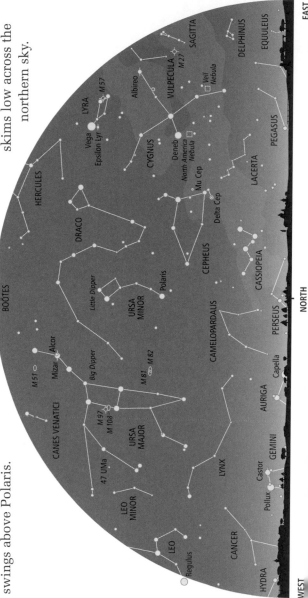

Northern Hemisphere

June ▪ Looking South

▪ View in late May at midnight, early June at 11 pm and late June at 10 pm.

Leo the Lion wanders off into the west carrying Regulus with it. Arcturus and Spica, the brightest stars of spring, are being joined by a new group of stellar companions, the more numerous bright stars of summer. Look for an orange star low in the south. That's Antares, the heart of Scorpius the Scorpion crawling along the southern horizon. Between Arcturus and Vega, now rising in the east, look for a crooked "H" that marks the main part of the Hercules. Between Hercules and Arcturus lies a semicircle of stars —Corona Borealis, the Northern Crown.

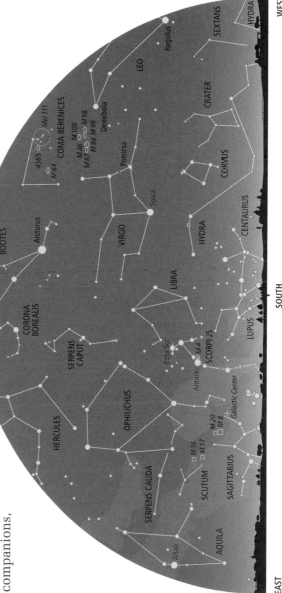

Northern Hemisphere

July ■ Looking North

■ View in late June at midnight, early July at 11 pm and late July at 10 pm.

In summer, the turning of the sky around Polaris sinks the Big Dipper into the northwest, swings the head of Draco the Dragon overhead, and raises Cassiopeia the Queen into the northeast. In the east, Vega, in Lyra the Harp, and Deneb, in Cygnus the Swan, form a large triangle in the sky with Altair, in Aquila the Eagle, found on the southern map (see facing page). These three stars, the brightest of summer, make up the Summer Triangle. Vega and Altair lie close by, only 25 and 17 light-years away respectively, but Deneb shines from a distance of 1,500 light-years.

Northern Hemisphere

July ■ Looking South

■ View in late June at midnight, early July at 11 pm and late July at 10 pm.

Straight overhead look for the crooked "H" pattern of Hercules. Arcturus and the sparse stars of spring still dominate the western sky. Due south, look for Antares amid the hook-shaped Scorpius the Scorpion. To the left, a teapot made of stars marks Sagittarius the Archer. In this direction you are looking toward the center of our Galaxy. If the sky is dark (with no Moon) and haze-free, you will see what looks like steam rising from the teapot and wafting up the sky past the stars Altair and Vega. That's the Milky Way, made up of millions of distant stars.

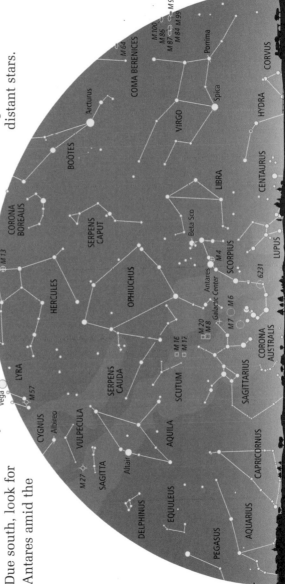

Northern Hemisphere
August ■ Looking North

■ View in late July at 11 pm, early August at 10 pm and late August at 9 pm.

The Big Dipper and Cassiopeia the Queen now lie on a horizontal line, seemingly balanced on opposite sides of the north celestial pole, marked by Polaris, the

North Star. Through the night, as Earth spins, the entire sky appears to turn about this star. Overhead, you will see blue-white Vega, the brightest star

of summer. Together with Deneb, in the east, and Altair, in the south, the three stars form the hall-mark of the summer sky, the Summer Triangle. The Milky Way, formed by our Galaxy's spiral arms, rises out of the northeast to sweep through the Triangle.

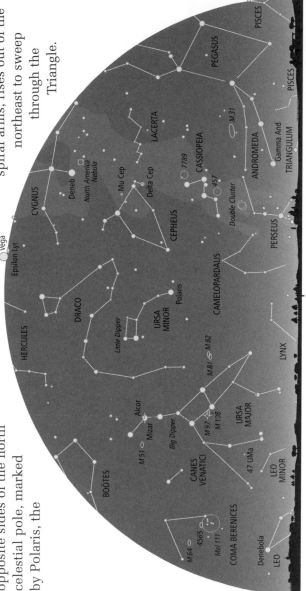

EAST

PISCES

PEGASUS

PISCES

M 31

Gamma And

LACERTA

TRIANGULUM

7789

CASSIOPEIA

ANDROMEDA

457

Double Cluster

PERSEUS

North America Nebula

Deneb

Mu Cep

Delta Cep

CYGNUS

CEPHEUS

CAMELOPARDALIS

Vega

Epsilon Lyr

NORTH

Polaris

DRACO

Little Dipper

URSA MINOR

HERCULES

M 81 ✎ M 82

LYNX

Alcor

Mizar

M 97

M 108

URSA MAJOR

M 51

Big Dipper

47 UMa

CANES VENATICI

LEO MINOR

BOÖTES

M 64

4565

Mel 111

COMA BERENICES

Denebola

LEO

WEST

Northern Hemisphere

August ■ Looking South

■ View in late July at 11 pm, early August at 10 pm and late August at 9 pm.

From a dark site on a moonless night, the Milky Way now dominates the sky, sweeping along the length of Cygnus the Swan, then flowing past Altair in Aquila the Eagle.

The Milky Way brightens in a small patch in the tiny constellation of Scutum the Shield, then brightens again in Sagittarius the Archer and Scorpius the Scorpion,

forming what might look like glowing clouds. These star clouds lie toward the center of our Galaxy, now due south. Scorpius' curving shape is unmistakable, but from north of 48°N latitude, the Scorpion's tail never rises above the horizon.

Northern Hemisphere ■ September ■ Looking North

■ View in late August at 10 pm, early September at 9 pm and late September at 8 pm.

Ursa Major, the Great Bear, now appears to be lumbering along the northern horizon. The Big Dipper, contained within Ursa Major, swings below the pole while the Little Dipper and the head of Draco the Dragon swing above the pole. To the east, the constellations of autumn—Cassiopeia the Queen, Andromeda the Chained Princess, and the Square of Pegasus the Flying Horse—are beginning to rise into the evening sky, gradually pushing all the summer stars off stage. The Milky Way now bisects the sky, running almost due north–south.

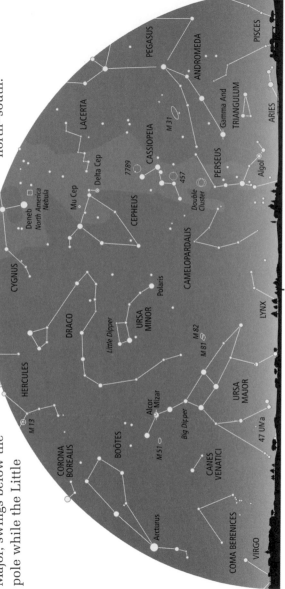

EAST

NORTH

WEST

PISCES

ARIES

ANDROMEDA

PEGASUS

TRIANGULUM

Gamma And

M 31

LACERTA

CASSIOPEIA

PERSEUS

Algol

457

7789

Double Cluster

Delta Cep

CEPHEUS

Mu Cep

CAMELOPARDALIS

Deneb

North America Nebula

LYNX

CYGNUS

Epsilon Lyr

Vega

Polaris

URSA MINOR

Little Dipper

DRACO

M 82

M 81

HERCULES

Alcor Mizar

M 13

URSA MAJOR

Big Dipper

47 UMa

CORONA BOREALIS

BOÖTES

M 51

CANES VENATICI

Arcturus

COMA BERENICES

VIRGO

Northern Hemisphere September ■ Looking South

■ View in late August at 10 pm, early September at 9 pm and late September at 8 pm.

The Summer Triangle stars, Vega, Altair, and to the north, Deneb, sparkle high overhead in the evening hours. Vega belongs to Lyra the Harp, a small parallelogram of stars. Altair belongs to Aquila the Eagle, depicted flying north along the Milky Way. To the right, or west, of Vega look for the H-shaped pattern of Hercules. To the west of Altair, stands Ophiuchus the Serpent Bearer. Below Altair, on the southern horizon between Sagittarius the Archer and Scorpius the Scorpion, lies the glowing heart of the Milky Way.

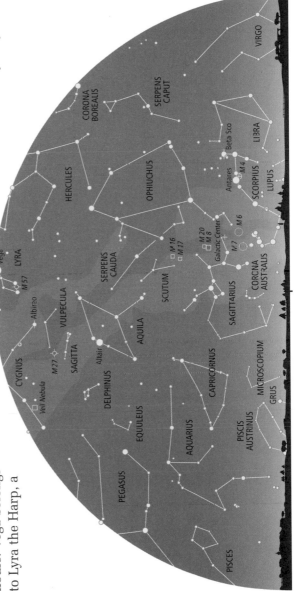

Northern Hemisphere   October ■ Looking North

■ View in late September at 10 pm, early October at 9 pm and late October at 8 pm.

The Big Dipper skims the horizon, while opposite the pole, Cassiopeia the Queen climbs high into the northeast. Below the "W" of Cassiopeia shine the stars of Andromeda, her daughter, and Perseus, the hero who rescued Andromeda from Cetus the Sea Monster, itself visible low in the south. Deneb, the most northerly star in the Summer Triangle, shines down from directly overhead. Two bright stars twinkle on the northern horizon: Arcturus setting in the northwest, and Capella rising in the northeast.

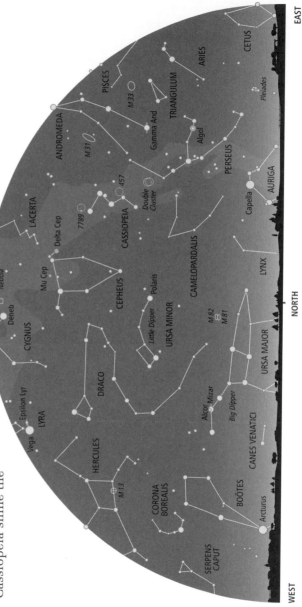

Northern Hemisphere   October ▪ Looking South

▪ View in late September at 10 pm, early October at 9 pm and late October at 8 pm.

Sagittarius the Archer and the center of the Galaxy sink into the southwest. Due south, look for a chevron of faint stars that marks Capricornus the Sea Goat. Below

shines lone Fomalhaut, in Piscis Austrinus, the Southern Fish. The Summer Triangle stars, Altair, Deneb, and Vega (on the north chart, see facing page) now

stand high in the west. They will continue to dominate the western sky through autumn. However, the true autumn constellations gradually take the scene, led by Pegasus the Flying Horse (marked by a square of four stars) rising into the east.

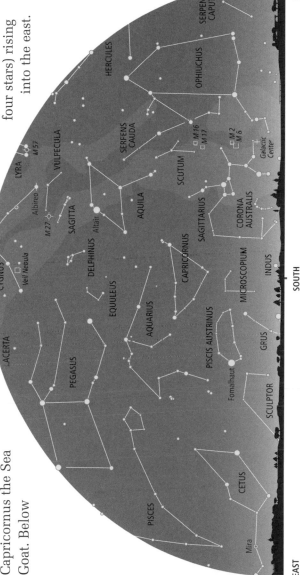

Northern Hemisphere ■ November ■ Looking North

■ View in late October at 10 pm, early November at 8 pm and late November at 7 pm.

The Big Dipper is now at its lowest point in the north, so low it may be hiding behind buildings and trees or, for those living south of 35°N latitude, below the horizon. High in the north, however, the five stars of Cassiopeia the Queen are easy to spot. Look for a letter "M" or an upside-down "W" of stars. To the left, or west, of Cassiopeia lies the faint house-shaped Cepheus the King. To the east of Cassiopeia, a Y-shaped chain of stars marks Perseus the Hero. Below, one of the first stars of winter, Capella, in Auriga the Charioteer, rises into the northeast.

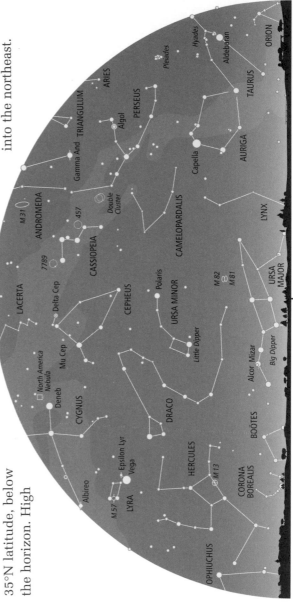

Northern Hemisphere   November ■ Looking South

■ View in late October at 10 pm, early November at 8 pm and late November at 7 pm.

High in the south, look for the square-shaped pattern marking Pegasus the Flying Horse. Connected to the top left corner of the Square, two arcs of stars stretch away to the east. They mark Andromeda the Chained Princess, rescued by Perseus from the clutches of Cetus the Sea Monster, a faint pattern low in the south, as Perseus flew in on the back of Pegasus. Between Cetus and Pegasus shines another faint "watery" constellation, Pisces the Fish. Another fish, Piscis Austrinus, is marked by a lonely bright star, Fomalhaut, low in the south.

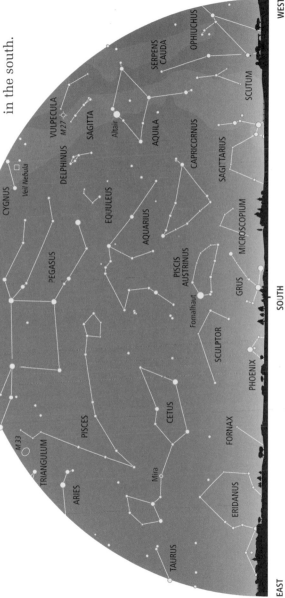

Northern Hemisphere   December ■ Looking North

■ View in late November at 9 pm, early December at 8 pm and late December at 7 pm.

The three persistent stars of the Summer Triangle, Vega, Altair, and Deneb, can still be seen, although they are now setting into the north-western sky. The Big

Dipper and Ursa Major, the Great Bear, graze the northern horizon while Cassiopeia the Queen now stands as high in the north as she gets for the year.

Stretching to the right, or east, of Cassiopeia, look for the Y-shaped pattern of Perseus the Hero. Below Perseus sparkle some stars of winter: Capella high in the northeast, and the twin stars of Castor and Pollux just rising.

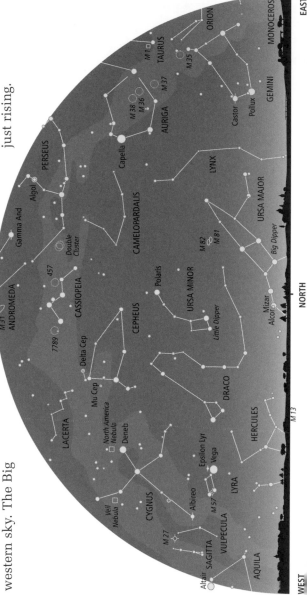

Northern Hemisphere   December ■ Looking South

■ View in late November at 9 pm, early December at 8 pm and late December at 7 pm.

Pegasus the Flying Horse flies high in the south while Andromeda the Chained Princess reclines overhead. Farther south, the sky is populated by faint, "watery"

constellations—Pisces the Fish, Aquarius the Water Bearer, Cetus the Sea Monster, Eridanus the River—all difficult to pick out in bright suburban skies.

However, the luminous stars of winter are set to replace the dim stars of autumn. To the east, the star-filled Orion the Hunter and Taurus the Bull, locked in battle, are scuffling into the sky. In Taurus, the star cluster called the Pleiades is sure to catch the eye.

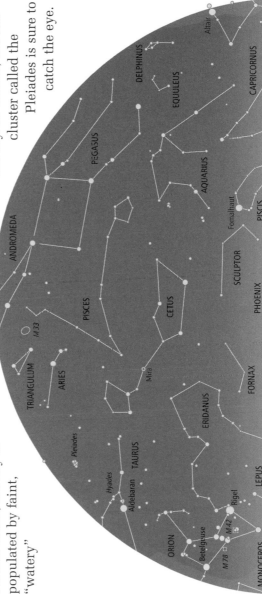

Highlights of the Southern Skies

The full wonder of the southern skies was hidden until the last few centuries from northern astronomers. The Messier scale does not include 47 Tucanae, for example, the second brightest globular cluster, as it is not visible from the Northern Hemisphere. The feature most people first look for in the southern skies is Crux—the Southern Cross. **Sirius** is the brightest star in the sky and can be found in the constellation of Canis Major. It is only 8.6 light-years away and 40 times brighter than our Sun. It has a companion, Sirius B, which is 10,000 times dimmer than Sirius. Sirius B was the first white dwarf star discovered. **Proxima Centauri** is the nearest star to Earth and part of the Alpha Centauri cluster of three stars. The other two members— Alpha [α and β] Centauri, a close binary—overshadow it completely. Alpha [α] Centauri, also known as Rigel Kentaurus, is the fourth brightest star in the sky, and the same type of star as our Sun.

Zubeneschamali is a 3rd-magnitude star in the constellation of Libra, and the only star to appear a green color, said to be impossible. Ancient astronomers recorded it as being brighter than 1st-magnitude Antares—another mystery. **The Jewel Box (NGC 4755)** is a beautiful compact aggregation of about 50 stars. It is a young cluster with many giant blue and white stars and can easily be seen with the naked eye. **Omega Centauri (NGC 5139)** is the largest-known globular cluster in our galaxy, containing over a million stars. At 17,000 light-years away it is also one of the nearest globular clusters to Earth.

47 TUCANAE is one of the glories of the southern sky and shows a pronounced central core of stars.

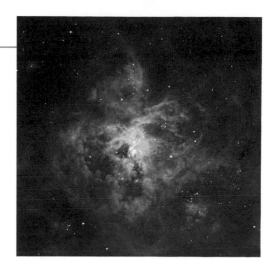

TARANTULA NEBULA The wispy tendrils of the Tarantula Nebula are clearly seen in this image. An emission nebula, it is illuminated by a cluster of hot, young stars at its heart.

47 Tucanae (NGC 104) is the brightest globular cluster after Omega Centauri, and exists at the center of our galaxy. It can be found near the Small Magellanic Cloud (SMC) in the constellation of Tucana, about 16,000 light-years away.

Eta Carinae Nebula (NGC 3372), the sky's finest nebula, is a diffuse nebula easily visible to the naked eye, and will reward any telescope viewing. The **Keyhole Nebula** (NGC 3324) is superimposed on the brightest part of this nebula.

The Helix Nebula (NGC 7293) is the closest known planetary nebula to Earth. The nebula is about 650 light-years away and can be found in the vicinity of the constellation of Aquarius.

The Lagoon Nebula (M8) is a beautiful nebula, just visible to the unaided eye on a dark night, another star factory.

The Coal Sack, near Crux, is the most famous of the dark nebulas.

Large and Small Magellanic Clouds The LMC and SMC are irregular galaxies in orbit around our own, part of the local group of over 35 galaxies. The eastern half of the LMC contains the giant **Tarantula Nebula** (NGC 2070), a star factory, which is 30 times larger than the Great Nebula.

Virgo A (M87), in the constellation of Virgo, is a giant, elliptical galaxy with a mass equivalent to more than 1 trillion of our Suns. There is a whirlpool-like disk of gas at the galaxy's core that rotates at approximately 300 miles per second (500 km/s) around a suspected black hole.

Southern Hemisphere January ■ Looking North

■ View in late December at 11 pm, early January at 10 pm and late January at 9 pm.

Orion the Hunter stands on his head due north. Look for Y-shaped Lepus the Hare cowering at his feet. A line drawn through the three stars of Orion's Belt and extended up to the right points to Sirius, the "dog star," and the brightest in the night sky. That same Belt line extended down points to orange-tinted Aldebaran, the eye of Taurus the Bull. Below Aldebaran sparkles a tight cluster of stars, the Pleiades. Capella twinkles just above the northern horizon, with the twin stars of Castor and Pollux rising to the right, or east.

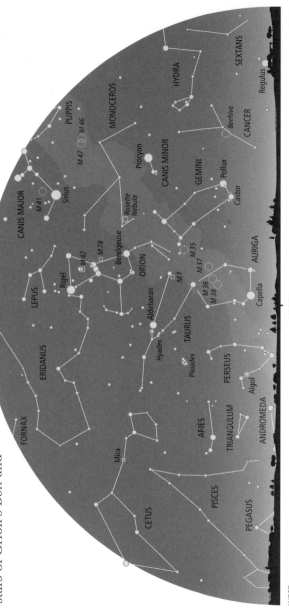

WEST

NORTH

EAST

Southern Hemisphere   January ■ Looking South

■ View in late December at 11 pm, early January at 10 pm and late January at 9 pm.

The Large and Small Magellanic Clouds (LMC and SMC) appear high in the south, as obvious hazy patches amid the faint starfields of Tucana, the Toucan,

Hydrus the Water Snake, and Dorado the Dolphinfish. The only bright star in the western half of the sky is Achernar at the mouth of Eridanus the River. Canopus,

the night sky's second brightest star, blazes above the LMC. To the left, or east, of the clouds, the Milky Way tumbles out of the northern sky's Puppis the Stern, down through Vela the Sail and Carina the Keel, then on past Crux the Southern Cross.

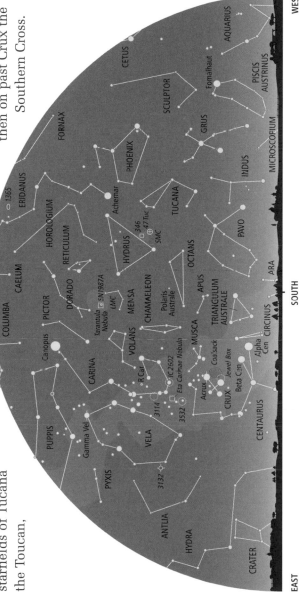

Southern Hemisphere

February ■ Looking North

■ View in late January at 11 pm, early February at 10 pm and late February at 9 pm.

The northern summer sky is filled with bright stars. Orion the Hunter, and its luminaries Betelgeuse and Rigel, shine high in the north. Above Orion sparkles Sirius in

Canis Major, the Great Dog. A lone bright star below Sirius, called Procyon, marks Canis Minor, the Little Dog. Below Procyon shine Castor and Pollux, the

twin stars of Gemini the Twins. Below and to the left, or west, of Orion look for reddish-orange Aldebaran in Taurus the Bull. Capella in Auriga the Charioteer, twinkling just above the northern horizon, rounds out the summer stars.

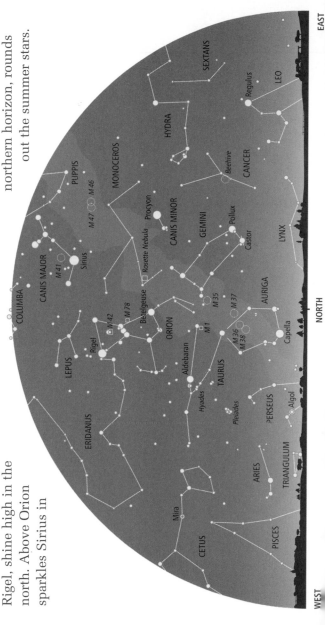

Southern Hemisphere ■ February ■ Looking South

■ View in late January at 11 pm, early February at 10 pm and late February at 9 pm.

During the short summer nights, the Large and Small Magellanic Clouds (LMC and SMC) remain ideally placed for exploration with binoculars or a telescope.

Canopus, in Carina the Keel, shines due south, while to the left, or east, the Milky Way flows past Vela the Sail and Carina the Keel, with each of these constellations contributing two stars to the False Cross, now climbing into the southeast. Crux, the real Southern Cross, is just rising low in the southeast. Below it shine the stellar pair of Beta and Alpha Centauri, also known as Hadar and Rigel Kentaurus.

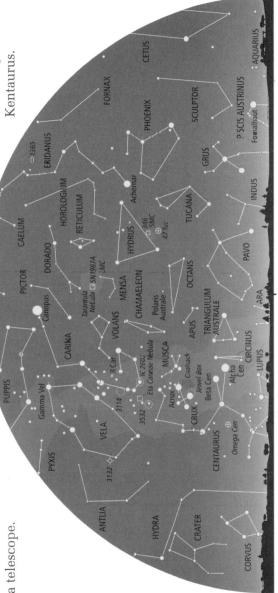

Southern Hemisphere   March ■ Looking North

■ View in late February at 10 pm, early March at 9 pm and late March at 8 pm.

Orion the Hunter, beginning his exit from the sky, shines in the northwest. Above the trio of stars that form his Belt look for the night sky's brightest star, Sirius, high in the north. Below Sirius shine Procyon and the close pair of Castor and Pollux. Low in the northeast, Regulus and the stars of Leo the Lion are creeping onto the sky.

Leo's front is marked by a dangling sickle or hook of stars, while his hindquarters are defined by a right-angle triangle of stars. Between Leo and Gemini the Twins look for a naked-eye star cluster, the Beehive in Cancer the Crab.

Southern Hemisphere

March ■ Looking South

■ View in late February at 10 pm, early March at 9 pm and late March at 8 pm.

The Milky Way is magnificent in autumn. It brightens as it comes out of the north and the constellation of Puppis the Stern now overhead above brilliant Canopus.

As it flows past Carina the Keel and Crux the Southern Cross, the Milky Way becomes filled with bright star clouds, clusters, and nebulas—all providing stunning panoramas for binoculars. Below Carina and Crux shine Beta and Alpha Centauri. Nowhere else do we find two stars as bright as these so close together. Beta is 526 light-years away, while Alpha lies a bit more than 4 light-years from Earth.

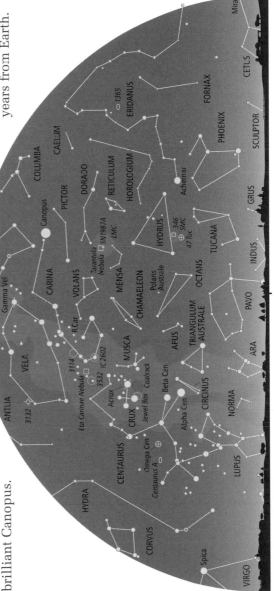

Southern Hemisphere
April ■ Looking North

■ View in late March at 9 pm, early April at 8 pm and late April at 7 pm.

Orion the Hunter, and the other bright stars of the northern summer sky, such as Sirius and Procyon, are gradually sinking into the western twilight. Taking their place is a relatively sparse area of sky. The most distinctive constellation of the northern autumn sky is Leo the Lion. The brightest star in the northeast is Regulus, the shining heart of Leo. A hook of stars hanging down from Regulus marks Leo's head and mane. Like many older constellations invented in the Northern Hemisphere, Leo appears upside down when viewed from southern latitudes.

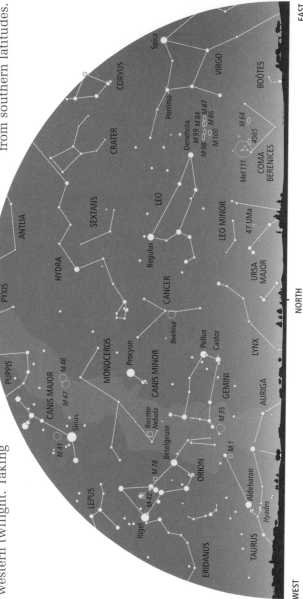

Southern Hemisphere

April ■ Looking South

■ View in late March at 9 pm, early April at 8 pm and late April at 7 pm.

The four stars of the False Cross stand due south. Though distinctive, it is not a proper constellation. The False Cross's two top stars belong to Vela the Sail, while its bottom two stars belong to Carina the Keel. Canopus, the brilliant star far to the right, or west, also belongs to Carina. Carina, Vela, Puppis the Stern, and Pyxis the Compass used to make up one huge constellation, the ship Argo Navis. Crux, the real Southern Cross, its stars bright enough to be seen even in city skies, is unmistakable high in the southeast, as are Beta and Alpha Centauri below it.

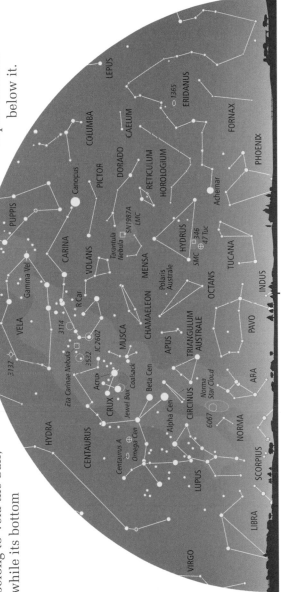

Southern Hemisphere   May ▪ Looking North

▪ View in late April at 9 pm, early May at 8 pm and late May at 7 pm.

As you gaze north, you are looking out of the plane of our Milky Way Galaxy (now behind you to the south) toward its north pole. The North Galactic Pole lies near the large naked-eye star cluster Melotte 111, also called the Coma Berenices Cluster. In this direction, you are looking through the thinnest part of our Galaxy's disk.

▪ So, looking north we see a sky with few bright stars. Regulus and the stars of Leo the Lion stand due north, while to the right, or east, shine Arcturus low in the sky in Boötes the Herdsman, and Spica high in the east in Virgo the Maiden.

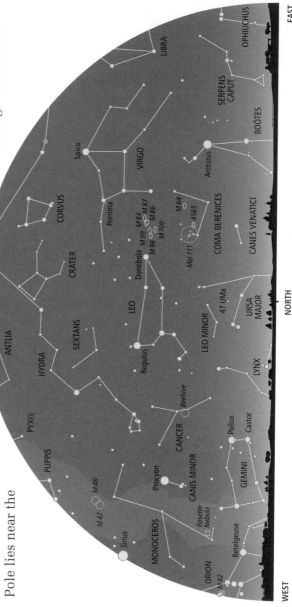

Southern Hemisphere   May ■ Looking South

■ View in late April at 9 pm, early May at 8 pm and late May at 7 pm.

There is no finer stellar panorama than what now lies to the south. The Milky Way and the plane of our Galaxy pours across the sky, from Sirius in the west

to Antares rising in the east. Crux the Southern Cross stands upright due south, its long axis pointing down to the south celestial pole in Octans the Octant. To

the east shine Alpha and Beta Centauri, also called the Pointers because a line drawn through them points to the Cross. The rest of Centaurus the Centaur, sprawling above and around Crux, prances high in the southeast.

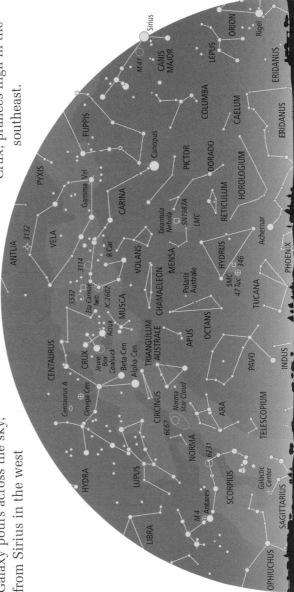

Southern Hemisphere

June ■ Looking North

■ View in late May at 9 pm, early June at 8 pm and late June at 7 pm.

Two bright stars dominate the otherwise star-poor northern winter sky—blue-white Spica high in the north in Virgo the Maiden, and yellow-white

Arcturus, lower in the sky in Boötes the Herdsman. A third star, Regulus, shines over in the northwest in Leo the Lion. Between these three stars lies the North

Galactic Pole, a region poor in stars but rich in galaxies beyond our Milky Way. Hundreds of galaxies, too faint to see with the unaided eye, await telescopic exploration in the constellations of Leo, Coma Berenices, and Virgo.

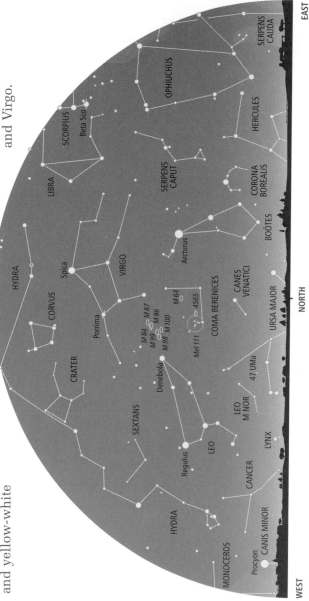

Southern Hemisphere

June ■ Looking South

■ View in late May at 9 pm, early June at 8 pm and late June at 7 pm.

The southern Milky Way is at its best, stretching from horizon to horizon across the south. In its midst stands Crux the Southern Cross, due south and upright in the sky. To the right, or west, of Crux look for the hazy patch of the Eta Carinae Nebula flanked by several bright clusters of stars. To the east of Crux,

Alpha and Beta Centauri, which are also known as Rigel Kentaurus and Hadar, shine high in the south. Between them and Crux, look for a "hole" in the Milky Way, the Coalsack, a dark cloud of interstellar dust at a distance of 500 light-years.

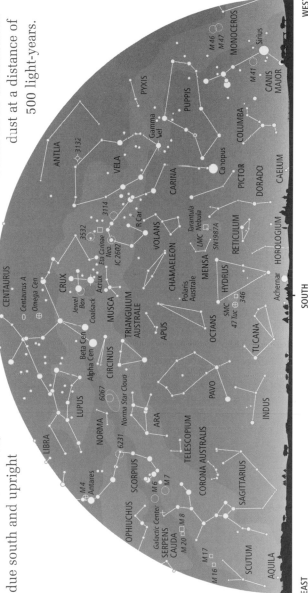

Southern Hemisphere

July ▪ Looking North

▪ View in late June at 9 pm, early July at 8 pm and late July at 7 pm.

The brightest star in the north is Arcturus in Boötes the Herdsman, the third brightest in the sky, after Sirius and Canopus. To the right, or east,

of Arcturus a neat semi-circle of stars forms Corona Borealis, the Northern Crown. Above Arcturus shines fainter Spica in Virgo the Maiden, while high

overhead ruddy Antares gleams as the heart of Scorpius the Scorpion. From Scorpius the Milky Way flows down into the northeastern sky through the constellations of Sagittarius the Archer, Scutum the Shield, and Aquila the Eagle.

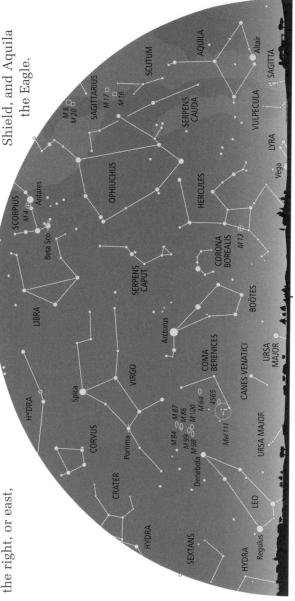

WEST

NORTH

EAST

Southern Hemisphere

July ■ Looking South

■ View in late June at 9 pm, early July at 8 pm and late July at 7 pm.

The Milky Way and the constellations of Crux the Southern Cross and Centaurus the Centaur begin their descent into the west. Rising high into the east is the "fish-hook" of stars that forms Scorpius the Scorpion, followed by a "teapot" of stars, Sagittarius the Archer. From a dark site, look for a giant "emu," formed by dark lanes in the Milky Way. The Coalsack near Crux forms his head, a dark band from Alpha Centauri to Scorpius forms his neck, while his legs are found in dark lanes streaming down from Scorpius.

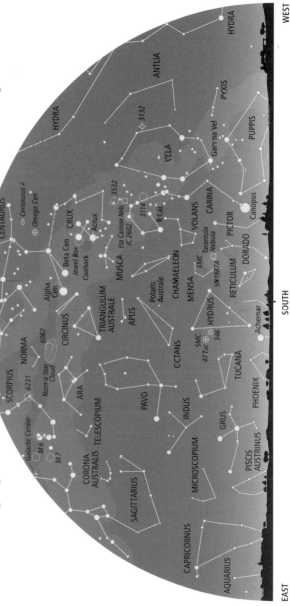

Southern Hemisphere   August ■ Looking North

■ View in late July at 9 pm, early August at 8 pm and late August at 7 pm.

The fish-hook form of Scorpius hangs overhead along with Antares, the reddish heart of the Scorpion. Straight up lies the center of the Milky Way Galaxy and collection of clusters and nebulas perfect for binocular scanning. Sweep down into the north and you will pass through Sagittarius the Archer, home to the richest collection of clusters and nebulas in the sky. The Milky Way narrows and dims below Sagittarius as it passes through Aquila the Eagle, marked by the bright star Altair. Just off the Milky Way shines blue-white Vega.

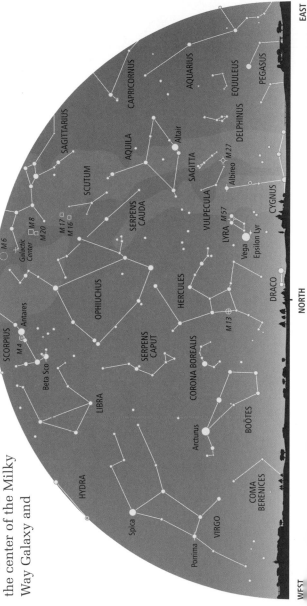

Southern Hemisphere   August ■ Looking South

■ View in late July at 9 pm, early August at 8 pm and late August at 7 pm.

It may be mid-winter but this is a superb time to travel to a dark site. The panorama of our galaxy now sweeps across the heavens from horizon to horizon.

Directly overhead lies the center of the galaxy. There, the Milky Way is at its brightest and widest, filled with rich star clouds and dark lanes that provide

marvelous fields for scanning with binoculars—just lie back and enjoy the view. To the south of Scorpius the Scorpion, the Milky Way narrows but remains spectacular through the starfields of Lupus the Wolf, Norma the Square, and Ara the Altar.

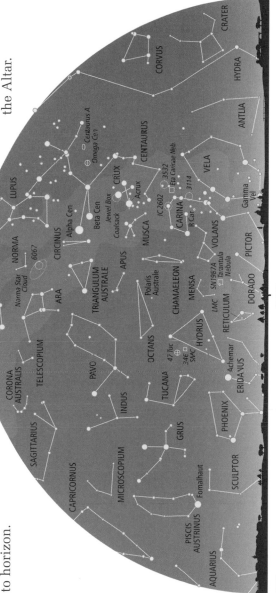

EAST

SOUTH

WEST

Southern Hemisphere   September ■ Looking North

■ View in late August at 9 pm, early September at 8 pm and late September at 7 pm.

The Milky Way bisects the northern sky as it flows down from Sagittarius the Archer, through Aquila the Eagle and Cygnus the Swan. Three bright

stars dominate the northern sky—Altair in Aquila, Vega in Lyra the Harp, and just above the horizon, Deneb in Cygnus. Northern Hemisphere observers know these stars as the Summer Triangle. Cygnus is also better known as the Northern Cross, now due north on the horizon. It is much larger than the Southern Cross and, from southern latitudes, appears to be upside down.

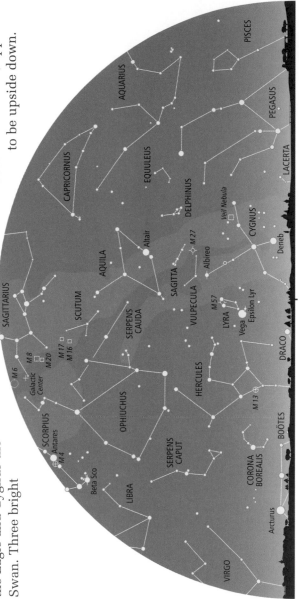

Southern Hemisphere ■ September ■ Looking South

■ View in late August at 9 pm, early September at 8 pm and late September at 7 pm.

The Milky Way Galaxy is magnificent, flowing from Sagittarius the Archer overhead, through the star-filled constellations of Scorpius the Scorpion, Lupus the Wolf, Norma the Square, Ara the Altar, Centaurus the Centaur, and Crux the Southern Cross. But as spring begins, these migrate toward the west, leaving the eastern half of the sky sparse by comparison. East of the celestial pole shines Achernar, the mouth of Eridanus the River and the brightest star in that half of the sky. Above, and alone in a star-poor region, shines Fomalhaut in Piscis Austrinus, the Southern Fish.

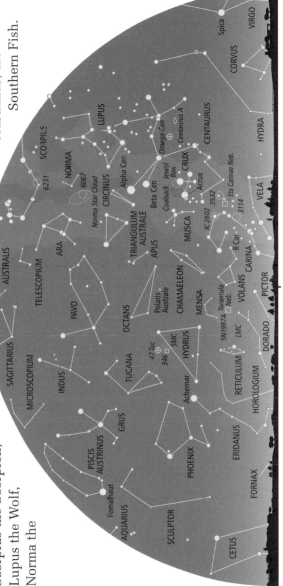

Southern Hemisphere   October ■ Looking North

■ View in late September at 9 pm, early October at 8 pm and late October at 7 pm.

The Milky Way edges westward but is still prominent as it cascades from the star clouds of Sagittarius the Archer to flow between the triangle formed by Altair, Vega, and Deneb, just skimming the northern horizon. As the Milky Way retreats to the west, new spring constellations appear in the east. The most notable is the square of four stars that marks Pegasus the Flying Horse. Above lie dim Aquarius the Water Bearer, Capricornus the Sea Goat, Cetus the Sea Monster, Pisces the Fish, and Piscis Austrinus, the Southern Fish, marked by Fomalhaut.

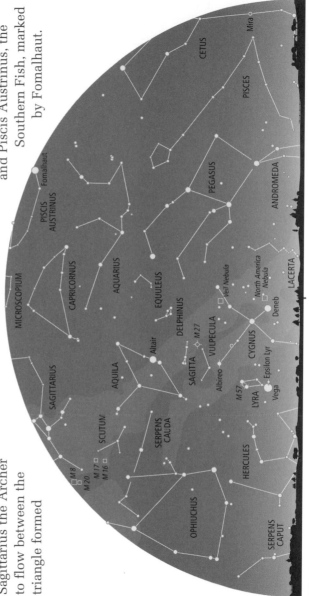

Southern Hemisphere ■ October ■ Looking South

■ View in late September at 9 pm, early October at 8 pm and late October at 7 pm.

As spring takes hold, Crux, the Southern Cross, and Alpha and Beta Centauri drop low into the southwest, with Scorpius the Scorpion and its rich star clouds following not far

behind. The departure of the winter Milky Way leaves a spring sky populated with faint constellations and few bright stars. High overhead, look for Grus the Crane, one

of the few constellations in this sky with an easy-to-identify pattern. Below Grus shines bright Achernar in Eridanus the River. Just to the right, or west, lies the Small Magellanic Cloud (SMC), now climbing into prominence.

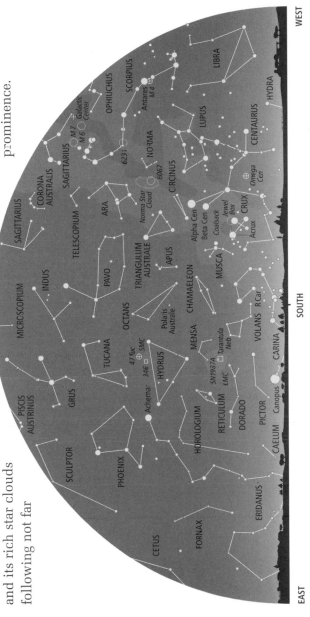

Southern Hemisphere   November ▪ Looking North

■ View in late October at 10 pm, early November at 9 pm and late November at 8 pm.

The Milky Way lies all around you on the horizon. In spring you gaze out the bottom of the Galaxy, at right angles to its disk of stars that forms the Milky Way. We are

looking through the thinnest part of the Galaxy, so this sky contains few bright stars. Across the north stretches a series of faint constellations: Cetus the Sea

Monster, Pisces the Fish, Aquarius the Water Bearer, Capricornus the Sea Goat, and Piscis Austrinus, the Southern Fish. Around the south galactic pole in Sculptor, and in nearby Fornax the Furnace, lie dozens of galaxies ripe for telescopic viewing.

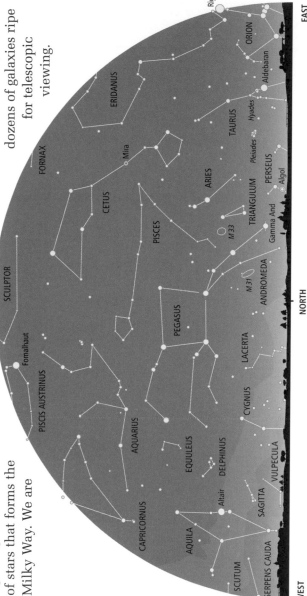

Southern Hemisphere   November ■ Looking South

■ View in late October at 10 pm, early November at 9 pm and late November at 8 pm.

A celestial aviary populates the southern sky. Apus, the Bird of Paradise, flits low in the southwest. Above struts Pavo the Peacock, while higher still flies Grus the Crane. High in the south perch Tucana the Toucan and Phoenix, the mythological bird reborn from the ashes of its predecessor. All these constellations were invented by 16th-century Dutch navigators. Other faint constellations named for scientific instruments (Telescopium, Microscopium, Octans the Octant, Horologium the Clock, Pictor the Compass) date from the 18th century.

Southern Hemisphere

December ■ Looking North

■ View in late November at 11 pm, early December at 10 pm and late December at 9 pm.

Pegasus the Flying Horse, Pisces the Fish, and Cetus the Sea Monster head off into the west, to be replaced by the brighter patterns of Taurus the Bull, Orion the Hunter, and

Canis Major, the Great Dog, now rising in the east. Nearly due south lies an eye-catching cluster of stars, the Pleiades in Taurus. In the east, a line of three stars

in a row, unique in the sky, marks the Belt of Orion. Compared with the way he is traditionally depicted, Orion stands upside down in the Southern Hemisphere sky, with his head and shoulders below the Belt and his legs above.

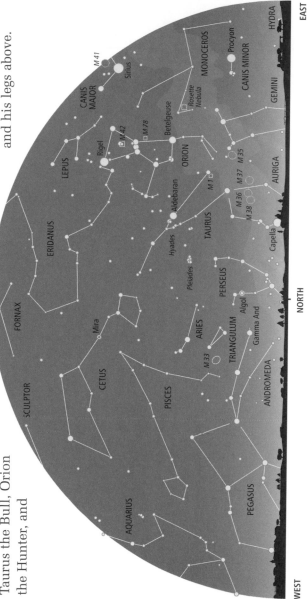

Southern Hemisphere   December ■ Looking South

■ View in late November at 11 pm, early December at 10 pm and late December at 9 pm.

The faint constellations of spring make way for the brighter star patterns of summer now rising into the east. In the transition, the two Magellanic Clouds (the LMC

and SMC) now appear at their best, high in the south just above the south celestial pole. From a dark site, these are rewarding objects for binoculars or a telescope

at low power. Above the SMC shines Achernar, while to the east of the LMC blazes Canopus, the second brightest star in the night sky. The lone bright star in the west is Fomalhaut in Piscis Austrinus, the Southern Fish.

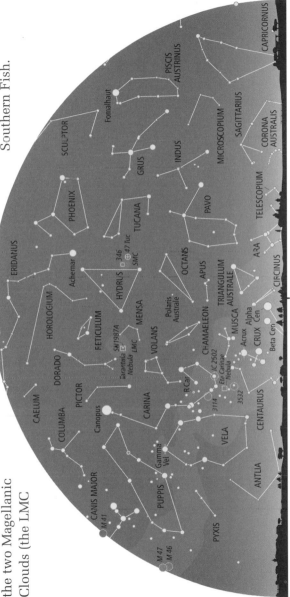

Constellation Charts

USING THE CHARTS

After some practice with the seasonal charts you will probably want to zero in on particular constellations.

THE A–Z OF CONSTELLATIONS

For ease of use, the charts (pp. 272–367) are presented in alphabetical order. North is at the top, and east is at the left—different from Earth maps, but necessary to match our view of the sky. All stars marked are visible to the naked eye, but near cities, binoculars may be needed to pick out the fainter ones.

Instruments Many of the deep-sky objects noted are within the range of binoculars or telescopes with apertures of 2.4 inches (60 mm). Of course, most objects will reveal more detail when viewed with a larger telescope.

Magnitude
The dimmest stars are magnitude 6.5.

Deep-sky objects
Many deep-sky objects visible in a small telescope are plotted.

Auriga

oh-RYE-gah

The Charioteer

This lovely multi-sided figure is easy to find in the sky, largely because of bright Capella. Ancient legends portray Auriga as a charioteer carrying a goat on his shoulder. EPSILON (ε) Ari... extraordinary ... supergian ... pa...

280

Icons
These show the "tool" needed to see the object. See the key below.

 naked eye

 binoculars

 telescope

KEY TO SYMBOLS

Magnitudes   -1   0   1   2   3   4   5   6 and under

Double stars   Variable stars   Open clusters

Globular clusters   Planetary nebulae

Diffuse nebulae   Galaxies   Quasar

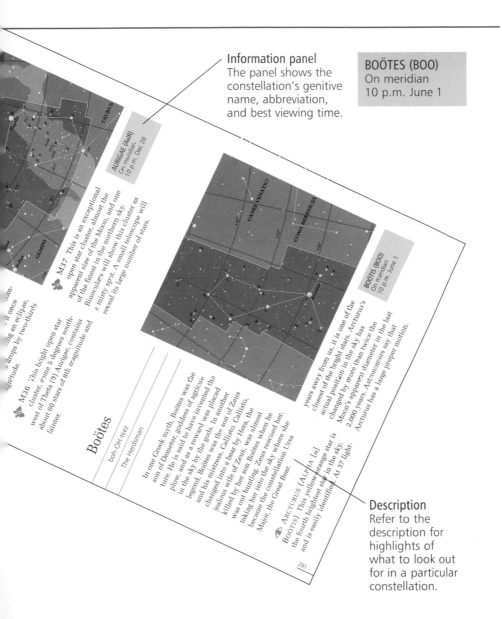

Information panel
The panel shows the constellation's genitive name, abbreviation, and best viewing time.

BOÖTES (BOO)
On meridian
10 p.m. June 1

AURIGAE (AUR)
On meridian:
10 p.m. Dec 20

BOÖTES (BOO)
On meridian
10 p.m. June 1

M37 This is an exceptional open star cluster, almost the apparent size of the Moon, and one of the finest in the northern sky. Binoculars will show this cluster as a misty spot. A small telescope will reveal its large number of stars.

...m-
...ng an eclipse,
...drops by two-thirds
...gnitude.

M36 This bright open star cluster spans 5 degrees south-west of Theta (θ) Aurigae, contains about 60 stars of 8th magnitude and fainter.

Boötes
boh-OH-teez

The Herdsman

In one Greek myth, Boötes was the son of Demeter, goddess of agriculture. He is said to have invented the plow, and as a reward was placed in the sky by the gods. In another legend, Boötes was the son of Zeus and his mistress, Callisto. Callisto, changed into a bear by Hera, the jealous wife of Zeus, was almost killed by her son Boötes when he was out hunting. Zeus rescued her, taking her into the sky where she became the constellation Ursa Major, the Great Bear.

ARCTURUS (ALPHA [α] BOÖTIS) This yellow orange star is the fourth brightest star in the sky, and is easily identified. At 37 light-years away from us, it is one of the closest of the bright stars. Arcturus's actual position in the sky has changed by more than twice the Moon's apparent diameter in the last 2,000 years. Astronomers say that Arcturus has a large proper motion.

281

Description
Refer to the description for highlights of what to look out for in a particular constellation.

Andromeda

an-DROH-me-duh

The Chained Princess

Although Andromeda is renowned for the great galaxy that resides within the constellation, its stars are not very bright. It is easy to find, however, located south of Cassiopeia's W, and just off one corner of the Great Square of Pegasus.

◆ THE ANDROMEDA GALAXY (M31) The closest major galaxy to us, the Andromeda Galaxy was first thought to be a nebula, and was listed in comet hunter Charles Messier's 18th-century catalog of nebulas. A spiral galaxy much like our own Milky Way, it is a maelstrom comprising 200 billion stars and clouds of dust and gas. It is bright enough to be seen with

binoculars from city sites and with the naked eye beneath a dark sky, being one of the most distant objects visible to the unaided eye. In the field of larger binoculars, or using a small telescope, you can see its two neighboring elliptical galaxies,

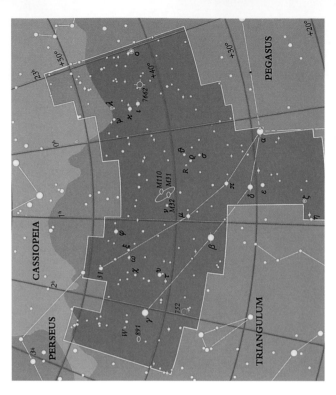

ANDROMEDAE (AND)
On meridian
10 p.m. Nov 1

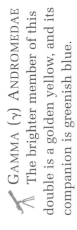

M32 and M110. M32 is small and compact; M110 is larger and more diffuse, and is thus harder to see.

 GAMMA (γ) ANDROMEDAE The brighter member of this double is a golden yellow, and its companion is greenish blue.

 R ANDROMEDAE This long-period Mira variable has a range of nine magnitudes.

 NGC 752 This open cluster lies about 5 degrees south of Gamma (γ) Andromedae and is easy to find because of its relatively bright stars. Because it is spread out over such a large area, it is actually easier to see through binoculars than through a telescope. If using a telescope, use it at its lowest power.

 NGC 7662 This fairly bright planetary nebula looks starlike through the smallest telescopes. However, through a 6 inch (150 mm) telescope at moderate power, it becomes a graceful, glowing spot of gas about 30 arcseconds across.

 NGC 891 This is a challenge even for 6 inch (150 mm) telescopes, but with a dark sky, you will see one of the best examples of a spiral galaxy, viewed edge-on.

ANDROMEDA GALAXY
With a telescope, use the lowest power you have to fit as much of Andromeda in the field of view as possible. Two companion galaxies are visible in this photo: M 110 (lower right) and M 32, the starlike blob left of Andromeda's center.

Antlia

ANT-lee-uh

The Air Pump

The Air Pump was named after the 17th-century physicist Robert Boyle's invention by Nicolas-Louis de Lacaille during the time he spent working at an observatory at the Cape of Good Hope, from 1750 to 1754. Antlia is a small, faint constellation just off the bright southern Milky Way, not far from Vela and Puppis. Its alpha (α) star is barely the constellation's brightest star and has been given no proper name. It is red in color and possibly varies slightly in magnitude.

NGC 2997 This is a large, faint spiral galaxy, with a star-like nucleus. It is quite difficult to observe with a small telescope.

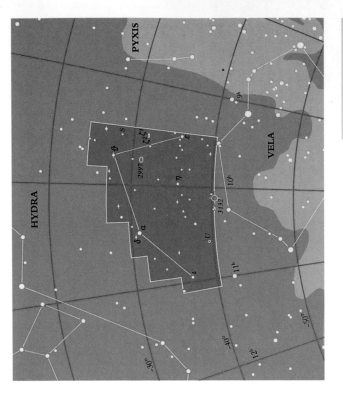

ANTLIAE (ANT)
On meridian
10 p.m. March 20

Apus

ay-pus

The Bird of Paradise

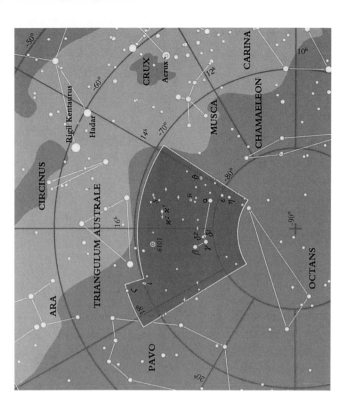

APODIS (APS)
On meridian
10 p.m. June 20

This faint constellation is directly below Triangulum Australe, the Southern Triangle. Being close to the southern pole, it cannot be seen from most northern latitudes.

THETA (ϑ) APODIS This variable star ranges from magnitude 6.4 to below 8 in a semiregular cycle over a hundred days.

NGC 6101 A faint globular cluster, NGC 6101 can be seen as a small, misty spot through a small telescope.

S APODIS This is a "backward" nova. Usually the star shines at about magnitude 10— bright enough to see through a small telescope—but at irregular intervals it erupts dark material. It then fades by about a hundred times, to around magnitude 15. After staying faint for several weeks, it slowly returns to its original brightness.

Aquarius

ah-KWAIR-ee-us

The Water Bearer

This is one of the sky's oldest constellations, dating from Babylonian times. Appropriately, the Water Bearer is not far from a dolphin, a river, a sea serpent, and a fish.

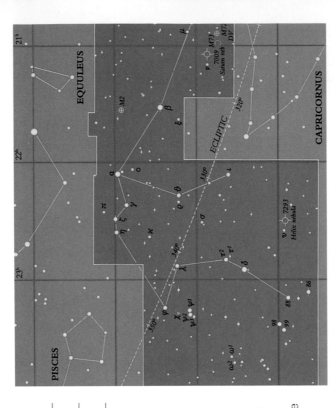

AQUARII (AQR)
On meridian
10 p.m. Sept 20

M2 This fine globular cluster appears as a fuzzy spot of light through binoculars and small telescopes. A 6 inch (150 mm) telescope resolves it into stars.

THE SATURN NEBULA (NGC 7009) This planetary nebula was so named because its protruding rays made it look like a dim version of Saturn with its rings. It is visible through a telescope as a greenish point of light.

THE HELIX NEBULA (NGC 7293) The Helix is a large planetary nebula. Because its brightness is spread over a large area, it appears best with a low-power, wide-field telescope or binoculars under a dark sky.

Aquila

uh-KWI-luh

The Eagle

Likened to an eagle by the sky-watchers of the Euphrates Basin, the constellation of Aquila takes its name from the bird that belonged to the Greek god Zeus. Aquila's main accomplishment was to bring the handsome mortal youth Ganymede to the sky to serve as his master's cup bearer.

 ETA (η) AQUILAE This supergiant star is a bright Cepheid variable that changes by about a magnitude in brightness (3.5 to 4.4) in a period of little more than a week. At its brightest, it rivals the nearby Delta (δ) Aquilae, and it fades to about the magnitude of Iota (ι) Aquilae.

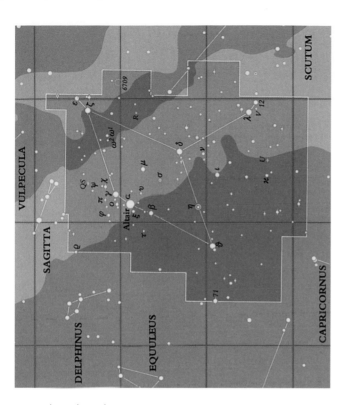

AQUILAE (AQL)
On meridian
10 p.m. Aug 10

 R AQUILAE This Mira star varies in magnitude from 6 to 11.5 over a period of 284 days.

NGC 6709 This open cluster is a closely knit group against a rich background of stars.

Ara

AR-ah

The Altar

Located south of Scorpius, Ara's original Latin name was Ara Centauri—the altar of the centaur Chiron. Half man and half horse, Chiron was thought to be the wisest creature on Earth. Ara has also been referred to variously as the altar of Dionysus; the altar built by Noah after the flood; the altar built by Moses; and even the altar from Solomon's Temple.

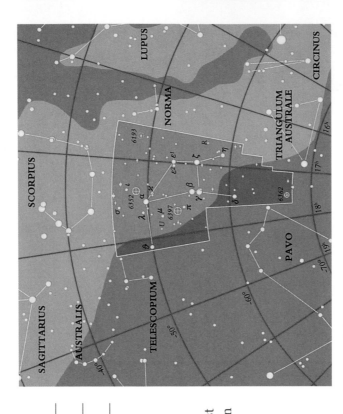

ARAE (ARA)
On meridian
10 p.m. July 10

NGC 6397 This globular cluster is placed between Beta (β) Arae and Theta (ϑ) Arae. It is relatively loose, so an observer with powerful binoculars should be able to detect it without difficulty and perhaps even resolve its faint stars.

U ARAE This Mira-type variable is bright enough to be seen through a small telescope when it is at its maximum of magnitude 8. However, it then drops a full five magnitudes before rising again over a period of more than seven months.

Aries

AIR-eez

The Ram

Aries is well known and is not hard to find, but it is small and contains few objects of interest.

The constellation has long been seen as a ram. For the Greeks, it represented the ram from which the golden fleece was taken. In one version of the legend, the god Hermes sent a ram with a golden fleece to carry Phrixus and Helle, the two children of the king of Thessaly, to safety from their cruel stepmother. Helle fell from the ram's back, but Phrixus was carried to safety on the shores of the Black Sea. Here, he sacrificed the ram, and its fleece was placed in the care of a sleepless dragon. It was from here that Jason and the Argonauts stole it.

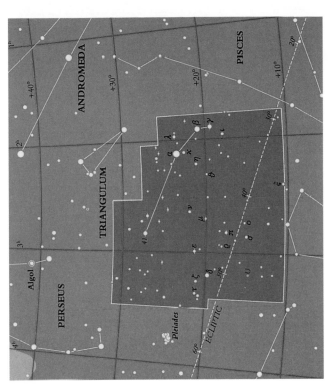

ARIETIS (ARI)
On meridian
10 p.m. Nov 20

GAMMA (γ) ARIETIS In 1664, the English scientist Robert Hooke was following the motion of a comet when he chanced upon this beautiful double star. It has a separation of 8 arcseconds, and is easy to find and observe.

Auriga

oh-RYE-gah

The Charioteer

This lovely multi-sided figure is easy to find in the sky, largely because of bright Capella. Ancient legends portray Auriga as a charioteer carrying a goat on his shoulder.

◆ EPSILON (ε) AURIGAE An extraordinary variable system, this supergiant star fades when its companion passes in front of it once every 27 years. During an eclipse, its brightness drops by two-thirds of a magnitude.

🔭 M36 This bright open star cluster, some 5 degrees southwest of Theta (ϑ) Aurigae, contains about 60 stars of 8th magnitude and fainter.

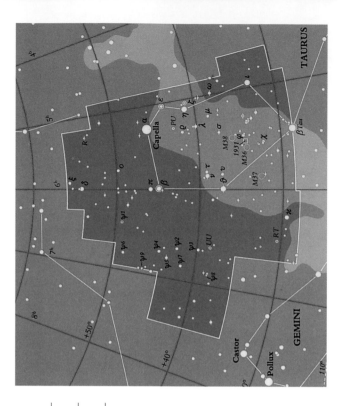

AURIGAE (AUR)
On meridian
10 p.m. Dec 20

🔭 M37 This is an exceptional open star cluster, almost the apparent size of the Moon, and one of the finest in the northern sky. Binoculars will show this cluster as a misty spot. A small telescope will reveal its large number of stars.

Boötes

boh-OH-teez

The Herdsman

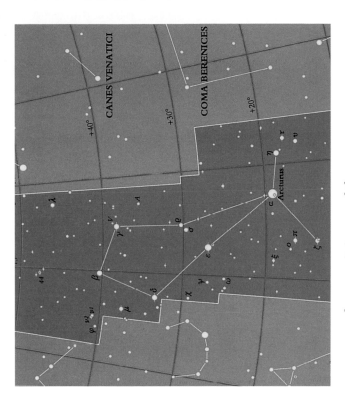

BOÖTIS (BOO)
On meridian
10 p.m. June 1

In one Greek myth, Boötes was the son of Demeter, goddess of agriculture. He is said to have invented the plow, and as a reward was placed in the sky by the gods. In another legend, Boötes was the son of Zeus and his mistress, Callisto. Callisto, changed into a bear by Hera, the jealous wife of Zeus, was almost killed by her son Boötes when he was out hunting. Zeus rescued her, taking her into the sky where she became the constellation Ursa Major, the Great Bear.

ARCTURUS (ALPHA [α] BOÖTIS) This yellow-orange star is the fourth brightest star in the sky, and is easily identified. At 37 light-years away from us, it is one of the closest of the bright stars. Arcturus's actual position in the sky has changed by more than twice the Moon's apparent diameter in the last 2,000 years. Astronomers say that Arcturus has a large proper motion.

281

Caelum

SEE-lum

The Chisel

Caelum is one of the least conspicuous of all the constellations, containing a few faint stars with a magnitude of 5 at best. Originally named Caela Sculptoris, the Sculptor's tool, it is one of the many regions in the Southern Hemisphere skies that was named by the 18th-century astronomer Nicolas-Louis de Lacaille. It comprises a largely empty region of the heavens between the constellations of Columba, the Dove, and Eridanus, the River.

R CAELI A bright Mira-type variable, this star changes from magnitude 6.7 to 13.7 over a period of about 13 months.

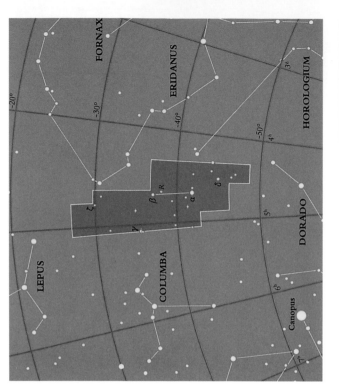

CAELI (CAEI)
On meridian
10 p.m. Jan 1

Camelopardalis

ka-mel-o-PAR-da-lis

The Giraffe

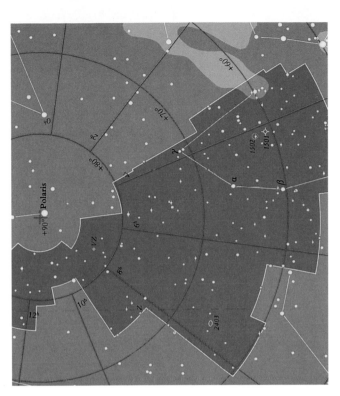

CAMELOPARDALIS
(CAM)
On meridian
10 p.m. Jan 10

Camelopardalis was dreamed up by the German astronomer Jakob Bartsch in 1624, who claimed that it represented the camel that brought Rebecca to Isaac. The constellation lies between Auriga and the two bears.

Z CAMELOPARDALIS This cataclysmic variable star erupts every two or three weeks from its minimum of magnitude 13 to a maximum of magnitude 9.6, which is still quite faint. Its resemblance to other such variables ceases when, while fading, it stops changing and hovers at an intermediate magnitude. This "standstill" might last for months before the decline resumes. In the late 1970s, Z Cam stayed around magnitude 11.7 for several years.

VZ CAMELOPARDALIS This star varies irregularly over the small range between magnitudes 4.8 and 5.2. It is located close to Polaris.

Cancer

CAN-ser

The Crab

Cancer is the faintest member of the zodiac, and its main claim to fame is the beautiful M44.

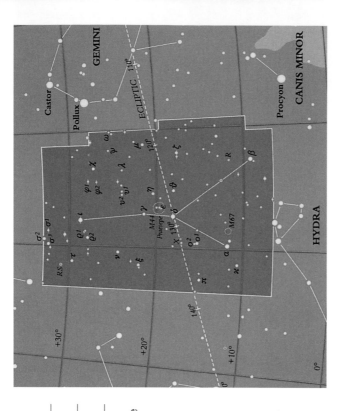

CANCRI (CNC)
On meridian
10 p.m. March 1

◉ THE PRAESEPE OR BEEHIVE (M44) One of the sky's finest open clusters, this is easy to see through binoculars from the city and with the naked eye from a dark site. There are over 200 stars in the Praesepe. Spread over 1½ degrees, they are best seen with binoculars.

M67 This open cluster has 500 faint stars spread over half a degree. Although you can find it with binoculars, your best view will be through a small telescope's low-power eyepiece.

R CANCRI This bright long-period variable is easily visible through a pair of binoculars when near its maximum magnitude of 6.2. R Cancri varies down to a faint 11.2 and back in almost precisely a year.

Canes Venatici

KAH-nez ve-NAT-eh-see

The Hunting Dogs

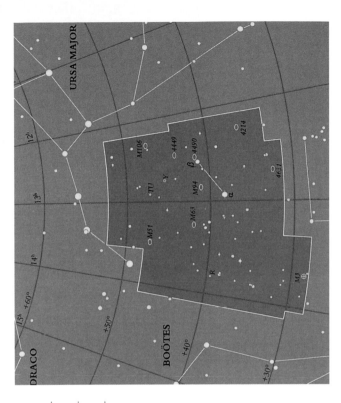

CANUM
VENATICORUM
(CVN)
On meridian
10 p.m. May 1

This constellation, tucked away just south of the Big Dipper's handle, contains a wide variety of deep-sky objects.

◈ COR CAROLI The heart of Charles, Alpha (α) Canum Venaticorum is believed to have been named by Edmond Halley after his patron, Charles II. This wide double is easily split.

⚹ M3   A rare gem of the northern sky, this globular cluster is midway between Cor Caroli and Arcturus. Some 35,000 light-years away and 200 light-years across, M3 begins to resolve into stars through a small telescope.

 THE WHIRLPOOL GALAXY (M51) In binoculars, this galaxy appears as a round, 8th-magnitude glow with a bright nucleus. A 12 inch (300 mm) telescope will show its spiral structure. M51 lies 23 million light-years away.

285

Canis Major

KAH-niss MAY-jer

The Great Dog

One of the most striking of all the constellations, the Great Dog is marked by the brilliant star Sirius, commonly known as the Dog Star—the brightest star in the entire sky.

Canis Major and its neighboring constellation, Canis Minor, the Little Dog, appear in a number of myths. One legend has the two dogs sitting patiently under a table at which the Twins are dining. The faint stars that can be seen scattered in the sky between Canis Minor and Gemini are the crumbs the Twins have been feeding to the animals.

According to the ancient Greeks, Canis Major could run incredibly fast. Laelaps, as they called him, is said to have won a race against a fox

that was the fastest creature in the world. Zeus placed the dog in the sky to celebrate the victory. Another myth has the Great Dog and Little Dog assisting Orion while he is hunting. In other versions of the story, Sirius is Orion's hunting dog.

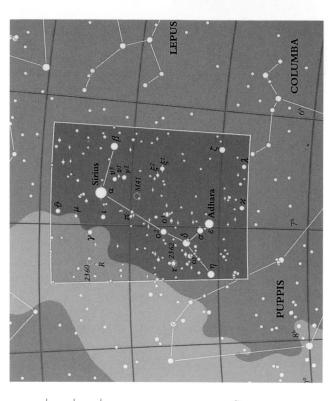

CANIS MAJORIS (CMA)
On meridian
10 p.m. Feb 1

For the ancient Egyptians, Sirius had special meaning. After being close to the Sun for several months, the star would rise just before dawn in late summer. This event heralded the annual flooding of the Nile Valley, the waters refertilizing the fields with silt.

◆ SIRIUS The sky's brightest star, Sirius is only 8.6 light-years from Earth. Its great brilliance is also due to its being some 40 times more luminous than the Sun. In 1834, Friedrich Bessel noted that Sirius had a strange wobble to its position, indicating an unseen companion. In 1862, the famous telescope maker Alvan Clark, while testing a new 18½ inch (460 mm) refractor on Sirius, discovered the faint star we now know as the Pup. It is a white dwarf star, its density being so great that a piece of it the size of this book might weigh

around 200 tons (203 tonnes). On its own, the Pup would be a respectable star visible through a telescope at magnitude 8.4, but its closeness to mighty Sirius makes it a very difficult target, requiring a telescope of 10 inch (250 mm) aperture and very steady viewing conditions.

◆ M41 A beautiful open cluster, M41 is surrounded by a rich field of background stars. If you look at it through a telescope, you will be able to see a distinctly red star near the cluster's center.

NGC 2362 This cluster of several dozen stars is tightly packed around Tau (τ) Canis Majoris. What is not clear is whether Tau (τ) is actually a member of the cluster or just a chance foreground star.

THE GREAT DOG

Canis Major has been depicted as a dog for thousands of years. The constellation is easily visible from most parts of Earth.

Canis Minor

KAH-niss MY-ner

The Little Dog

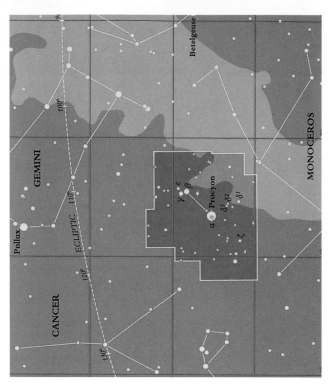

Canis Minor has only two stars brighter than 5th magnitude—Procyon and Gomeisa (Beta [β] Canis Minoris). Besides being one of Orion's dogs, Canis Minor was also said to be one of Actaeon's hounds. Actaeon surprised Artemis, goddess of the hunt, while she was bathing outdoors. Spellbound by her beauty, he paused for a moment and she saw him. Furious that a mortal had seen her naked, Artemis turned him into a stag, set her hounds upon him, and he was devoured.

◈ PROCYON (ALPHA [α] CANIS MINORIS) This beautiful deep yellow star follows Orion across the sky. Only 11.4 light-years away, it is accompanied by a white dwarf that is much fainter than the Pup that accompanies Sirius.

 BETA (β) CANIS MINORIS This is set in a beautiful field that includes one quite red star.

Capricornus

kap-reh-KOR-nuss

The Sea Goat; Capricorn

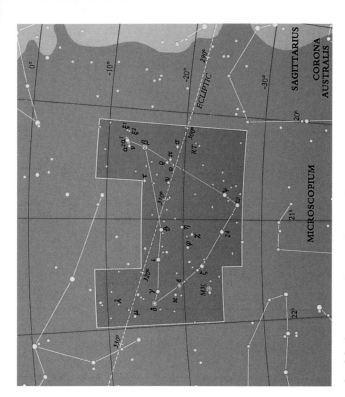

CAPRICORNI (CAP)
On meridian
10 p.m. Sept 1

The triangle of stars forming Capricornus is easily recognized, although the stars are no brighter than 3rd magnitude.

The constellation has been named for a goat since Babylonian times, and it is often depicted as a goat with the tail of a fish. This might relate to a story about the god Pan, who, when fleeing the monster Typhon, leaped into the Nile. The part of him that was underwater turned into a fish tail, while his top half remained that of a goat.

◈ ALPHA (α) CAPRICORNI This double has a separation of 6 arcminutes—a naked-eye test for a night's clarity and steadiness. The pair is a double by coincidence, but each star is itself a true binary.

 M30 Perhaps 40,000 light-years away, this globular cluster has a fairly dense center. It is not well resolved in small telescopes.

Carina

ka-RYE-nah

The Keel

This constellation lies in one of the richest parts of the Milky Way, and under a dark sky it is breathtaking.

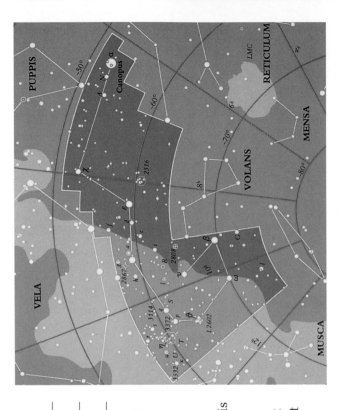

CANOPUS (ALPHA [α] CARINAE) This yellow supergiant is the second brightest star in the sky.

NGC 3532 This is the finest of the clusters in Carina, with about 150 stars visible in a telescope at low magnification.

THE ETA (η) CARINAE NEBULA (NGC 3372) This exquisite nebula will reward any size of binoculars or telescope. It is 2 degrees across, with dark rifts appearing to break it up. The dark

Keyhole Nebula (NGC 3324) is superimposed on its brightest part.

IC 2602 This open cluster around Theta (ϑ) Carinae is best seen in binoculars or in the eyepiece of a wide-field telescope.

CARINAE (CAR)
On meridian
10 p.m. March 1

Cassiopeia

kass-ee-oh-PEE-uh

The Queen

This striking W-shaped figure is on the other side of Polaris from the Big Dipper. Most prominent in the Northern Hemisphere's winter sky, Cassiopeia is visible all year from mid-northern latitudes.

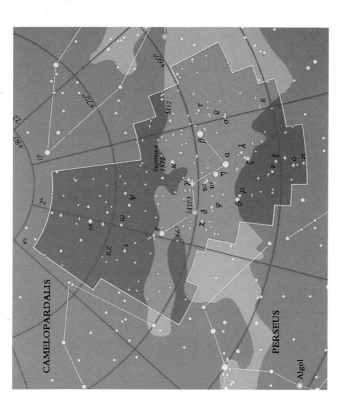

CASSIOPEIAE (CAS)
On meridian
10 p.m. Nov 1

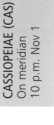

GAMMA (γ) CASSIOPEIAE
This star lies at the center of Cassiopeia's W figure. Normally the constellation's third brightest star, it is an irregular variable. It is slowly losing mass into a disk or shell that surrounds it, and alterations in the shell's thickness might be responsible for its variations in brightness.

M52 This group of a hundred or so stars is one of the richest in the northern half of the sky, but only one of several open clusters scattered throughout Cassiopeia.

NGC 663 This small open cluster of quite faint stars is an attractive sight in a small telescope.

Centaurus

sen-TOR-us

The Centaur

These stars represent Chiron, one of the Centaurs—creatures that were half man, half horse. Unlike the other Centaurs, who were brutal, Chiron was extremely wise, and tutored Jason and Hercules.

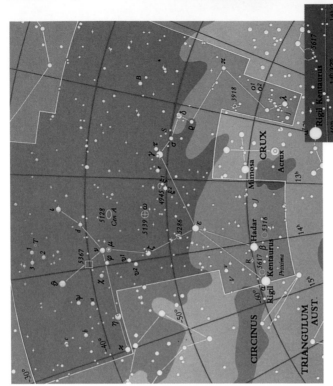

◆ ALPHA (α) CENTAURI At the foot of the Centaur, this star is only 4.4 light-years away and is the Sun's nearest neighbor. One of the prettiest binary stars, its two components revolve around each other once every 80 years. The separation is around 16 arcseconds, but this will close to 2 arcseconds by about the year 2035. Alpha (α) and Beta (β) Centauri are the bright "pointers" to the Southern Cross.

✧ PROXIMA CENTAURI A tiny red dwarf only 25,000 miles (40,000 km) across, this star is actually a little closer to us than the two stars of Alpha (α) Centauri, but it is thought to be their companion. It flares occasionally, jumping by half

a magnitude or more, usually returning to its normal brightness within half an hour.

◉ OMEGA (ω) CENTAURI This is perhaps the finest globular cluster in the entire sky. With the naked eye it is visible as a fuzzy star of magnitude 4. Unlike most globulars, it is oval rather than round in shape. A 3 inch (75 mm) telescope will show a large, fuzzy disk with mottled edges, while a 6 inch (150 mm) one will resolve it into stars. Viewed in an even larger telescope, under a dark sky, it looks magnificent, with the field of a low-power eyepiece overflowing with faint stars.

 NGC 5128 Located only 4½ degrees north of Omega (ω) Centauri, this galaxy is distinguished by a dark band that runs across its center—probably the result of a collision with another galaxy. It is a strong source of radio energy, known to radio astronomers as Centaurus A. The dust lane is apparent in dark skies with a 4 inch (100 mm) or larger telescope.

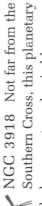 NGC 3918 Not far from the Southern Cross, this planetary nebula presents a classic blue-green disk 12 arcminutes across, like a larger version of Uranus.

 NGC 5128 A dark band of dust cuts across NGC 5128. This galaxy emits more than a thousand times the radio energy of our own Galaxy.

CENTAURI (CEN)
On meridian
10 p.m. May 10

Cepheus

SEE-fee-us

The King

Cepheus is an inconspicuous constellation. Its five bright stars are easy to find only because they face the open side of the W shape of Cassiopeia. It looks a little like a house with a pointed roof. Although the top of the roof does not really point to Polaris, it offers the general direction to the pole at a time of year when the Big Dipper's pointer stars are not readily accessible.

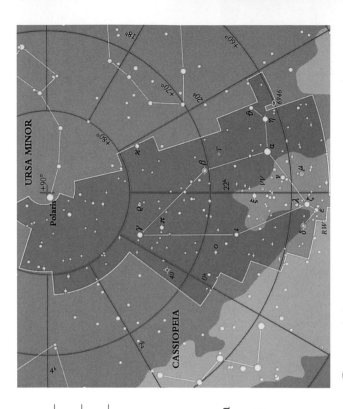

CEPHEI (CEP)
On meridian
10 p.m. Oct 1

◆ DELTA (δ) CEPHEI   This star is the prototype for the Cepheid variables. Its highest magnitude is 3.5, as bright as neighboring Zeta (ζ) Cephei, and it fades to 4.4, the brightness of Epsilon (ε) Cephei. It completes a cycle every 5.4 days.

◆ MU (μ) CEPHEI   This star is so strikingly red that William Herschel called it the Garnet Star. Using Zeta (ζ) and Epsilon (ε) as comparison stars, you can watch it vary in brightness irregularly over hundreds of days.

Cetus

SEE-tus

The Whale; The Sea Monster

The constellation Cetus consists of faint stars, but it occupies a large area of sky. This sea monster's head is a group of stars not far from Taurus and Aries, and his body and tail lie toward Aquarius.

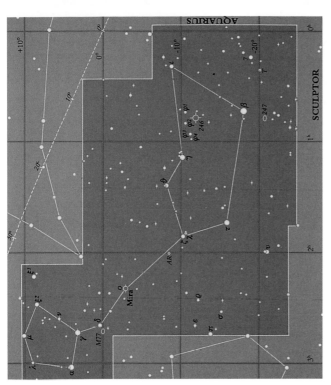

👁 MIRA Omicron (o) Ceti, known as Mira, is the most famous long-period variable of all. On August 13, 1596, David Fabricius, a Dutch skywatcher, saw a new star in Cetus. Over the following weeks, it faded, disappeared, then reappeared in 1609. In 1662 Johannes Hevelius named it Mira Stella, the Wonderful Star. Mira varies from a magnitude of about 3.4 to a minimum of 9.3 over 11 months.

M77 Cetus contains several galaxies, the brightest of which is M77, near Delta (δ) Ceti. It is a 9th-magnitude spiral galaxy with a bright core. A 4 inch (100 mm) telescope shows a faint circular disk around the core.

Chamaeleon

ka-MEE-lee-un

The Chameleon

Johann Bayer drew this constellation early in the 17th century, following descriptions given by early south sea explorers. One of the smallest and least conspicuous of the constellations, Chamaeleon does a good job hiding in the sky. Consisting of a few faint stars, it lies close to the south celestial pole, south of Carina and right beside the south polar constellation of Octans.

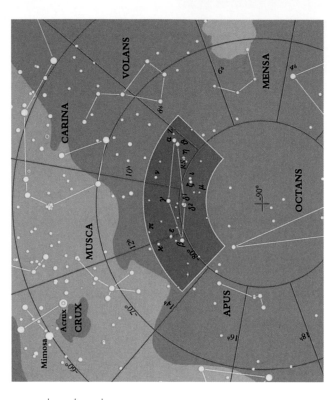

CHAMAELEONTIS (CHA)
On meridian
10 p.m. April 1

Z CHAMAELEONTIS This faint variable star erupts periodically. At its minimum it shines at magnitude 16.2, invisible except in a telescope with an aperture of at least 12 inches (300 mm). However, every three to four months it undergoes an outburst, rising within just a few hours to about magnitude 11.5, and for a few days it is visible through a 6 inch (150 mm) telescope. Even so, this does not constitute an easy target in a corner of the sky with few stars.

Circinus

SUR-seh-nus

The Drawing Compass

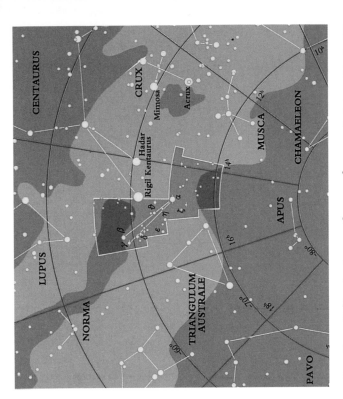

CIRCINI (CIR)
On meridian
10 p.m. June 1

The early explorers in the south seas were less interested in mythology than in the modern instruments on which they relied to find their way around uncharted waters. The Drawing Compass is one of a number of obscure constellations that were designated by the French astronomer Nicolas-Louis de Lacaille. He worked at an observatory at the Cape of Good Hope from 1750 to 1754, where he compiled a catalog of more than 10,000 stars. The constellation is not visible to most northern observers.

ALPHA (α) CIRCINI This, at only 3rd magnitude, is the constellation's brightest star and chief attraction. It lies just near the much brighter Alpha (α) Centauri. It is about 53 light-years away and has a faint 9th-magnitude companion. Alpha (α) Circini represents the hinge of the compass; Beta (β) Circini is one of the points.

Columba

koh-LUM-bah

The Dove

Immediately south of Canis Major, the constellation Columba was named by Petrus Plancius, a 16th-century Dutch theologian and mapmaker. This inconspicuous group of stars honors the dove that Noah sent out from the ark after the rains had stopped, to see if it could find dry land. According to at least one source, the name for the constellation's alpha (α) star, Phakt, is the Arabic word for "ring dove."

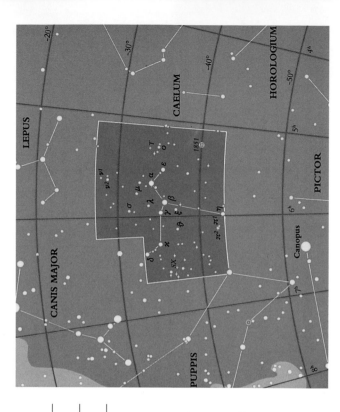

COLUMBAE (COL)
On meridian
10 p.m. Jan 20

NGC 1851   Bright and large, this 7th-magnitude globular cluster appears as a misty spot through binoculars under a good sky. A 6 inch (150 mm) telescope will begin to resolve the cluster's brightest stars.

T COLUMBAE   This star is a Mira variable, with a maximum magnitude of 6.7. It drops down to magnitude 12.6 and then rises again over a period of seven and a half months.

Coma Berenices

KOH-mah bear-eh-NEE-seez

Berenice's Hair

Coma Berenices has no bright stars and is hard to distinguish, but it is a remarkable area of sky. It is a sprinkling of faint stars superimposed on a cloud of galaxies.

M53 This fine globular cluster is about 3 arcminutes in diameter and lies close to Alpha (α) Comae Berenices.

The Blackeye Galaxy (M64) This looks like an ordinary spiral galaxy, with tightly wound arms, but seen with a 4 to 6 inch (100 to 150 mm) telescope or larger, a huge cloud of dust can be seen dominating its center, giving it the look of a black eye.

NGC 4565 Under a dark sky, a small telescope should show this 10th-magnitude object as a pencil-thin line of haze. It is a spiral galaxy seen edge-on, with a dust lane that becomes apparent in 8 inch (200 mm) telescopes.

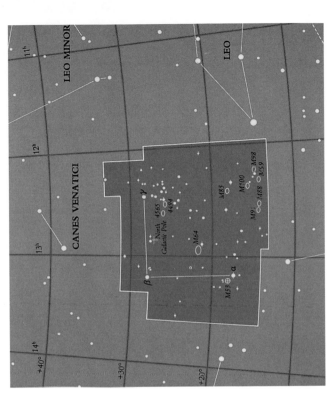

LEO MINOR

LEO

CANES VENATICI

11ʰ
12ʰ
13ʰ
14ʰ

+40°
+30°
+27°

γ

North Galactic Pole
4565
494

M85
M100
M99
4188
M98
M59

M64

β

α

M53

COMAE BERENICES (COM)
On meridian
10 p.m. May 1

Corona Australis

kor-OH-nah os-TRAH-lis

The Southern Crown

This small semicircular group of faint stars lies just south of Sagittarius and is said to represent a crown of laurel or olive leaves. One story relating to the crown comes from Ovid's *Metamorphoses*. Juno discovered that her husband, Jupiter, was the lover of Semele, a human. Masquerading as Semele's maid, Juno suggested that Semele ask Jupiter to appear before her in all his glory. Jupiter was appalled at her request, but did not refuse it. When she saw him in his splendor she was consumed by fire. Her unborn child was saved, however, to become Bacchus, god of wine, who honored his mother by placing the crown in the sky.

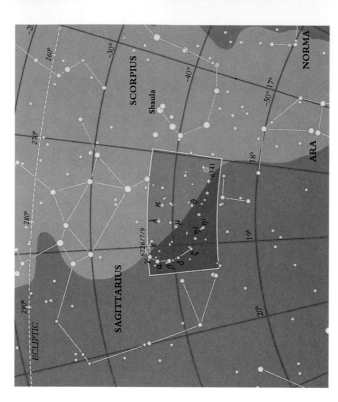

CORONAE AUSTRALIS (CRI)
On meridian
10 p.m. Aug 1

NGC 6541 Viewed through smaller telescopes, this globular cluster looks like a small nebulous disk. An 8 inch (200 mm) telescope only begins to resolve the edge into stars. The cluster is located about 22,000 light-years away.

Corona Borealis

kor-OH-nah bor-ee-AL-is

The Northern Crown

Just 20 degrees northeast of Arcturus lies the Northern Crown, a small semicircle of stars that are faint but very distinct. In Greek mythology, the crown belongs to Ariadne, daughter of Minos, King of Crete.

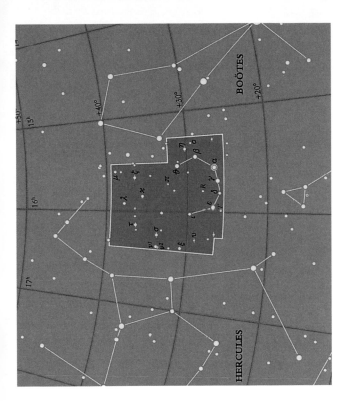

 R CORONAE BOREALIS One of the more remarkable stars in the sky, R Cor Bor, as it is generally known, is a nova in reverse.

Normally shining at magnitude 5.9, at completely irregular intervals the star will suddenly fade, sometimes by as much as eight magnitudes, as dark material erupts in its atmosphere. It then slowly recovers as the material dissipates.

T CORONAE BOREALIS Now shining at magnitude 10.2, in 1866 this star suddenly rose to magnitude 2. Known as a recurrent nova, the star repeated the performance unexpectedly in 1946, and will probably do so again.

CORONAE BOREALIS (CRB)
On meridian
10 p.m. June 30

Corvus and Crater

KOR-vus   KRAY-ter

The Crow   The Cup

Arc to Arcturus, speed to Spica, then turn west and you will see a small foursome of stars that the ancients called the Crow or the Raven. Crater is a fainter constellation alongside that looks like a cup, and that represents the chalice of the Greek god Apollo.

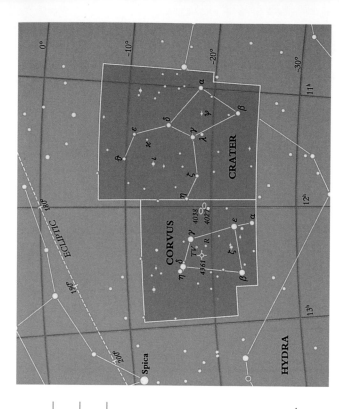

CORVI (CRV)
CRATERIS (CRT)
On meridian
10 p.m. April 20

R CORVI This Mira-type variable star ranges from magnitude 6.7 to 14.4 over a period of about 10 months.

THE RING-TAILED GALAXY Also called the Antennae or Rat-tailed Galaxy, NGC 4038 and NGC 4039 form a faint, 11th-magnitude pair of galaxies that are in the process of interacting or colliding. Needing an 8 inch (200 mm) telescope to see, it is still one of the brightest pairs of connected galaxies. Long-exposure photographs show the galaxies have a pair of "tails," hence the common names.

Crux

KRUKS

The Southern Cross

The most famous southern constellation, the Southern Cross appears on the flags of several nations.

ACRUX Acrux, or Alpha (α) Crucis, is the double star at the foot of the cross, separated by 4½ arcseconds. A third star, of 5th magnitude, lies 90 arcseconds away.

GAMMA (γ) CRUCIS This optical double consists of a magnitude 6.4 star lying almost 2 arcminutes from an orange primary.

THE JEWEL BOX Superimposed on Kappa (κ) Crucis, this is one of the finest open clusters. Although small, it sparkles in any instrument, and has several stars of contrasting color.

THE COAL SACK This large and dense dark nebula is clearly visible in a dark sky against the star clouds of the Milky Way.

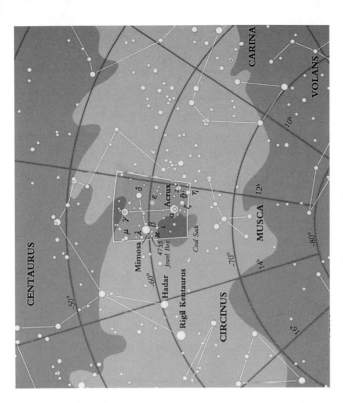

CRUCIS (CRU)
On meridian
10 p.m. May 1

303

Cygnus

SIG-nus

The Swan

Cygnus is the Northern Hemisphere's answer to Crux. Looking like a large cross, Cygnus straddles the northern Milky Way.

◈ DENEB (ALPHA [α] CYGNI) In Arabic Deneb means "tail," which is where this star is positioned on the swan. This mighty star is 25 times more massive and 60,000 times more luminous than the Sun.

◈ ALBIREO (BETA [β] CYGNI) The unaided eye sees Albireo as one star; a telescope transforms it into a double with a separation of 34 arc-seconds. One member is yellow with a magnitude of 3, and the other is bluish with a magnitude of 5.

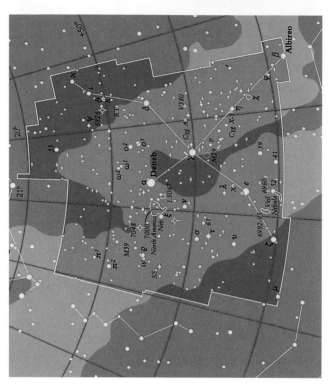

CYGNI (CYG)
On meridian
10 p.m. Aug 20

✎ 61 CYGNI Dubbed the Flying Star because of its rapid motion relative to more distant stars, this double is easily separated in small telescopes. The two components revolve around each other over the course of about 650 years.

VEIL NEBULA Also known as the Cygnus Loop, the Veil Nebula is the expanding blast-wave from a supernova that exploded about 15,000 years ago.

◇ THE NORTH AMERICA NEBULA (NGC 7000) This giant cloud is illuminated by Deneb, which lies only 3 degrees to the west. Because of its size, the nebula is difficult to see in a telescope: it is best seen with the naked eye on a dark night. Photographs show this nebula to look surprisingly like the shape of North America, but this resemblance is not readily apparent to the eye when observing.

 M39 This open star cluster is seen at its best through binoculars. On a clear night you might be able to see it with the naked eye.

 CHI (χ) CYGNI At maximum brightness, magnitude 4 or 5, this long-period variable is bright enough to be seen with the naked eye. It fades to about magnitude 13 and then climbs back in a period of a little more than 13 months.

 THE VEIL NEBULA (NGC 6960, 6992, 6995) The lacy remnants of an ancient supernova, this beautiful nebulosity requires at least a 6 inch (150 mm) telescope. NGC 6960, the nebula's western arc, passes through the star 52 Cygni, which makes it easier to find but harder to see. The Veil Nebula lies 2,500 light-years away.

Delphinus

del-FIE-nus

The Dolphin

This small group of faint stars has a distinctive shape, a little like a kite. Its alpha (α) star is named Sualocin and its beta (β) star is known as Rotanev. These names honor a relatively recent observer, Niccolo Cacciatore, long-time associate of the famous 19th-century observer Giuseppe Piazzi. Star atlases at the time included these names without comment, but the Reverend Thomas Webb worked out that the names, spelled backward, are Nicolaus Venator—the Latinized version of Cacciatore's name.

GAMMA (γ) DELPHINI This is an optical double with a separation of 10 arcseconds. The brighter component is magnitude 4.5 and the fainter, which is slightly green in color, is 5.5.

R DELPHINI This Mira star has a magnitude range of 8.3 to 13.3 over a period of 285 days.

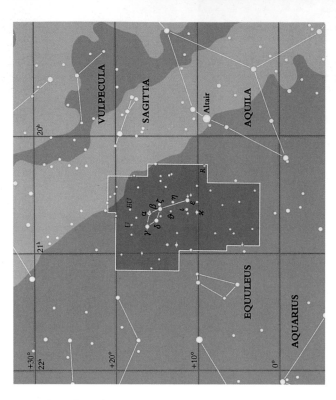

DELPHINI (DEL)
On meridian
10 p.m. Sept 1

Dorado

doh-RAH-doh

The Goldfish; The Dolphinfish

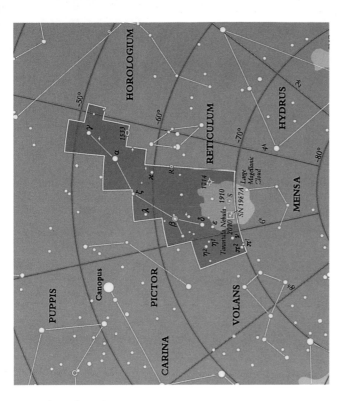

DORADUS (DOR)
On meridian
10 p.m. Jan 1

Lying far to the south, this constellation was first recorded by Bayer in his star atlas of 1603.

◉ THE LARGE MAGELLANIC CLOUD (LMC) This is a companion galaxy to the Milky Way, lying only 160,000 light-years away. The LMC spans about 11 degrees of the sky. It was from this galaxy that supernova 1987A blazed forth. The LMC is plainly visible in a dark sky, but it is easily lost in the glare of city lights.

◉ THE TARANTULA NEBULA (NGC 2070) This is one of the finest emission nebulas in the sky. It is enormous, perhaps 30 times the size of the more famous Orion Nebula (M42).

 S DORADUS Located within the open cluster NGC 1910, this star varies irregularly in brightness between magnitudes 9 and 11.

307

Draco

DRAY-koh

The Dragon

This constellation is circumpolar from much of the Northern Hemisphere and is best seen during the warmer months of the year. Large and faint, the Dragon is hard to trace as it winds about between the constellations of Ursa Major, Boötes, Hercules, Lyra, Cygnus, and Cepheus.

◆ QUADRANTIDS This is one of the strongest meteor showers. The time of maximum activity is around January 3, although the shower lasts only a few hours.

◆ DRACONIDS The Draconids meteor shower reaches its peak around October 8.

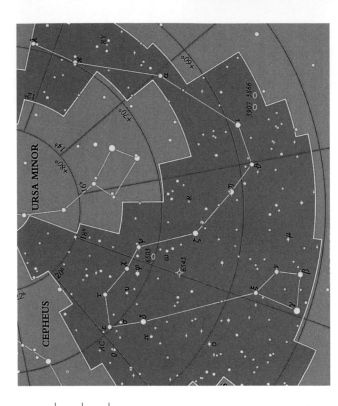

NGC 6543 This 8th-magnitude planetary nebula lies midway between the stars Delta (δ) and Zeta (ζ) Draconis. It is bright blue-green in color, but high power is needed in order to make out its small, hazy disk.

Equuleus

eh-KWOO-lee-us

The Little Horse

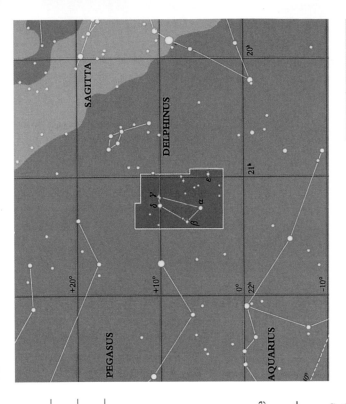

EQUULEI (EQU)
On meridian
10 p.m. Sept 1

With the exception of Crux, Equuleus occupies a smaller patch of sky than any other constellation. It lies just to the southeast of Delphinus and because it has no bright stars it is of limited interest. The famous Greek astronomer Hipparchus is thought to have made up the constellation in the second century BC. It has been said to represent Celeris, brother of Pegasus (the Winged Horse), given to Castor (one of the twins represented by Gemini) by Mercury.

ALPHA (α) EQUULEI The constellation's brightest star is named Kitalpha, which is Arabic for "little horse."

Eridanus

eh-RID-an-nus

The River

This constellation has been seen as a river since ancient times—usually the Euphrates or the Nile. In *Metamorphoses*, the Roman poet Ovid writes of Phaethon being tossed out of the chariot of the Sun to drown in Eridanus.

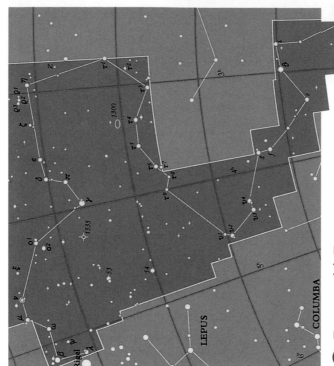

ERIDANI (ERI)
On meridian
10 p.m. Dec 10

OMICRON 2 (o_2) ERIDANI This remarkable triple consists of a 4th-magnitude orange dwarf, a 9th-magnitude white dwarf, and an 11th-magnitude red dwarf. The red and white dwarfs form a pair (separation 8 arcseconds), and are separated from the brighter star by 80 arcseconds. The white dwarf is the only one of its class that is easy to see in a small telescope.

EPSILON (ϵ) ERIDANI Only 10.5 light-years away, this is one of the closest stars to Earth. It is a smaller version of our Sun. Radio telescopes have searched for but been unsuccessful in discovering signals that indicate intelligent life.

Fornax

FOR-nax

The Furnace

This constellation was originally named Fornax Chemica, in honor of the Chemical Furnace, in honor of the chemist Antoine Lavoisier, who was guillotined during the French Revolution in 1794. Today it is simply known as the Furnace.

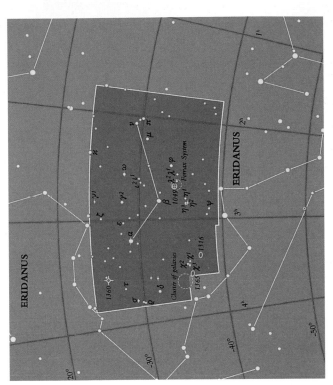

FORNACIS (FOR)
On meridian
10 p.m. Dec 1

THE FORNAX GALAXY

CLUSTER While there are no bright points of interest in Fornax, if you have a large telescope you will enjoy this challenging cluster of galaxies near the Fornax–Eridanus border. With a wide-field eyepiece, you may see up to nine galaxies in a single field of view. The brightest galaxy, at 9th magnitude, NGC 1316, is also the radio source Fornax A.

THE FORNAX SYSTEM This dwarf galaxy is too faint to see with a backyard telescope, but one of its globular clusters, NGC 1049, is, at magnitude 12.9, visible in a 10 inch (250 mm) telescope under a good sky.

311

Gemini

JEM-eh-nye

The Twins

The Greeks named Gemini's two brightest stars Castor and Pollux after the twins who were the offspring of Leda, princess of Sparta, and Zeus, king of the gods.

CASTOR (ALPHA [α] GEMINORUM) This sextuple star can be seen only as a double through a small telescope.

ETA (η) GEMINORUM This bright semi-regular variable ranges from magnitude 3.2 to 3.9 and back over about eight months.

M35 This open cluster is beautiful through binoculars and spectacular in a small telescope.

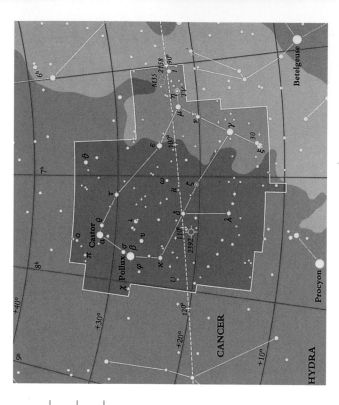

GEMINORUM (GEM)
On meridian
10 p.m. Feb 1

NGC 2158 is a smaller, fainter open cluster on its southwest edge.

THE CLOWNFACE OR ESKIMO NEBULA (NGC 2392) This 8th-magnitude planetary nebula has a bright central star.

Grus

GROOS

The Crane

Grus has little to offer the small telescope user, although some faint galaxies provide targets for telescopes of 8 inch (200 mm) aperture or larger. Grus has only three fairly bright stars, which can be used as a simple illustration of magnitude.

ALPHA (α) GRUIS Also known as Alnair, this is a large, blue main-sequence star about seventy times as luminous as the Sun. Being 100 light-years away, it is the brightest of the three stars only because it is relatively close to us.

BETA (β) GRUIS This is a much larger red giant star, 800 times as luminous as the Sun and 170 light-years away, but its color makes it appear fainter than Alpha (α) Gruis.

GAMMA (γ) GRUIS This blue giant is more luminous than the others, but appears fainter than them, as it is 200 light-years away.

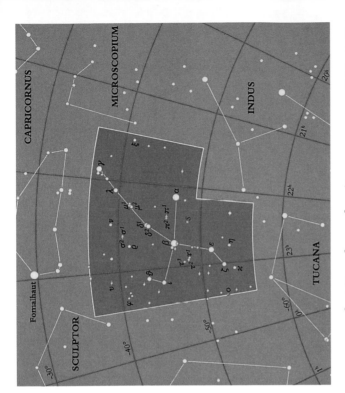

Hercules

HER-kyu-leez

Hercules

For northern observers, Hercules, with its "keystone" of four stars—Epsilon (ε), Zeta (ζ), Eta (η) and Pi (π)—is one of the best of the summer constellations.

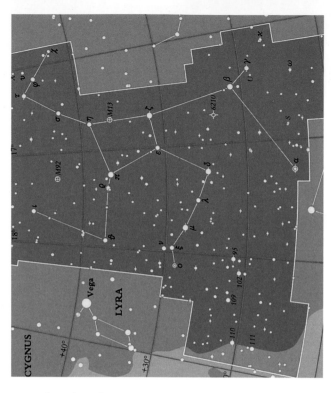

◈ THE HERCULES CLUSTER (M13) This globular cluster is faintly visible to the naked eye as a fuzzy spot, but through a telescope it is a sight to behold. The edges begin to resolve into stars in a 6 inch (150 mm) telescope. When you view this cluster, you are looking 23,000 years into the past.

◈ RAS ALGETHI (ALPHA [α] HERCULIS) This is a very red star, varying from magnitude 3.1 to 3.9. It is also a splendid colored double, with a 5th-magnitude blue-green companion about 5 arcseconds away from an orange primary.

M92 M13's slightly smaller and fainter cousin, this cluster of stars is 26,000 light years away.

Horologium

hor-oh-LOH-jee-um

The Clock

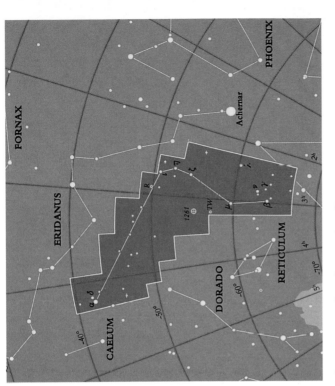

HOROLOGII (HOR)
On meridian
10 p.m. Dec 10

A small group of stars lying east of Achernar, this is one of the constellations mapped by the 18th-century French astronomer Nicolas-Louis de Lacaille. Originally called Horologium Oscillatorium, it honors the invention of the pendulum clock by the Dutch scientist Christiaan Huygens in 1656 or 1657. By applying the law of the pendulum, discovered by Galileo, to clockmaking, he significantly increased the accuracy of timekeeping.

 R HOROLOGII This long-period variable star was discovered from an observing station that Harvard University used to run in Peru. In 13½ months, it completes its cycle of variation from 5th to 14th magnitude and back.

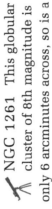 NGC 1261 This globular cluster of 8th magnitude is only 6 arcminutes across, so is a target for a larger telescope.

Hydra

HY-dra

The Sea Serpent

In Greek mythology, Hydra was the nine-headed serpent that Hercules had to kill as one of his 12 labors. Each time he lopped off one head, two others grew in its place. Hercules emerged from this nightmare by having his nephew burn the stump of each severed neck, preventing new heads from sprouting.

R HYDRAE   This Mira star's light changes were first seen in the late 1600s. It varies over 13 months from a maximum of magnitude 3.5 to a minimum of 10.

V HYDRAE   A rare example of a carbon star, this is a low-temperature red giant producing carbon. It is so deeply red that you can be sure you have found it merely by its color. The star varies erratically between magnitudes 6 and 12, with two superimposed periods—one about 18 months, and the other 18 years.

M48 (NGC 2548)   Long thought to be a missing Messier object because he wrongly reported its position, M48 is now considered to be the same as NGC 2548—a large open cluster best seen using binoculars or a wide-field telescope.

M83   This is a odd-looking spiral galaxy with three obvious spiral arms. At magnitude 8, it

HYDRA   Although in mythology, Hydra was the nine-headed serpent killed by Hercules, it is generally portrayed as a sea serpent. It snakes a quarter of the way across the sky.

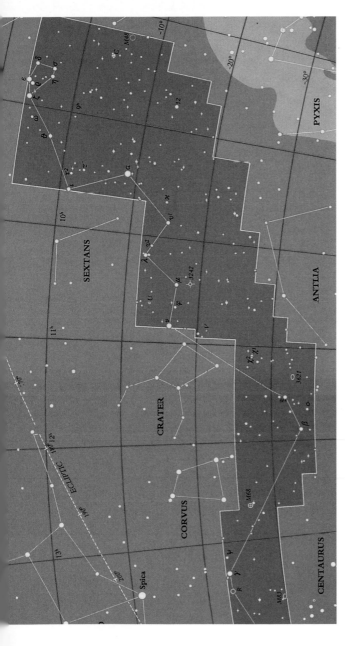

THE GHOST OF JUPITER
NEBULA (NGC 3242) This nebula is the brightest planetary nebula in this part of the sky. It is about 16 arcseconds across and shows its structure well in a 10 inch (250 mm) telescope.

is one of the brighter galaxies visible in binoculars and will show more detail at higher magnification in a telescope. Keep a lookout for "new" stars here, as M83 has been the location of four supernovas in the last 60 years.

Hydrus

HY-drus

The Water Snake

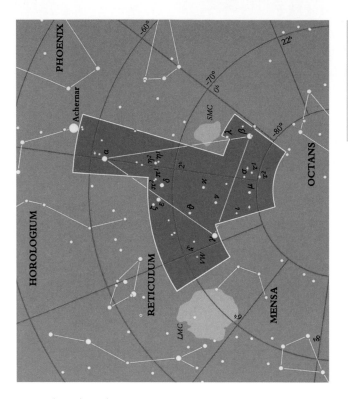

HYDRI (HYI)
On meridian
10 p.m. Dec 1

The German astronomer Johann Bayer created this constellation, publishing it in his 1603 star atlas. He placed it near Achernar, the mouth of the River Eridanus, between the Large and Small Magellanic Clouds. It is sometimes called the Male Water Snake, to avoid confusion with Hydra.

VW HYDRI This star is the most popular cataclysmic variable with Southern Hemisphere observers. When in its usual state, it shines at a faint 13th magnitude, but when it goes into outburst, an event which occurs about once a month, it can become brighter than 8th magnitude in just a few hours.

Indus

IN-dus

The Indian

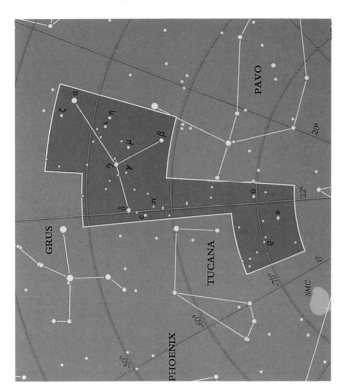

INDI (IND)
On meridian
10 p.m. Sept 1

This constellation was added to the southern sky by the German astronomer Johann Bayer to honor the Native Americans that European explorers encountered on their travels. The figure of Indus is positioned between three birds: Grus, the Crane; Tucana, the Toucan; and Pavo, the Peacock.

◈ EPSILON (ε) INDI   Only 11.8 light-years away, this is one of the closest stars to the Sun and is somewhat similar to it. With four-fifths of the Sun's diameter and one-eighth its luminosity, scientists consider Epsilon (ε) Indi to be worth investigating for planets and for evidence of extraterrestrial intelligence, such as radio signals. In the early 1960s, when Frank Drake began searching for signs of life elsewhere in the galaxy, he used this star as one of his targets. In 1972, the Copernicus Satellite searched unsuccessfully for laser signals from this star.

Lacerta

lah-SIR-tah

The Lizard ʼ

Lacerta is far enough north to be circumpolar at the higher mid-northern latitudes. It lies, inconspicuously, to the south of Cepheus. The German astronomer Johannes Hevelius suggested that this group of stars be named Lacerta, the Lizard, in his star catalog published in 1690.

BL LACERTAE Since this object varies from 13.0 to 16.1, it is invisible to any but the largest amateur telescopes. However, BL Lacertae is worth a look, since it is not a star at all but the nucleus of a distant elliptical galaxy. Some of this class of BL Lacertae-type (BL Lac) objects have been known to

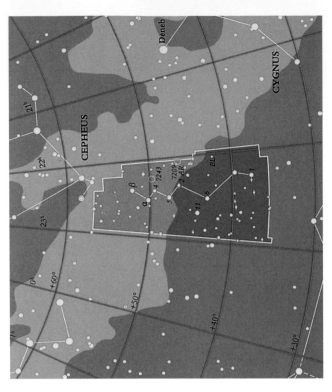

change by as much as two magnitudes in a single day. Theories suggest that BL Lac objects, quasars, and other high-powered galaxies are all closely related "active galaxies." The powerful energy source at the center may be a black hole.

LACERTAE (LAC)
On meridian
10 p.m. Oct 1

Leo and Leo Minor

LEE-oh   LEE-oh MY-ner

The Lion   The Little Lion

Unlike many constellations, Leo, with its sickle tracing out a head, really can be pictured as its namesake, a lion. Leo Minor was introduced during the 17th century.

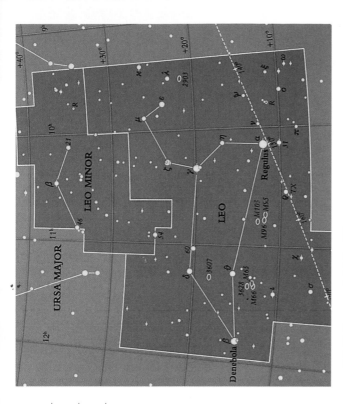

LEONIS (LEO)
LEONIS MINORIS
(LMI)
On meridian
10 p.m. April 1

GAMMA (γ) LEONIS   This double star has orange-yellow components of 2nd and 3rd magnitude separated by 5 arcseconds.

R LEONIS   A Mira variable, this ranges from magnitude 5.8 to 11 over about 10½ months.

R LEONIS MINORIS   Another Mira star, this one takes about a year to vary between magnitudes 7.1 and 12.6.

M65 AND M66   These two spiral galaxies near Theta (ϑ) Leonis are visible in binoculars but give a better view in a telescope.

LEONIDS   This meteor shower peaks annually on November 17.

321

Lepus

LEE-pus

The Hare

A faint constellation, Lepus is nevertheless easy to find because it is directly south of Orion.

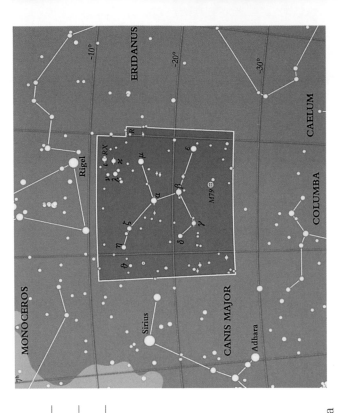

GAMMA (γ) LEPORIS Easy to separate in virtually any telescope, this wide double star with contrasting colors has a separation of 96 arcseconds.

HIND'S CRIMSON STAR Likened by some observers to a drop of blood in the sky, R Leporis is the variable that the 19th-century British astronomer J. Russell Hind called the Crimson Star. Over a period of 14 months, the star varies in magnitude from a maximum of as much as 5.5 to a minimum of 11.7.

Its coloring is at its most striking when the sky is dark and the star is near maximum brightness.

 M79 This globular cluster is best observed using a telescope 8 inches (200 mm) or larger.

Libra

LEE-bra

The Scales; The Balance

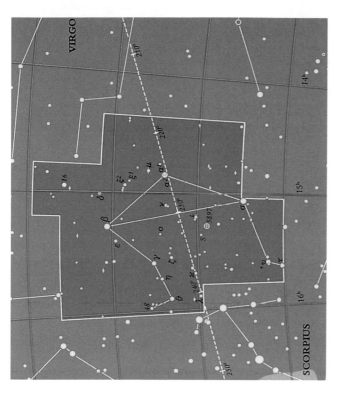

Looking like a high-flying kite, Libra is easy to find by extending a line westward from Antares and its two bright neighbors in Scorpius. The line reaches a point between Alpha (α) and Beta (β) Librae. Libra is one of the constellations of the zodiac and was associated with Themis, the Greek goddess of justice, whose symbol was a pair of scales.

Originally these stars were seen as the claws of Scorpius. But Roman skylore fancied placing a set of scales here, reviving a figure that dated from Sumerian times.

DELTA (δ) LIBRAE Similar to Algol, this eclipsing variable star fades by about a magnitude every 2.3 days, from 4.9 to 5.9. The entire cycle is visible to the naked eye.

S LIBRAE A Mira star, S Librae varies from an 8.4 maximum to a 12.0 minimum over a period of just over six months.

323

Lupus

LOO-pus

The Wolf

South of Libra and east of Centaurus, Lupus, the Wolf, is a small constellation with some 2nd-magnitude stars. It is almost joined with Centaurus, as if the Centaur is stroking the wolf like a pet. The ancient Greeks and Romans called this group of stars Therion—an unspecified wild animal. Lying within the band of the Milky Way, this constellation is home to a number of open and globular clusters.

RU LUPI (Read this name out loud. After immersing yourself in constellation lore to this point, you possibly are!) RU Lupi is a faint nebular variable, with a maximum of only 9th magnitude. Its irregular

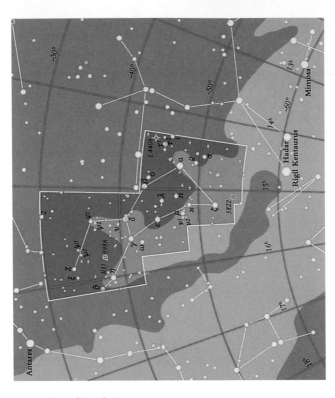

variation is characteristic of young stars still wrapped in nebulosity.

NGC 5986 This globular cluster is visible in binoculars, and sits close to some 6th- and 7th-magnitude stars.

LUPI (LUP)
On meridian
10 p.m. June 10

Lynx

LINKS

The Lynx

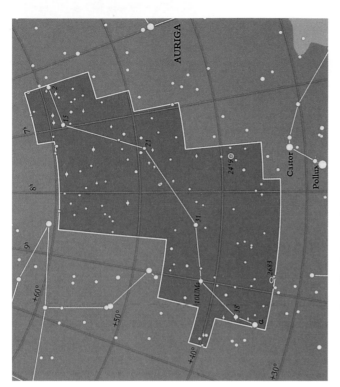

LYNCIS (LYN)
On meridian
10 p.m. Feb 20

With only one 3rd-magnitude star, Lynx is one of the hardest constellations to find. Johannes Hevelius charted this figure around 1690, apparently naming it Lynx because you need to have the eyes of a lynx to spot it. The same is true of its deep-sky objects.

THE INTERGALACTIC TRAMP (NGC 2419) Lying some 7 degrees north of Castor, the brightest star in Gemini, this is a very faint and distant globular cluster. It is more than 60 degrees from any other globular. At 210,000 light-years, it is more distant than the Large Magellanic Cloud and is so far away that it might escape the gravitational pull of our galaxy. It is for this reason that the U.S. astronomer Harlow Shapley called it the Intergalactic Tramp. Through a 10 inch (250 mm) or larger telescope, NGC 2419 appears as a fuzzy knot of light.

Lyra

LYE-rah

The Lyre

This constellation is dominated by Vega, one of the sky's brightest stars. You can imagine the lyre strings stretched across the parallelogram of four stars that accompany it.

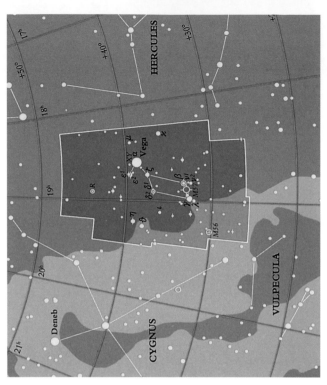

LYRAE (LYR)
On meridian
10 p.m. Aug 1

EPSILON (ε) LYRAE This is a "double double" star. The slightest optical aid shows two 5th-magnitude stars—ε¹ and ε². Both are themselves doubles, with separations under 3 arcseconds. A 4 inch (100 mm) telescope operating at a magnification of 100 or more will split both of them.

BETA (β) LYRAE This eclipsing variable ranges from magnitude 3.3 to 4.4 in 13 days.

THE RING NEBULA (M57) This planetary nebula lies between Beta (β) and Gamma (γ) Lyrae. It appears in 3 inch (75 mm) telescopes as a star out of focus at low magnification. Higher power will show its ring shape.

Mensa

MEN-sah

The Table; The Table Mountain

The only constellation that refers to a specific piece of real estate, Mensa was originally called Mons Mensae by Nicolas-Louis de Lacaille, after Table Mountain, south of Cape Town, South Africa, where he did a good deal of his work. He created this small constellation from stars between the Large Magellanic Cloud and Octans. The northernmost stars of the constellation, representing the summit of the mountain, are hidden in the Large Magellanic Cloud, in the same way that Table Mountain is often shrouded in clouds.

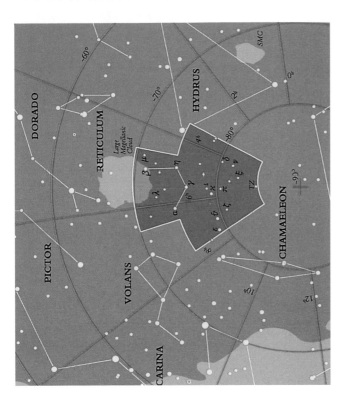

MENSAE (MEN)
On meridian
10 p.m. Jan 10

◈ ALPHA (α) MENSAE This dwarf star has an apparent magnitude of 5.1. It lies comparatively close to us, its light taking only 33 years to reach Earth.

◈ BETA (β) MENSAE Lying very near the Large Magellanic Cloud, this faint star of magnitude 5.3 is 640 light-years away.

Microscopium

my-kro-SKO-pee-um

The Microscope

This small, faint constellation, which lies just south of Capricornus and east of Sagittarius, is made up of 5th-magnitude stars. A modern creation, it was formulated in about 1750 by the French astronomer Nicolas-Louis de Lacaille. It commemorates the microscope, the invention of which is credited to the Dutch spectacle-maker Zacharias Janssen, around 1590, and to Galileo, among others.

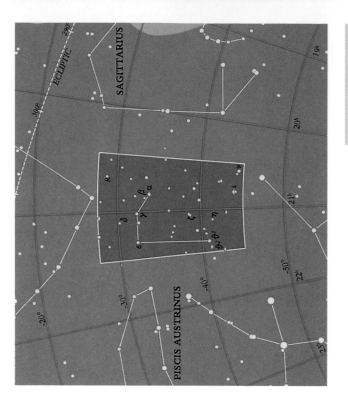

MICROSCOPII (MIC)
On meridian
10 p.m. Sept 1

R Microscopii   This faint Mira variable star has a rapid cycle lasting only 4½ months, during which it drops from magnitude 9.2 to 13.4 and then climbs back again.

Monoceros

moh-NO-ser-us

The Unicorn

This faint constellation was formed in about 1624 by the German Jakob Bartsch. Monoceros is the Latin form of a Greek word meaning "one-horned," a reference to the unicorn.

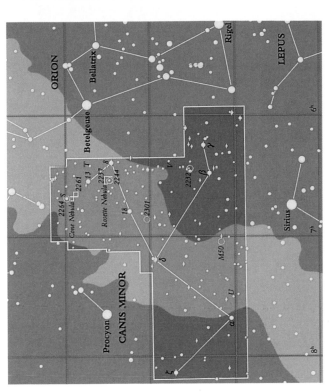

MONOCEROTIS (MON)
On meridian
10 p.m. Feb 1

M50 This beautiful open cluster, lying slightly more than one-third of the way from Sirius to Procyon, is easy to find. Some of the cluster's stars are arranged in pretty arcs.

THE ROSETTE NEBULA (NGC 2237) In a 10 inch (250 mm) telescope, this ring-shaped nebula, and the open cluster it contains (NGC 2244), offer a scene of delicate beauty. Binoculars and small telescopes will reveal the nebula on very clear nights.

THE CHRISTMAS TREE CLUSTER (NGC 2264) This open cluster really does look like a Christmas tree.

329

Musca

MUSS-kah

The Fly

Musca is an easy constellation to find, just to the south of the Southern Cross.

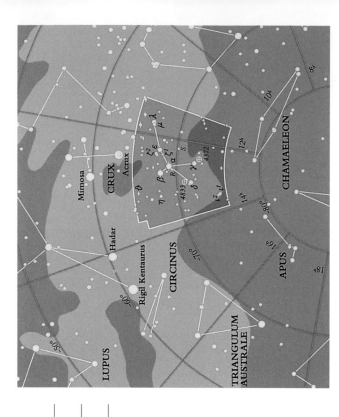

MUSCAE (MUS)
On meridian
10 p.m. May 1

BETA (β) MUSCAE This elegant double star consists of two 4th magnitude stars that revolve around each other in a period that spans several hundred years. The pair is some 310 light-years from Earth. The separation of 1.6 arcseconds is very tight, presenting a challenge for a 4 inch (100 mm) telescope.

NGC 4372 This globular cluster is close to Gamma (γ) Muscae and has faint stars spread over 18 arcminutes.

NGC 4833 This is a large, faint globular cluster, 18,000 light-years away. It lies within 1 degree of Delta (δ) Muscae. A 4 inch (100 mm) or larger telescope is needed to begin to resolve the cluster into individual stars.

Norma

NOR-muh

The Square

East of Centaurus and Lupus is a small constellation called Norma, the Square. When he named this group of stars, Nicolas-Louis de Lacaille decided to call it Norma et Regula, the Level and Square, after a carpenter's tools. Since those days, however, the Regula has been forgotten. The constellation lies alongside Circinus, the Drawing Compass, which he named at the same time. Set in the southern Milky Way, Norma presents good fields for binoculars, containing a number of open clusters. For such a small constellation, Norma has also been quite lucky with the appearance of novas: there was one in 1893 and another in 1920.

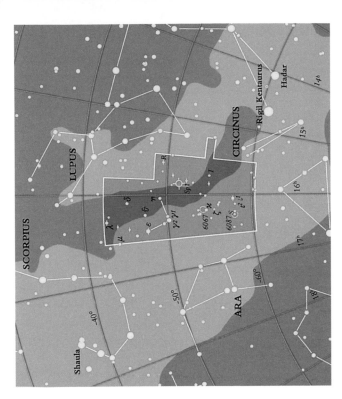

NORMAE (NOR)
On meridian
10 p.m. June 10

 NGC 6067 This is a small open cluster. Large binoculars or a telescope reveal about a hundred stars within a stunning field.

 NGC 6087 This is another of Norma's striking open clusters.

Octans

OCK-tanz

The Octant

To honor the invention of the octant in 1730, Nicolas-Louis de Lacaille formed this south polar constellation. The forerunner of the sextant, the octant was used for measuring the altitude of a celestial body.

◇ SIGMA (σ) OCTANTIS   This is the south pole star. At magnitude 5.4, it is barely visible to the naked eye on a dark night, so while it does mark the pole, it is not as convenient a marker star as the north's Polaris. The celestial poles move as the axis of the Earth precesses, or wobbles like a top, over some 26,000 years. Sigma (σ) Octantis was at its closest to the pole in about 1870, at just under half a

degree. It is now just over 1 degree. In about another 3,000 years, the pole will begin to move through Carina, and it will pass near Delta (δ) Carinae in about 7,000 years. At 2nd magnitude, this is the brightest south pole star the Earth ever sees.

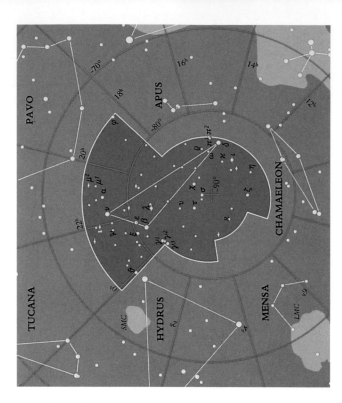

OCTANTIS (OCT)
On meridian
10 p.m. Sept 10

Ophiuchus

oh-fee-YOO-cuss

The Serpent Bearer

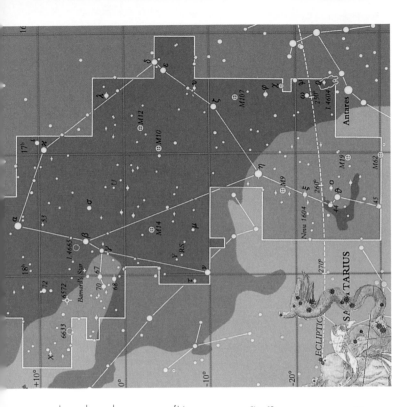

OPHIUCHI (OPH)
On meridian
10 p.m. July 10

Ophiuchus, entwined with the constellation Serpens, covers a large expanse of sky and contains some of the Milky Way's richest star clouds.

 M9, 10, 12, 14, 19, 62
These globular clusters provide examples of different concentrations of stars. M9 and 14 are rich; M10 and 12 are looser; M19 is oval; M62 is somewhat irregular in outline. All are visible in binoculars but require a 6 or 8 inch (150 or 200 mm) telescope to do them justice.

RS Ophiuchi This nova has had a number of outbursts. Its magnitude ranges from 11.8 to as high as 4.3 during outbursts.

Barnard's Star This magnitude 9.5 red dwarf star has the greatest proper motion of any known star.

Orion

oh-RYE-un

The Hunter

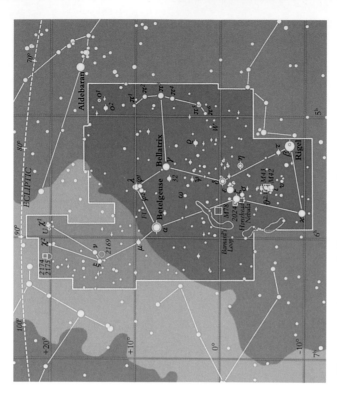

ORIONIS (ORI)
On meridian
10 p.m. Jan 10

Orion is a treasure, with Rigel, Betelgeuse and its three belt stars in a row lighting up the sky from December to April.

◆ BETELGEUSE (ALPHA [α] ORIONIS) Betelgeuse (pronounced BET-el-jooze but sometimes corrupted to BEETLE-juice) is fabulous. (Its name comes from the Arabic for "hand of al-jauza," an obscure term which may refer to a female character in Arabic mythology.) A variable star, it ranges in magnitude from 0.3 to 1.2 over a period of about six years. However, the semi-regular nature of the variation means that it is often possible to detect changes over just a few weeks.

◆ RIGEL (BETA [β] ORIONIS) The name Rigel is derived from the Arabic word for "foot," a reference to the star's position in Orion. This mighty supergiant, some 775 light-years from Earth, is about 40,000 times as luminous as the Sun.

THE ORION NEBULA (M42)

This star nursery, one of the marvels of the night sky, is also known as the Great Nebula. Plainly visible to the naked eye under a dark sky, it can be clearly seen through binoculars even in the city. The swirls of nebulosity spread out from its core of four stars called the Trapezium, which power the nebula. Photographs usually "burn out" the inner region of the nebula and obscure the Trapezium stars.

M43 This is a small patch of nebulosity just north of the main body of the Orion Nebula. In fact, the M42 complex is simply the brightest part of a gas cloud covering the constellation of Orion at a distance of some 1,500 light-years.

THE HORSEHEAD NEBULA

(IC 434) Also known as Barnard 33, this dark nebula is projected against a background of diffuse nebulosity, alongside the bright belt star Zeta (ζ) Orionis. It can be quite difficult to see, usually requiring a dark sky and at least an 8 inch (200 mm) telescope.

NGC 2169 This open cluster is made up of about 30 stars.

ORION NEBULA The Orion Nebula is one of the most impressive sights for skywatchers. It is pictured here with its companion, M43 (the ball-like shape at top right).

Pavo

PAH-voh

The Peacock

Pavo, the Peacock, lies not far from the south celestial pole, south of Sagittarius and Corona Australis.

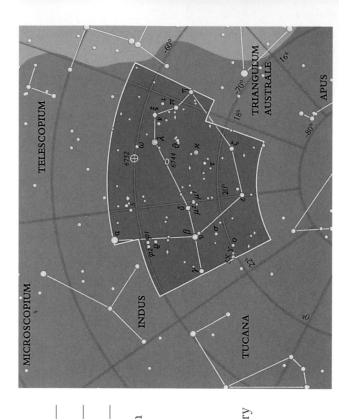

THE PEACOCK STAR

(ALPHA [α] PAVONIS) This star is 180 light-years away. It is a binary system whose members orbit each other in less than two weeks, but the pair is too close to separate telescopically.

NGC 6752 A spectacular globular cluster at a relatively close distance of 17,000 light-years, this huge family of stars is the third largest globular cluster (in apparent size); only Omega (ω) Centauri and 47 Tucanae exceed it.

NGC 6744 This faint but beautiful galaxy is one of the largest known barred spirals. Smaller telescopes reveal only the nuclear regions, a 10 inch (250 mm) telescope being necessary to reveal anything more.

Pegasus

PEG-a-sus

The Winged Horse

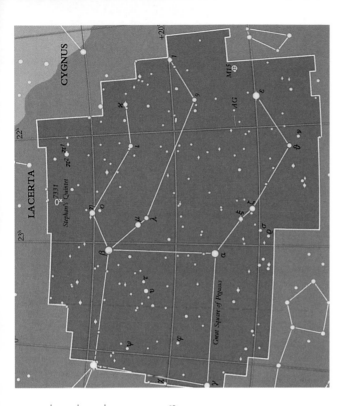

PEGASI (PEG)
On meridian
10 p.m. Oct 1

Although this constellation has no really bright stars, it is easy to spot because its three brightest stars, plus Alpha (α) Andromedae, form the Great Square of Pegasus.

M15   This is one of the best of the northern sky globular clusters. Binoculars show it as a nebulous patch, but in a telescope it is a real showpiece.

NGC 7331   This spiral galaxy is the brightest one in Pegasus, but is still only 9th magnitude.

STEPHAN'S QUINTET   This very faint group of galaxies lies half a degree south of NGC 7331.

Four of the five galaxies appear to be interacting, distorting each other, and drawing out long streamers of stars. Stephan's Quintet is not really a target for the beginner, as it needs at least a 10 inch (250 mm) telescope to be seen clearly.

Perseus

PURR-see-us

The Hero

A pretty constellation that straddles the Milky Way, Perseus is in the northern skies from July to March.

◉ ALGOL This is the most famous of the eclipsing variables. Every 2 days, 20 hours and 48 minutes, it begins to drop in brightness from magnitude 2.1 to 3.4 in an eclipse lasting 10 hours.

✸ M34 This bright open cluster sits in the middle of a rich field of stars.

◉ THE DOUBLE CLUSTER (NGC 869 AND 884) Two of the best examples of open clusters, NGC 869 and 884 (h Persei and Chi [χ]

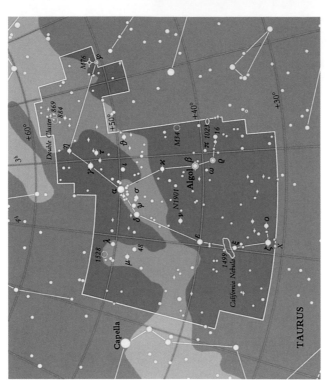

PERSEI (PER)
On meridian
10 p.m. Dec 10

Persei respectively) are magnificent through binoculars or the low-power field of a small telescope.

◉ PERSEIDS One of the best meteor showers, the Perseids peak on August 11 and 12.

Phoenix

FEE-nicks

The Phoenix

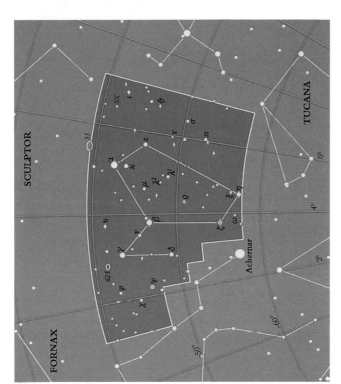

A symbol of rebirth, in mythology the Phoenix was a bird of great beauty that lived for 500 years. It would then build a nest of twigs and fragrant leaves which would be lit by the noontime rays of the Sun. The Phoenix would be consumed in the fire, but a small worm would wriggle from the ashes, bask in the sun, and evolve into a new Phoenix.

SX PHOENICIS The best example of a "dwarf Cepheid" variable, this star changes from magnitude 7.1 to 7.5 and back again in only 79 minutes and 10 seconds! Cepheid periods are usually very exact. In this case, however, the range varies, with some maxima as bright as 6.7. The variation probably occurs because the star has two different oscillations occurring at once. Such a small range in brightness can be difficult to monitor, requiring careful comparison with neighboring stars.

339

Pictor

PIK-tor

The Painter's Easel

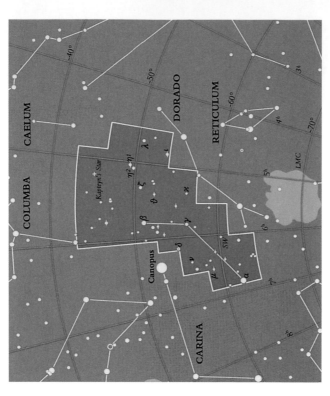

This southern constellation was originally named Equuleus Pictoris, the Painter's Easel, by Nicolas-Louis de Lacaille. Nowadays its shortened name refers solely to the painter. It is a dull group of stars lying south of Columba and alongside the brilliant star Canopus.

◈ BETA (β) PICTORIS This 4th-magnitude star is host to a disk of dust and ices that could be a planetary system in formation. The surrounding nebula is only visible using large telescopes.

✦ KAPTEYN'S STAR Only 12.8 light-years away, this star was discovered by the Dutch astronomer Jacobus Kapteyn in 1897. It moves quickly among distant background stars, crossing 8.7 arcseconds of sky per year—the width of the Moon every two centuries. At magnitude 8.8, the star is visible in binoculars and small telescopes.

PICTORIS (PIC)
On meridian
10 p.m. Jan 10

Pisces

PIE-seez

The Fish

For thousands of years, this faint zodiacal constellation has been seen either as one fish or two. The ring of stars in the western fish, which is beneath Pegasus, is called the Circlet. The eastern fish is beneath Andromeda.

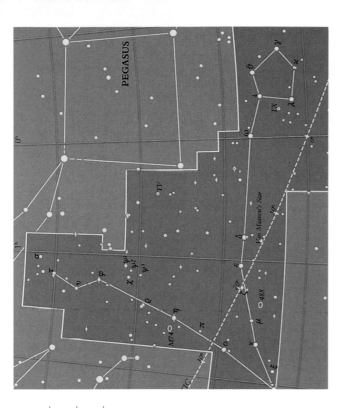

PISCIUM (PSC)
On meridian
10 p.m. Nov 1

🔭 ZETA (ζ) PISCIUM A fine double star of magnitudes 5.6 and 6.5, separated by 24 arcseconds.

🔭 M74 This is a large spiral galaxy, seen face-on, close to Eta (η) Piscium. While it is the brightest Pisces galaxy, it is still rather faint and requires a dark sky and an 8 inch (200 mm) telescope or larger to be seen. Photographs highlight its prominent nucleus and well-developed spiral arms.

🔭 VAN MAANEN'S STAR An 8 inch (200 mm) telescope will identify this magnitude 12.2 white dwarf star.

341

Piscis Austrinus

PIE-sis oss-STRINE-us

The Southern Fish

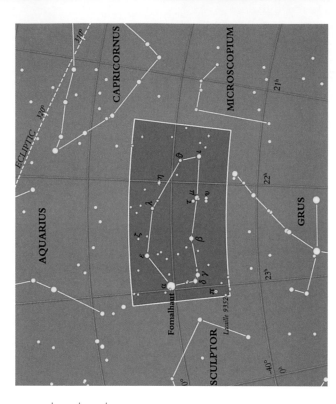

PISCIS AUSTRINUS
(PSA)
On meridian
10 p.m. Oct 1

Lying to the south of Aquarius and Capricornus, Piscis Austrinus, the Southern Fish, is relatively easy to spot because of its lone, magnitude 1.2 star, Fomalhaut, which is often referred to as the Solitary One.

For the Persians, 5,000 years ago, this was a Royal Star that had the privilege of being one of the guardians of heaven. Many early charts of the heavens show the Southern Fish drinking water that is being poured from Aquarius's jar.

◆ FOMALHAUT This bright star is 25 light-years away—close by stellar standards. It is about twice as large as our Sun and has 14 times its luminosity. Some 2 degrees of arc southward is a magnitude 6.5 dwarf star that seems to be sharing Fomalhaut's motion through space. They are so far apart that it is hard to call them a binary system. Maybe these two stars are all that is left of a cluster that dissipated long ago.

Puppis and Pyxis

PUP-iss   PIK-sis

The Stern   The Compass

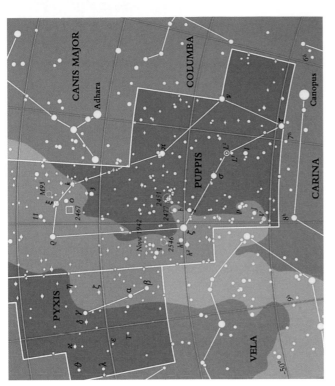

With the Milky Way running along it, Puppis provides a feast of open clusters for binoculars or telescopes. Right alongside is the smaller and fainter constellation of Pyxis.

◆ ZETA (ζ) PUPPIS This blue supergiant sun is one of our galaxy's largest. It shines at 2nd magnitude.

◆ L² PUPPIS One of the brightest of the red variable stars, L² Puppis varies from magnitude 2.6 to 6.2 over a period of five months.

M46 A beautiful open star cluster, through small telescopes, M46 is a cloud of faint stars the apparent diameter of the Moon.

A larger telescope is needed to see NGC 2438, a planetary nebula superimposed on the cluster.

T PYXIDIS This recurrent nova sometimes reaches 7th magnitude during its outbursts.

343

Reticulum

reh-TIK-u-lum

The Reticule

A small constellation of faint stars halfway between the bright stars Achernar and Canopus, Reticulum was first set up as Rhombus by Isaak Habrecht of Strasburg. Nicolas-Louis de Lacaille changed its name to Reticulum to honor the reticule—the grid of fine lines in a telescope eyepiece that aids with centering and focusing. It is occasionally also known as the Net.

R RETICULI This Mira-type variable star is quite red, and at maximum light it shines at about magnitude 7. Over a period of nine months, R Reticuli drops to magnitude 14, then returns to maximum brightness.

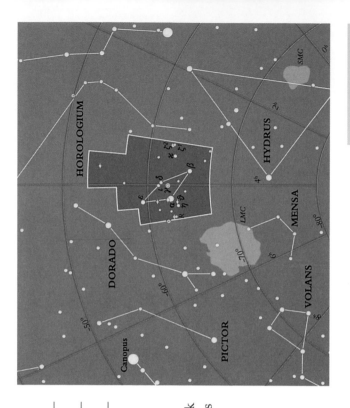

RETICULI (RETI)
On meridian
10 p.m. Dec 10

Sagitta

sa-JIT-ah

The Arrow

Although only a small constellation, Sagitta is easy to find halfway between Altair in Aquila, and Albireo (Beta [β] Cygni). The ancient Hebrews, Persians, Arabs, Greeks, and Romans all saw this group of stars as an arrow.

U SAGITTAE Every 3.4 days, this eclipsing binary drops from magnitude 6.5 to a minimum of 9.3.

V SAGITTAE Although this star is faint, varying erratically from magnitude 8.6 to magnitude 13.9, it is interesting because of the way it alters a little almost every night. It might have been a nova a long time ago.

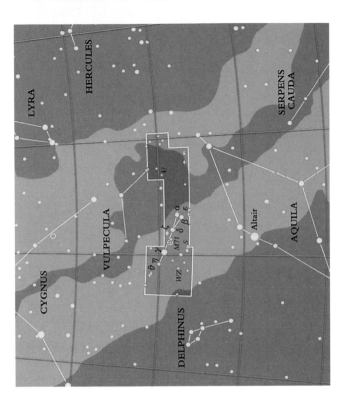

SAGITTAE (SGE)
On meridian
10 p.m. Aug 20

M71 A little south of the midpoint of a line joining Delta (δ) and Gamma (γ) Sagittae, M71 is a fertile cluster of faint stars. It is generally regarded as a poor globular cluster, rather than as a rich open cluster.

Sagittarius

sadge-ih-TAIR-ee-us

The Archer

This constellation is located in the Milky Way in the direction of the center of the galaxy. Here the band of the Milky Way is at its broadest, although cut by dark bands of dust. It is a treasure trove of galactic and globular clusters, plus bright and dark nebulas.

◈ M22 The Great Sagittarius star cluster is a very large globular. At magnitude 5.1, it is an easy object to see in binoculars, but a telescope really brings out the cluster's beauty. Only 10,000 light-years away, it is one of the closest globulars, and with an 8 inch (200 mm) telescope you should be able to resolve it into countless stars.

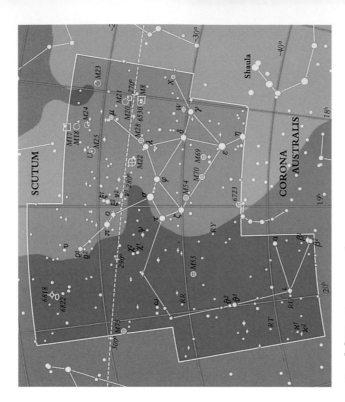

SAGITTARII (SAG)
On meridian
10 p.m. Aug 1

⊕ M23 Just one of many galactic clusters in Sagittarius, M23 presents more than a hundred stars in an area about the size of the Moon. It is a striking sight in binoculars or a telescope using low magnification.

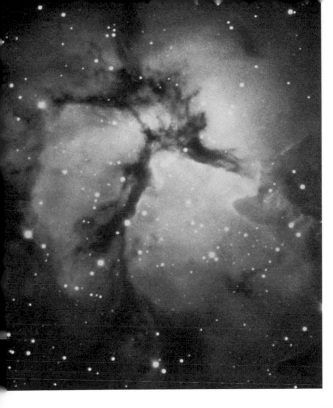

THE LAGOON NEBULA (M8)
This spectacular diffuse nebula envelops the cluster of stars called NGC 6530. On a dark night the nebula is visible to the naked eye as a milky-white spot of light just to the north of one of the richest part of the Milky Way. In photographs, the extensive nebula is marked by several tiny dark splotches. Dutch astronomer Bart Bok identified these as globules in which new stars are being formed.

THE TRIFID NEBULA (M20)
Found only 1½ degrees to the northwest of the Lagoon Nebula, the Trifid Nebula is likely to be part of the same complex of nebulosity. It is known as the Trifid because three lanes of dark clouds divide the nebula in the most beautiful way. You should be able to detect these dark lanes with a 6 inch (150 mm) telescope under a good sky.

THE OMEGA NEBULA (M17)
Also called the Swan, the Horseshoe or the Checkmark, this nebula can be seen quite clearly in binoculars. In a 4 inch (100 mm) telescope it looks like the figure 2 with an extended baseline. It is a stunning sight in a larger telescope.

TRIFID NEBULA The photo clearly show the dust lanes which trisect M20 and give it its popular name.

Scorpius

SKOR-pee-us

The Scorpion

A beautiful constellation of the zodiac, filled with bright stars and rich star fields of the Milky Way, Scorpius really does resemble a scorpion, complete with head and stinger. Near the northern end is a line of three bright stars, with red Antares at its center.

ANTARES The Romans called this magnitude 1 star Cor Scorpionis, meaning "heart of the scorpion." Antares is a red super-giant 600 million miles (1 billion km) across and is 9,000 times more luminous than the Sun. However, with a mass only 10 or 15 times that of the Sun, it is not very dense. The star lies about 520 light-years away.

BETA (β) SCORPII This is a double star whose 2.6 and 4.9 magnitude components are 13.7 arcseconds apart, making resolution possible even in a 2 inch (50 mm) telescope. Beta (β) Scorpii is also known as Graffias.

THE SCORPION In Greek mythology, Scorpius is the tiny Scorpion that stung and killed Orion the Hunter.

M4 This strange globular cluster has a different appearance with each instrument you use. Binoculars show a fuzzy patch of light; a small telescope shows a large patch of mottled haze; and 4 or 6 inch (100 to 150 mm) instruments begin to show the individual stars. This is one of the best globulars for viewing in small telescopes.

THE BUTTERFLY CLUSTER (M6) The stars of this bright open cluster really resemble a butterfly when viewed at high power.

M7 This large, bright open cluster, lying to the southeast of M6, needs to be seen through the large field of view of binoculars to be fully appreciated.

NGC 6231 Half a degree north of Zeta (ζ) Scorpii, this bright open cluster lies in a rich region of the Milky Way. It is best surveyed in binoculars or at very low power in a telescope.

M80 This bright globular cluster can be seen in binoculars but needs a 10 inch (250 mm) telescope to resolve its stars.

SCORPIUS X-1 This is a close binary star in which one star expels gas onto a dense neighbor that could be either a white dwarf, a neutron star, or a black hole. It is a bright source of X-rays, but appears visually as a 13th-magnitude star.

Sculptor

SKULP-tor

The Sculptor

This constellation lies to the south of Aquarius and Cetus. Its most significant feature is a small cluster of nearby spiral galaxies.

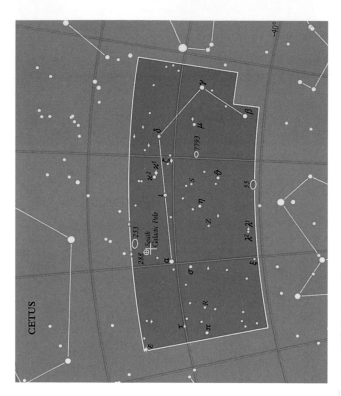

SCULPTORIS (SCL)
On meridian
10 p.m. Oct 20

NGC 253   For a small telescope user, this magnitude 7 galaxy is one of the most satisfying, especially for observers in the Southern Hemisphere. It is very large and is viewed almost edge-on. It was discovered by Caroline Herschel one night in 1783, while she was searching for comets. It appears as a thick streak in binoculars and begins to show the texture evident in photographs when larger instruments are used. The galaxy is 10 million light-years distant.

NGC 55   This is another very fine edge-on galaxy, similar to NGC 253, although fainter at 8th magnitude. Those using an 8 inch (200 mm) telescope or larger will see that it is distinctly brighter at one end than the other.

Scutum

SKU-tum

The Shield

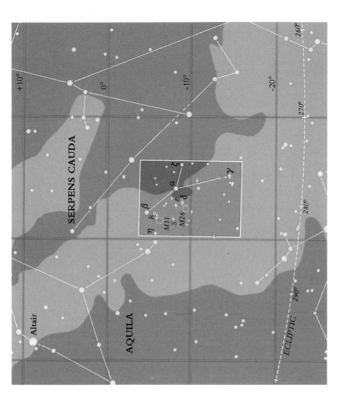

Although Scutum is not a large constellation and has no bright stars, it is not difficult to find in a dark sky because it is the home of one of the Milky Way's most dramatic clouds of stars. The constellation was created at the end of the 17th century, and named Scutum Sobiescianum (Sobieski's Shield) in honor of King John Sobieski of Poland.

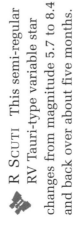 R SCUTI This semi-regular RV Tauri-type variable star changes from magnitude 5.7 to 8.4 and back over about five months.

 THE WILD DUCK CLUSTER (M11) This spectacular open cluster is clearly visible in binoculars, rewarding in a small telescope, and stunning in an 8 inch (200 mm) one. One of the most compact of all the open clusters, the presence of a bright star in the foreground adds to its beauty.

Serpens

SIR-penz

The Serpent

This is the only constellation that is divided into two parts. The head (Serpens Caput) and the tail (Serpens Cauda) are separated by the constellation of Ophiuchus, the Serpent Bearer.

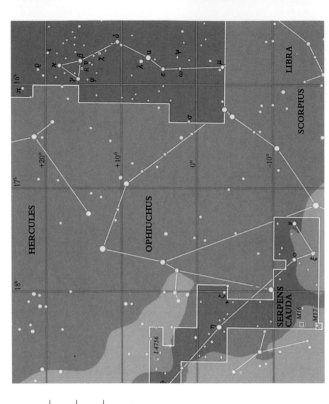

R SERPENTIS A Mira star almost midway between Beta (β) and Gamma (γ) Serpentis, this variable has a bright maximum of 6.9. It fades to about 13.4, although it sometimes can become fainter. Its period is about one year.

M5 This very striking 5th-magnitude globular cluster in Serpens Cauda is about 26,000 light-years away.

SERPENTIS (SER)
On meridian
10 p.m. June 20
(Serpens Caput)
10 p.m. July 20
(Serpens Cauda)

THE EAGLE NEBULA (M16) Through an 8 inch (200 mm) or larger telescope on a dark night, this combination of nebula and star cluster is stunning. But you can still enjoy the sight of the cluster in smaller telescopes.

Sextans

SEX-tanz

The Sextant

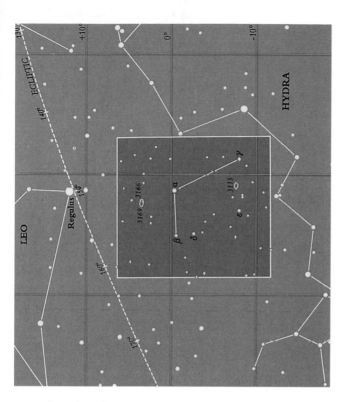

SEXTANTIS (SEX)
On meridian
10 p.m. Mar 20

Sextans Uraniae, now known simply as Sextans, was the creation of the 17th-century German astronomer Johannes Hevelius. He chose this name for the new constellation to commemorate the loss of the sextant he once used to measure the positions of the stars. Along with all his other astronomical instruments, the sextant was destroyed in a fire that took place in September 1679. "Vulcan overcame Urania," Hevelius remarked sadly, commenting on the fire god having defeated astronomy's muse.

THE SPINDLE GALAXY (NGC 3115) Because we see this 10th-magnitude galaxy almost edge-on, it appears to be shaped like a lens, with a bright center. Unlike many faint galaxies, the Spindle Galaxy gives quite satisfying views at high power. It seems to be somewhere between an elliptical and a spiral.

353

Taurus

TORR-us

The Bull

Taurus is a prominent constellation clearly visible from both Northern and Southern Hemispheres, from February through April.

◆ THE PLEIADES (M45) Also known as the Seven Sisters, this is the most famous open star cluster in the sky and forms the bull's shoulder. Alcyone (Eta [η] Tauri) is the most dazzling sister. She is accompanied by: Maia (20 Tauri); Asterope I and II (the double star 21 Tauri); Taygeta (19 Tauri); Celaeno (16 Tauri); and Electra (17 Tauri). Finally, there is Merope (23 Tauri), a star surrounded by a beautiful cloud of cosmic grains producing a blue reflection nebula. On a

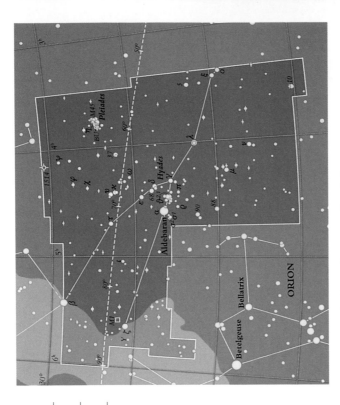

TAURI (TAU)
On meridian
10 p.m. Jan 1

reasonably dark night, you should be able to see at least six of the stars in the Pleiades with the naked eye; under good conditions, you might be able to see as many as nine. Containing more than 500 stars, the Pleiades is about 375 light-years

away and covers an area four times the size of the Full Moon. It is best seen with binoculars.

THE HYADES
Like the Pleiades, this is also an open cluster, but it is so close to us (only 150 light-years away) that even when viewed with the naked eye the stars appear to be spread out. The stars of the Hyades form the bull's head.

ALDEBARAN (ALPHA [α] TAURI)
This is an orange giant and is the brightest star in Taurus. Only 65 light-years away, it marks the bull's eye.

THE CRAB NEBULA (M1)
This nebula is clearly visible in a 4 inch (100 mm) telescope on a dark night as an oval glow, 5 arcminutes across. Details in the cloud can be detected in 10 inch (250 mm) scopes or larger.

MARVELS OF TAURUS The Crab Nebula (above) marks the site of a supernova seen in 1054. High-magnification photographs such as this reveal the Crab's complex structure. Another highlight of Taurus is the Pleiades cluster, whose brightest stars are charted at left.

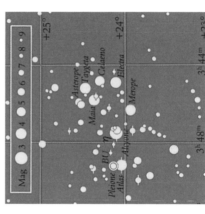

Telescopium

tel-eh-SKO-pee-um

The Telescope

Originally bearing the name Tubus Telescopium, this constellation was created by Nicolas-Louis de Lacaille during the 18th century to honor the invention of the telescope. Lacaille "borrowed" stars from large surrounding constellations in order to create his new one.

RR TELESCOPII Although this star is normally too faint for small telescopes, it is one of the most interesting novas on record. Before 1944, this star varied over about 13 months between 12.5 and 15th magnitude, but in that year it began a rise to magnitude 6.5 that took some five years. As the nova declined in the following years, it still displayed its original 13-month period. It is thought that the star may be a binary system, in which a large red star is responsible for the minor variations that take place, and a smaller, hotter star puts on the nova part of the performance.

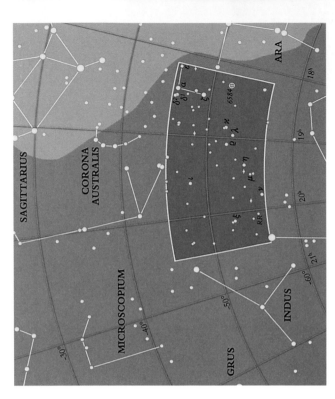

TELESCOPII (TEL)
On meridian
10 p.m. Aug 10

Triangulum

tri-ANG-gyu-lum

The Triangle

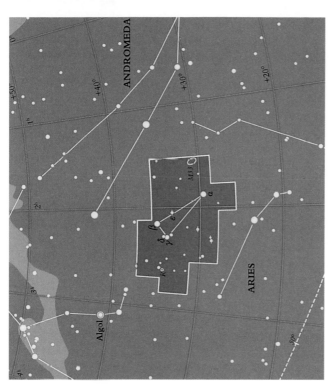

TRIANGULI (TRI)
On meridian
10 p.m. Nov 20

This is a small, faint constellation extending just south of Andromeda, near Beta (β) and Gamma (γ) Andromedae. The group of stars was known to the ancients, and because of its similarity to the Greek letter delta (Δ) it was sometimes called Delta or Deltoton. The ancient Hebrews gave it the name of a triangular musical instrument.

◆ THE PINWHEEL GALAXY

(M33) This is one of the brightest members of our Local Group and we have a front-row view because it appears face-on. It shines at magnitude 5.5 but its light is spread out over such a large area that it is difficult to see. Although it can be seen by the naked eye on very clear nights, you need a dark sky and binoculars to see a fuzzy glow larger than the Full Moon. A telescope with a wide field of view will also show the galaxy, but one with a narrow field will show nothing at all.

357

Triangulum Australe

tri-ANG-gyu-lum os-TRAH-lee

The Southern Triangle

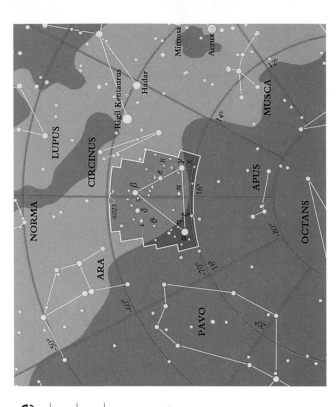

Triangulum lies just to the south of Norma, the Level, and to the east of Circinus, the Drawing Compass—tools used by woodworkers and navigators on early expeditions to the Southern Hemisphere.

 **R TRIANGULI AUSTRALIS** One of several Cepheids in the constellation, this variable alters by about a magnitude—from 6.0 to 6.8. Because it is a Cepheid variable, we know its period precisely, which is 3.389 days. For Cepheids with this rapid variation, magnitude estimates at least once a night are worthwhile.

 **S TRIANGULI AUSTRALIS** Another Cepheid variable, S varies from magnitude 6.1 to 6.7 and back over a period of 6.323 days.

 **NGC 6025** This is a small open cluster of about 30 stars of 9th magnitude, with fainter background stars.

Tucana

too-KAN-ah

The Toucan

Johann Bayer first published this constellation in his star atlas of 1603. From the earliest drawings, the Tucan sat on the Small Magellanic Cloud, one of the two closest galaxies to the Milky Way, tending it like an egg.

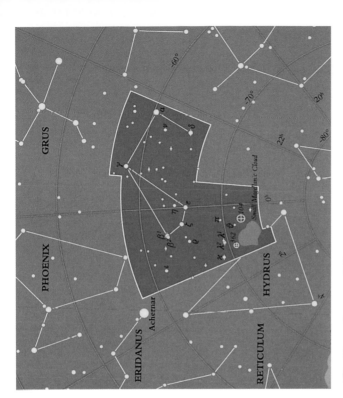

◉ 47 TUCANAE (NGC 104)
From its perch 16,000 light-years away, this glorious globular cluster shines brightly at magnitude 4.5. Although it is a naked-eye object under dark skies, a 4 inch (100 mm) or larger telescope really brings out the best in this cluster, which competes with Omega (ω) Centauri for the title of the most splendid globular cluster in the entire sky.

◉ THE SMALL MAGELLANIC CLOUD (SMC) This galaxy is visible to the naked eye on a good night, with the great globular cluster 47 Tuc alongside. About 192,000 light-years away, the cloud is some 30,000 light-years wide.

Ursa Major

ER-suh MAY-jer

The Great Bear

This well-known constellation contains the group of seven stars that make up the Big Dipper. In Greek myth, Zeus and Callisto, a mortal, had a son called Arcas. Hera, Zeus's jealous wife, turned Callisto into a bear, and one day while out hunting, her son, not knowing that the bear was his mother, almost killed her. Zeus rescued Callisto, placing both her and her son, whom he also turned into a bear, in the sky together. Callisto is Ursa Major and Arcas is Ursa Minor.

◈ MIZAR (ZETA [ζ] URSAE MAJORIS) AND ALCOR Mizar and Alcor make up the famous apparent double star in the middle of the Big

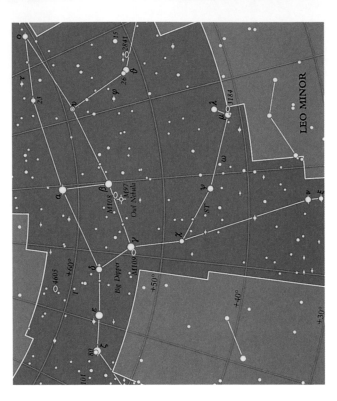

URSAE MAJORIS
(UMA)
On meridian
10 p.m. April 20

Dipper's handle. The two stars are separated by 12 arcminutes and it is thus possible to see them as a pair with the naked eye, although your eyesight needs to be sharp. Mizar is itself a true binary star, its components separated by 14 arcseconds.

M81 This spiral galaxy can be easily seen through binoculars, even when observing in the city, and it is dramatic when observed under good conditions. The oval disk becomes more apparent with increasing telescope size. M81 is probably a fair representation of how the Milky Way Galaxy would look from the outside.

M82 This is a long, thin, peculiar galaxy, half a degree from M81. It appears as a thin, gray nebulosity in a 4 inch (100 mm) telescope, but begins to show some detail in an 8 inch (200 mm) or larger one. Even in large telescopes or photographs, however, it is not clear what type of galaxy this is.

M101 This large, spread-out spiral galaxy is visible through small telescopes if the sky is dark enough. It needs a wide field and a low-power eyepiece. At 16 million light-years, it is one of the closer spiral galaxies to the Milky Way.

THE OWL NEBULA (M97) This is an oval planetary nebula that takes the shape of an owl when it is seen in a 12 inch (300 mm) telescope. It is large and dim, and a 4 inch (100 mm) or larger telescope is needed to find it.

ANCIENT BEAR Ursa Major is one of the oldest constellations, and many civilizations depicted it as a bear. The ancient Egyptians, however, considered this group of stars to be either a hippo or a Nile River boat for the god Osiris.

Ursa Minor

ER-suh MY-ner

The Little Bear

Ursa Minor looks a bit like a spoon whose handle has been bent back by a playful child. This group of stars was recognized as a constellation in 600 BC by the Greek astronomer Thales. The Little Bear, according to Greek legend, is Arcas, son of Callisto—Ursa Major, the Great Bear. Placed in the heavens by Zeus, he and his mother follow each other around the north celestial pole.

POLARIS (ALPHA [α] URSAE MINORIS) The pole star for the Northern Hemisphere, this Cepheid variable is currently almost 1 degree from the exact pole. Precession of the Earth's axis will carry the pole to within about 27 arcminutes of

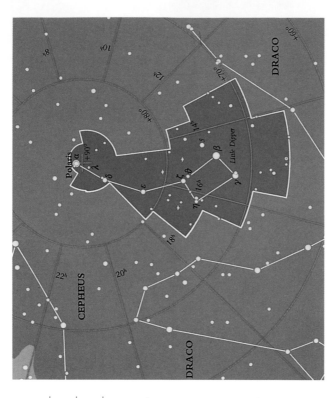

Polaris around the year 2100, and then it will start to move away again. Polaris is 430 light-years away, with a 9th magnitude companion some 18½ arcseconds away. Splitting this pair is an interesting test for a 3 inch (75 mm) telescope.

URSAE MINORIS (UMI)
On meridian
10 p.m. June 10

Vela

VEE-lah

The Sail

This constellation was created in the 1750s and represents the sail of the ship *Argo*, in which Jason and the Argonauts sailed to search for the Golden Fleece.

 THE FALSE CROSS Delta (δ) and Kappa [κ] Velorum, together with Epsilon (ε) and Iota (ι) Carinae, make up a larger but fainter version of the Southern Cross which is known as the False Cross.

 GAMMA (γ) VELORUM This double star is resolvable in a steady pair of binoculars.

NGC 3132 This bright planetary nebula accompanies the many clusters in Vela, but lies right on the border with Antlia. Being 8th magnitude and almost 1 arcminute across, it is considered the southern version of Lyra's Ring Nebula, but with a much brighter central star.

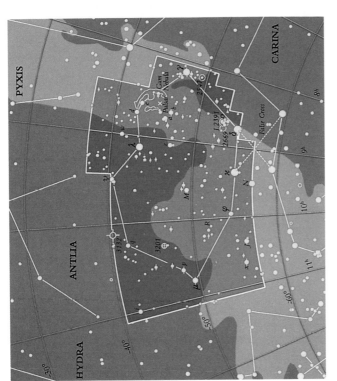

VELORUM (VEL)
On meridian
10 p.m. March 10

Virgo

VER-go

The Maiden; The Virgin

Scattered throughout Virgo and Coma Berenices are more than 13,000 galaxies. Known as the Virgo Cluster or Coma-Virgo Cluster, this mighty club of distant systems of stars repays sweeping with a small, wide-field telescope on a dark night.

SPICA (ALPHA [α] VIRGINIS) A bright, white star, Spica is almost exactly 1st magnitude, although it has a slight variation. It is 260 light-years away and more than 2,000 times as luminous as the Sun.

PORRIMA (GAMMA [γ] VIRGINIS) This is one of the best double stars in the sky, each component shining at magnitude

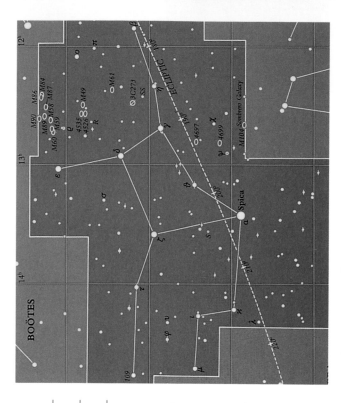

VIRGINIS (VIR)
On meridian
10 p.m. May 10

3.7. At 3 arcseconds separation, the pair is easy to separate.

M84 AND 86 These two elliptical galaxies are close enough to be seen in the same low-power telescope field. On a dark night, an 8 inch (200 mm) telescope will show several smaller galaxies in the same view.

M87 This elliptical galaxy is one of the mightiest galaxies we know. Through a small telescope it appears as a bright patch of fuzzy light about a magnitude brighter than M84 and 86. Interestingly, larger telescopes do not show a great deal more. In the professional size range, however, more details do emerge. With a 60 inch (1.5 m) telescope, for example, you can see a jet emerging from the galaxy's center.

THE SOMBRERO GALAXY (M104) Although M104 is quite a distance south of the main concentration of galaxies, it seems to be gravitationally attracted to the swarm and so is thought to be a part of it. The brightest of the Virgo galaxies, a dark lane cuts along its equator, making it look a little like a sombrero hat in an 8 inch (200 mm) telescope.

3C273 VIRGINIS This is the brightest known quasar, but being only 13th magnitude, an 8 inch (200 mm) scope is needed.

SOMBRERO GALAXY
The Sombrero Galaxy presents a bright, 8th-magnitude glow, just 8 arcminutes across, but is readily seen in smaller telescopes.

Volans

VOH-lanz

The Flying Fish

Piscis Volans, the Flying Fish, lies south of Canopus, and was introduced in 1603. It is now known only as Volans. Sailors in the south seas had reported seeing schools of flying fish, which may have been the inspiration for the name. The pectoral fins of these fish are as large as the wings of birds and they glide across the water for distances of up to a quarter of a mile (400 m).

 S VOLANTIS A Mira star, S Volantis usually has a maximum magnitude of 8.6, but it has occasionally risen to 7.7. Its faint minimum averages 13.6. The star completes its cycle in a little less than 14 months.

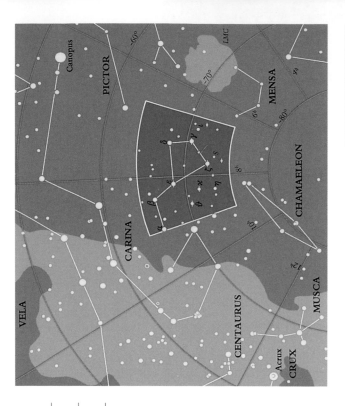

VOLANTIS (VOL)
On meridian
10 p.m. Feb 20

Vulpecula

vul-PECK-you-lah

The Fox

This constellation, invented by Johannes Hevelius in 1690, is without an exciting story or a moral tale. Hevelius's name for it was Vulpecula cum Anser, the Fox with the Goose, but now the constellation is simply referred to as the Fox.

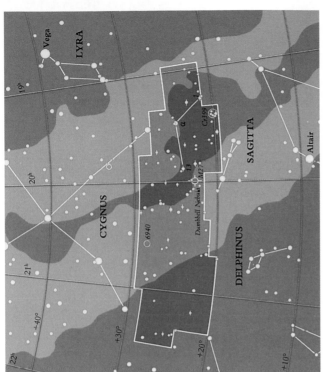

THE DUMBBELL NEBULA (M27) This is one of the finest planetary nebulas in the sky and is well suited to small telescopes. Bright and large, it is easy to find just north of Gamma (γ) Sagittae. Being 7th magnitude, it can be found through binoculars, but it appears only as a faint nebulous spot. If you use a small telescope, you can make out its odd shape. A larger telescope will reveal its 13th-magnitude central star. Although the nebula's gases are expanding at the rate of 17 miles (27 km) per second, there will be no noticeable change in the appearance of the nebula within a human lifetime.

STARHOPPING GUIDE

*Enjoy a journey around the sky
visiting the sights and stars
of your choice.*

The 20 starhops on the following pages cover a selection of some of the best-known areas across the night sky. They are intended as an introduction to the technique of starhopping, with the hope that you will move on from here to discover for yourself some of the multitude of other amazing objects appearing elsewhere in the sky.

M42 and M43 (above) form the pink glow in the sword of the Orion constellation (right).

The Stellar Nursery of Orion

Orion straddles the celestial equator, making its star nursery visible to observers in both the Northern and Southern hemispheres. With his mighty club raised, Orion, the Hunter, dominates the night sky early in the year as he prepares to battle Taurus, the Bull. Behind Orion's back is the mythical Monoceros, the Unicorn, partly obscured by a maze of Milky Way star fields.

The Hunter's starry sword dangles from his three-star belt. The sword harbors the Great Nebula in Orion (also known as the Orion Nebula), where gas covering the sky throughout the constellation is unmasked by the blazing light of young, hot blue-white stars. Even younger stars lie hidden within the gas clouds around it, only revealed by their infrared glow.

The introductory text provides historical, mythological, or general information about the constellations on the starhop.

The locater map outlines the region surrounding the starhop. The darker blue rectangle is the same 30 x 20 degree area that is shown on the main sky chart.

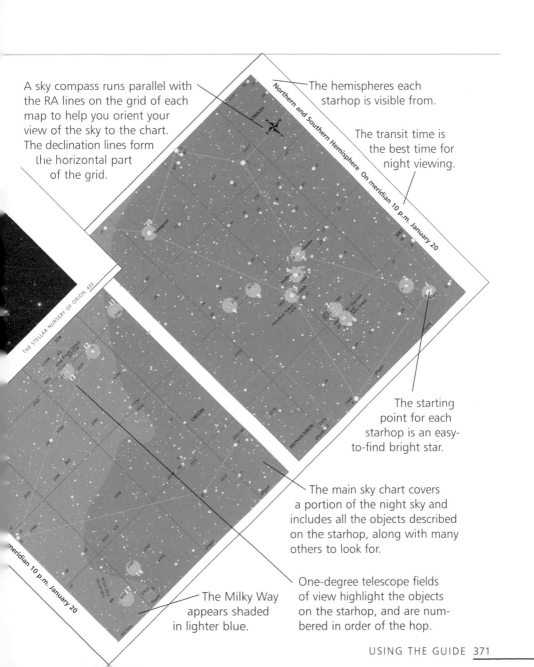

A sky compass runs parallel with the RA lines on the grid of each map to help you orient your view of the sky to the chart. The declination lines form the horizontal part of the grid.

The hemispheres each starhop is visible from.

The transit time is the best time for night viewing.

The starting point for each starhop is an easy-to-find bright star.

The main sky chart covers a portion of the night sky and includes all the objects described on the starhop, along with many others to look for.

The Milky Way appears shaded in lighter blue.

One-degree telescope fields of view highlight the objects on the starhop, and are numbered in order of the hop.

The starhopping text takes you on a guided tour of the night sky and is frequently cross-referenced to other relevant chapters in the book. It provides important observer-based information about each of the objects on the starhop, along with tips for finding fainter objects and some interesting historical facts.

Color photographs supplement the text by showing some of the objects described on the starhop.

Each object on the starhop is numbered to correspond with the 1-degree telescope fields of view (circles) on the main sky chart.

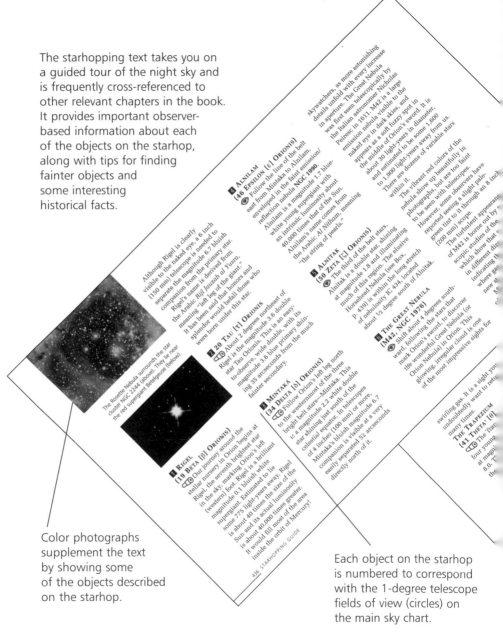

The Rosette Nebula surrounds the star cluster NGC 2244 (above). They lie near the red supergiant Betelgeuse (below).

Although Rigel is clearly visible to the naked eye, a 6 inch (150 mm) telescope is needed to separate the magnitude 6.7 bluish companion from the primary star. Rigel's name is derived from the Arabic *Rijl Jauzah al Yusra*, meaning "left leg of the giant." It has been said that honors and splendor would befall all those who were born under this star.

1 RIGEL (β) ORIONIS) (19 BETA [β] ORIONIS)
Our journey around the stellar nursery in Orion begins at Rigel, the seventh brightest star in the sky, marking Orion's left (western) foot. Rigel is a brilliant magnitude 0.1 bluish white supergiant. Estimated to lie some 775 light-years away, Rigel is about 40 times the size of the Sun and its actual luminosity is about 40,000 times greater. It would fill most of the area inside the orbit of Mercury!

2 20 TAU [τ] ORIONIS
Rigel is the magnitude 3.6 double star Tau Orionis, located about 2 degrees northeast of Rigel. This is an easy-to-observe, wide double, with its magnitude 3.6 blue primary shining 35 arcseconds from the much fainter secondary.

3 MINTAKA (34 DELTA [δ] ORIONIS)
Follow Orion's left leg north to the westernmost of the three bright belt stars—Mintaka. This is a magnitude 2.2 white double star shining just south of the celestial equator. In telescopes of 4 inches (100 mm) or more, Mintaka's bluish magnitude 6.7 companion is visible at a very easily separated 52 arcseconds directly north of it.

4 ALNILAM (46 EPSILON [ε] ORIONIS)
Follow the line of the belt east from Mintaka to Alnilam, enveloped in the faint emission/reflection nebula NGC 1990. Alnilam is a magnitude 1.7 blue-white young supergiant with an intrinsic luminosity about 40,000 times that of the Sun. Alnilam's name comes from the Arabic *Al Nitham*, meaning "the string of pearls."

5 ALNITAK (50 ZETA [ζ] ORIONIS)
The third of the belt stars, Alnitak is a double star, shining at magnitude 1.8 and illuminating much of this region. The elusive Horsehead Nebula (see Box, p. 439) is within the long stretch of nebulosity IC 434, located about 1/2 degree south of Alnitak.

6 THE GREAT NEBULA (M42, NGC 1976)
Shift about 4 degrees southward, following the stars that mark Orion's sword, to discover the wonderful Great Nebula (or Orion Nebula) in Orion. This glowing, irregular cloud is one of the most impressive sights for

skywatchers, as more astonishing details unfold with every increase in aperture. The Great Nebula was first seen telescopically by the Italian astronomer Nicholas Peiresc in 1611. M42 is a large emission nebula visible to the naked eye in dark skies, and appears as a soft fuzzy spot in the middle of Orion's sword. It is about 30 light-years in diameter, and estimated to be some 1,600 to 1,900 light-years away from us.

There are dozens of variable stars within it.

The vibrant red colors of the nebula show up beautifully in photographs, but are too faint to be seen with telescopes. However, some observers have reported seeing a slight pale-green tint to it through an 8 inch (200 mm) scope.

The turbulent appearance of M42 is borne out by spectro-scopic studies of the gas, which show that it is moving in different dir[...] indicating [...] where gas [...] new st[...]

swirling gas. It is a sight you undoubtedly want to return to many times.

THE TRAPEZIUM (41 THETA [θ] [...]
The Trap[...] four young [...] at magni[...] 8.0. T[...] the [...]

The illustrated feature box takes a closer look at one of the more interesting objects on the starhop, elaborating on aspects of the science behind it.

The Horsehead Nebula (B33)

An interesting, but exceedingly difficult, object to observe is the famous Horsehead Nebula (below). The Horsehead is a thick black cloud of dust and gas that can be seen only because it blots out some of the light coming from the faintly glowing stream-ers of the diffuse emission nebula IC 434. The Horsehead is estim-ated to be 1 light-year across and is composed of a thin haze of dust in non-luminous gas.

You need a clear dark sky to have any chance of observing this elusive object—probably the most challenging you will encounter. To locate the nebula, scan the area about halfway between Alnitak and the 11th and 12th magnitude stars directly south of it. An H-beta filter that screws into your eyepiece may help you to observe it.

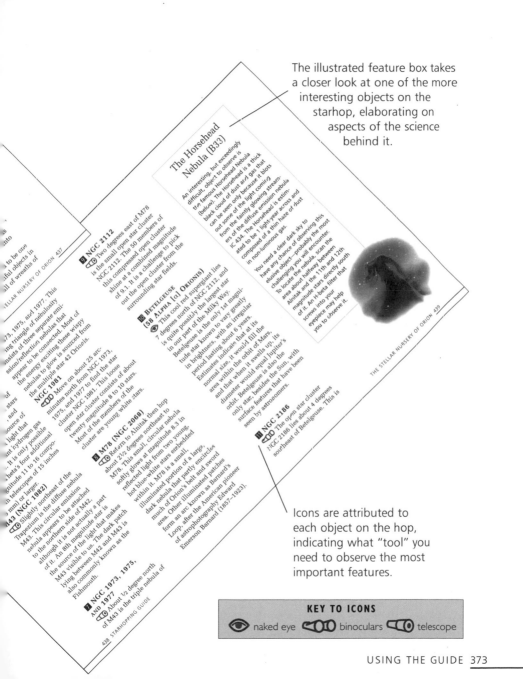

9 NGC 2112
Two degrees east of M78 is the small open star cluster NGC 2112. The 50 members of this compressed open cluster shine at a combined magnitude of 9.1. It is a challenge to pick out the open cluster from the surrounding star fields.

10 BETELGEUSE (58 ALPHA [α] ORIONIS)
This cool red supergiant lies 7 degrees north of NGC 2112 and is quite possibly the largest star in our part of the Milky Way. Betelgeuse is the only 1st magni-tude star known to vary greatly in brightness, with an irregular period lasting about 6 years. Estimates indicate that at its normal size, it would fill the area within the orbit of Mars, and that when it swells up, its diameter would equal Jupiter's orbit. Betelgeuse is also the only star besides the Sun with surface features that have been seen by astronomers.

11 NGC 2186
NGC 2186 lies about 4 degrees southeast of Betelgeuse. This is

NGC 1981
Move on about 25 arc-minutes north from NGC 1973, 1975, and 1977 to find the star cluster NGC 1981. This loose open star cluster consists of about twenty magnitude 8 to 10 stars. Most of the members of the cluster are young white stars.

8 M78 (NGC 2068)
Return to Alnitak then hop about 2½ degrees northeast to M78. This small, circular nebula softly glows at magnitude 8.3 in reflected light from two young, hot blue-white stars embedded within it. M78 is a small, illuminated portion of a large, dark nebula that partly encircles much of Orion's belt and sword area. Other illuminated patches form an arc known as Barnard's Loop, after the American pioneer of astrophotography Edward Emerson Barnard (1857–1923).

73, 1975, and 1977. This ng triangle of nebulosity onsists of three separate emi-ssion/reflection nebulas that appear to be connected. Most of the energy exciting these wispy nebulas to glow is sourced from the multiple star 42 Orionis.

M43 (NGC 1982)
Slightly northeast of the Trapezium is the diffuse emission nebula M43. This circular emission nebula appears to be attached to the northern side of M42, although it is not actually a part of it. An 8th magnitude star is the source of the light that makes M43 visible to us. The dark patch lying between M42 and M43 is also commonly known as the Fishmouth.

7 NGC 1973, 1975, AND 1977
About ½ degree north of M43 is the triple nebula of

Icons are attributed to each object on the hop, indicating what "tool" you need to observe the most important features.

KEY TO ICONS

👁 naked eye   binoculars   telescope

How to Starhop

For novice stargazers, navigating your way among the stars and searching for faint deep-sky objects can be daunting, until you learn how to starhop.

Basically, starhopping is a technique that uses bright stars as a guide to finding fainter objects. All you need to be able to starhop is an idea of how much sky you can see (the field of view) in your finderscope and telescope eyepieces, and how that view will compare with the same amount of sky on your star chart.

Even if you are fortunate enough to have a computerized telescope to take you from one object to the next, the techniques of starhopping will help you pick out a faint deep-sky object from a field of stars. The 20 starhops on the following pages are a great way to get started.

How Much Sky Can You See?

To start out, you will need a variety of templates of some sort to represent the fields of view of your binoculars or finderscope, and of your telescope eyepieces.

Illustrators' plastic circle templates work well, as they come in a wide variety of sizes and are available from most artists' and office supply stores.

To find out what diameter circle represents your finderscope field of view on the sky charts, center your finder on an easy-to-locate star, such as Mizar (Zeta [ζ] Ursae Majoris) (see p. 478). Southern Hemisphere skywatchers can use brilliant Alpha [α] Centauri (see p. 504). Look at the fainter stars around Mizar or Alpha Centauri, and study the view. Notice which stars you can see along the edges of the field, then find those same stars on your chart. Center your template circle on the same bright star on the map and try out different diameter circles until you find the one that closely matches your finderscope view.

To locate fainter objects, it helps to have an idea of how large the object will appear to be in your telescope eyepiece. The apparent size of an object is its angular diameter, usually measured in minutes or seconds of arc. Measure the field of view of your eyepieces by using a bright star located close to the celestial equator, such as Mintaka (Delta [δ] Orionis) (see p. 436), and follow these simple steps: place the star on the eastern edge of your view; time, in seconds, how long it takes for the star to drift across the center of the field and exit on the opposite (western) side; divide this time by four. The result represents the angular diameter of your field of view in arcminutes.

You should multiply the answer by 60 to obtain your field diameter in arcseconds—many faint objects and the separations of most double stars are smaller than an arcminute across. It is a good idea to measure the field of view for all of your eyepieces, along with the finderscope, and record this information in your observation logbook.

THE TRIFID NEBULA appears as a small, faint patch of light in a binocular-field view (above), but is revealed as a colorful nebula in the photograph at left.

A RED FLASHLIGHT is essential for reading star charts under a dark sky.

USING THE SKY CHARTS

It is important to have a feel for the size of your chart in relation to what you are looking at. All the main sky charts in the Star-hopping Guide are to the same scale (about 30 x 20 degrees). The span of your outstretched hand at arm's length measures close to 20 degrees—equivalent to the area represented by the main sky charts' vertical edge. Look for the brightest stars on your chart, then match the chart orientation to the same arrange-ment of stars in the sky.

Starhopping is like moving down the link of a chain, with each link represented by your field-of-view circle. On your chart, each selected object is centered in a 1 degree field—about the same size as a low-power eyepiece—but remember that each eyepiece's field size will be different. Estimate how many fields to move your tele-scope in making each hop, using your template circle. As you move the telescope, look out for the patterns of fainter stars along the hop.

One of the most difficult aspects of starhopping is being sure to move your telescope in the right direction, as the view of the sky through a telescope is often upside down or back to front. The easiest way to orient yourself is to nudge your scope toward the north (or south) celestial pole to see where stars enter the northern (or southern) edge of the field. Nudge your scope at right angles to this to find east and west. A compass symbol is also marked on the grid of each main sky chart to help keep you on track.

The stars on the star charts are marked from magnitude −1 down to magnitude 8. The deep-sky objects are marked to as faint as magnitude 12.5.

Now that you know how to starhop, you are ready to embark on any of the guided sky tours featured in the following pages.

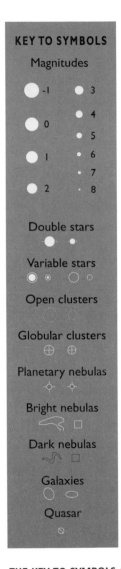
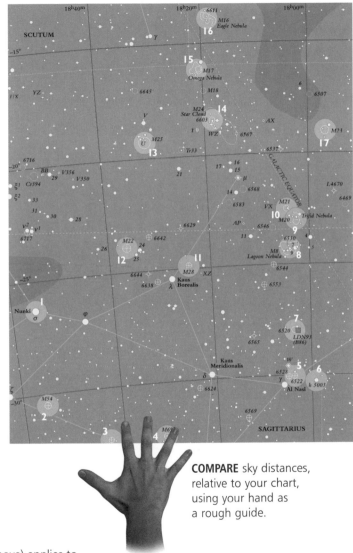

COMPARE sky distances, relative to your chart, using your hand as a rough guide.

THE KEY TO SYMBOLS (above) applies to all the main sky charts in this chapter.

KEY MAPS

Finding some constellations can be difficult, depending on your location, but a map of the whole sky is a great way to orient yourself to the overall picture.

It is easy to get around the night sky if you have some knowledge of the constellations and their position in relation to each other. A naked-eye view of the sky is the best way to learn the positions of the constel-lations, regardless of whether you own a telescope or not. When you are familiar with the constellations, you can then move on to particular regions, such as those in the starhops.

The key maps below represent the entire night sky. The projec-tion used on these pages halves the celestial sphere from top to bottom (celestial north to south). The north celestial and south celestial poles are at +90° and −90°, respectively. To avoid the distortion of the constellation patterns that occurs as the sphere narrows toward the two poles, the key maps have been

The Starhops

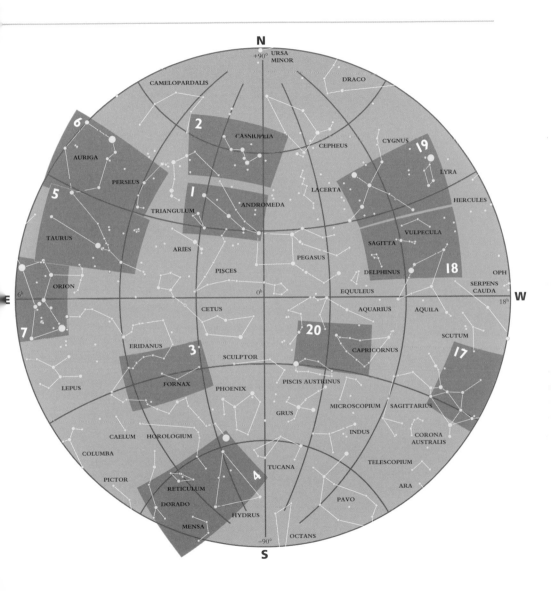

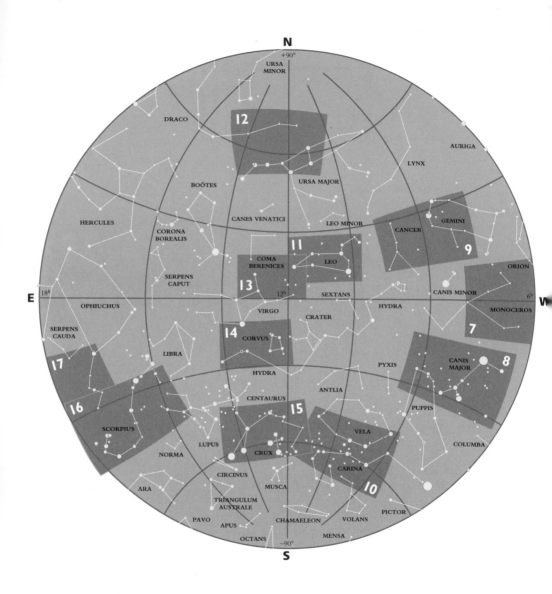

presented in stereographic projection. The only "distortion" from this projection comes from an increase in scale toward the edge of each map, giving them a more rounded appearance, making the star patterns easier to recognize.

The starhops are represented by the darker blue patches on the key maps, and are numbered from 1 to 20. The key maps are shown at a larger size on the opening page of each starhop to assist you as a locator tool. They are ordered west to east across the sky according to the times that they come into view in the evening throughout the year. These regions have been chosen for their variety of objects as well as their location. One or two starhops might be too far north or south for you to observe but most of them can be enjoyed by anyone with a telescope and the desire to learn about the night skies.

The Starhops
(continued)

A Galaxy Hunt around Andromeda

V isible from both the Northern and Southern hemispheres, this starhop offers skywatchers plenty of celestial treasures. The tour highlights are the Andromeda and Pinwheel galaxies, providing unforgettable views in a clear, dark sky.

The Andromeda Galaxy, in the constellation of Andromeda, is one of the brightest and most accessible galaxies for observers, and has been well known since ancient times. The earliest extant drawing of it is on a sky chart published in AD 964 by the Persian astronomer Abderrahaman al-Sufi.

The Pinwheel Galaxy lies in the neighboring constellation of Triangulum, the Triangle.

Keep in mind, though, that these galaxies are not the sum total of the area. This starhop is also rich in many other interesting deep-sky objects.

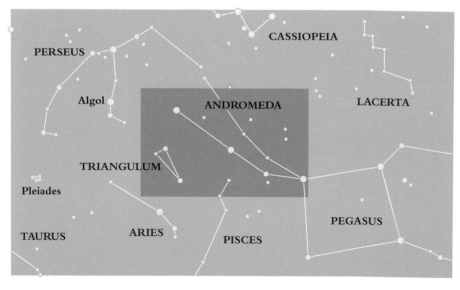

The Andromeda Galaxy
(M31) (left) is vastly more
distant than the open
cluster NGC 752 (above),
its neighbor in the
Andromeda constellation.

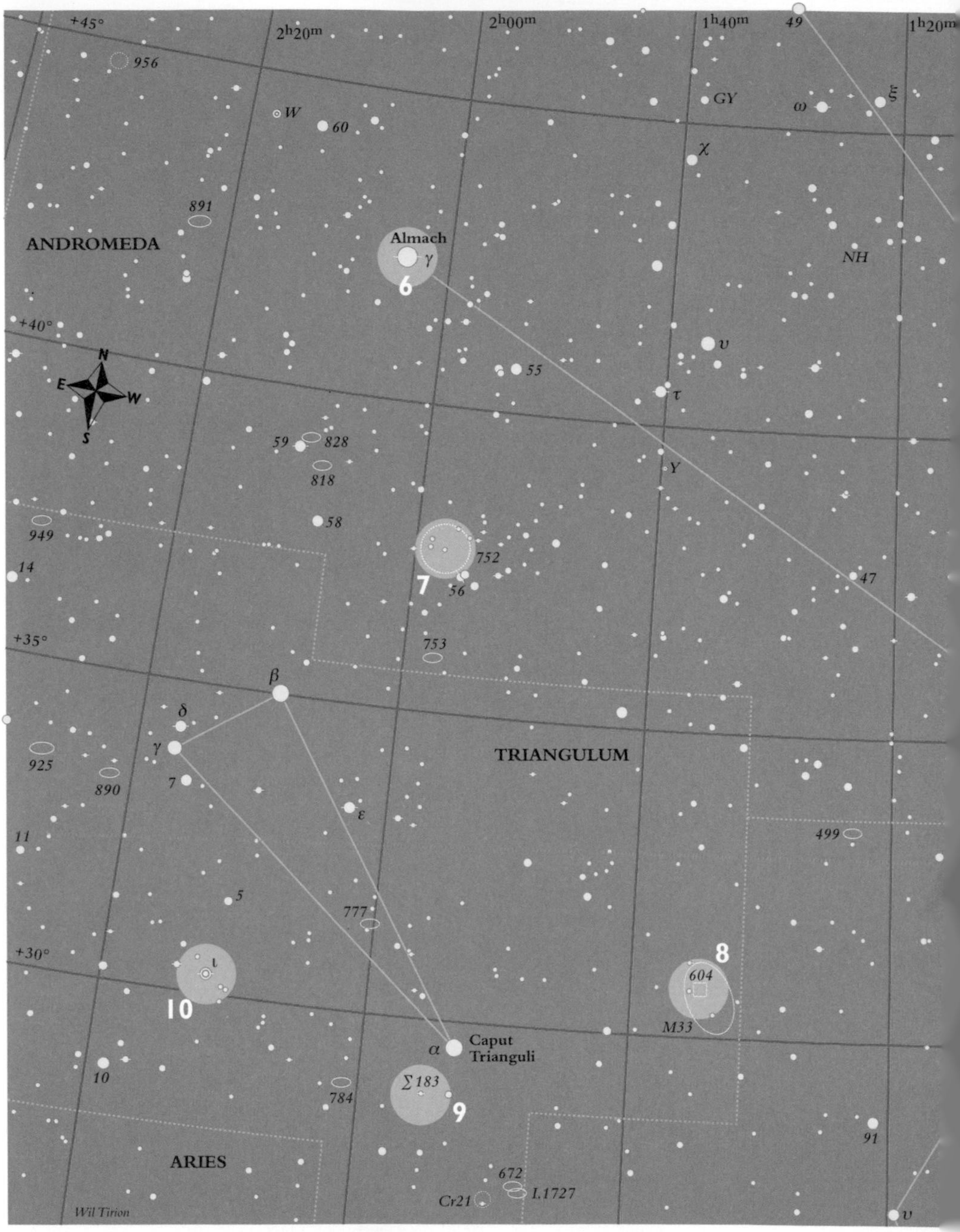

ANDROMEDA

TRIANGULUM

ARIES

Almach

Caput
Trianguli

Wil Tirion

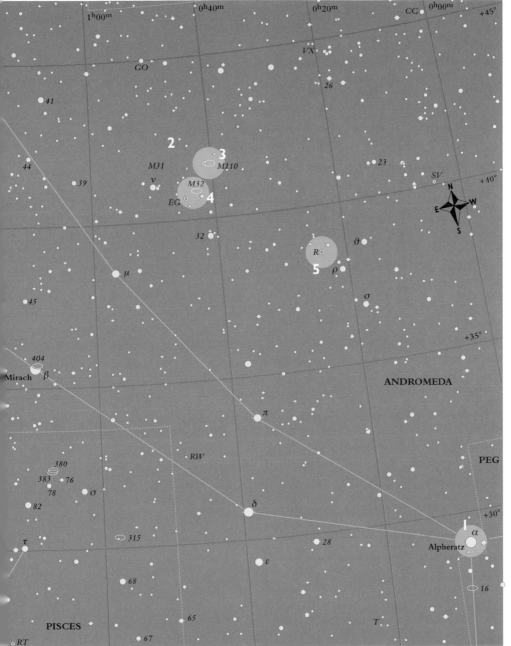

Northern and Southern Hemisphere On meridian 10 p.m. November 10

1 ALPHERATZ
(21 ALPHA [α] ANDROMEDAE)

 Alpheratz marks the northeastern corner of the Great Square of Pegasus, shown in the locater map (p. 382). Our starhop begins with this magnitude 2.1 blue-white double star, the brightest in the Andromeda constellation. Using a scope of 8 inches (200 mm) or more, you might be able to spot the very faint magnitude 11.3 secondary star, 82 arcseconds from the primary star.

Alpheratz was once known as Delta [δ] Pegasi because it was considered to be a part of the constellation of Pegasus before being renamed and allocated to Andromeda. You might see it labeled as Delta [δ] Peg on some sky charts.

To find the Andromeda Galaxy, use the stars **Mirach (43 Beta [β] Andromedae)** and **37 Mu [μ] Andromedae**, located in the twin chains of stars northeast of Alpheratz, as pointers to help you on your way.

2 THE ANDROMEDA GALAXY (M31, NGC 224)

👁 The spectacular Andromeda Galaxy is the most distant object we can see with the naked eye. As you gaze at the soft glow of the closest spiral galaxy to the Milky Way, you are looking across about 2,900,000 light-years. M31 is a large, bright object measuring 160 x 50 arc-minutes. In a dark sky it is clearly visible to the unaided eye, appearing as a broad, hazy-white cloud. However, city observers need binoculars to catch a satisfying view. In a 4 inch (100 mm) telescope, the core of M31 seems flattened, flowing evenly into the disk of the galaxy. A telescope fitted with a low-power, wide-field eyepiece is an advantage when observing M31 because of its sheer size. A higher power eyepiece will reveal only its nucleus.

In 1924, Edwin Hubble proved that M31 was not a part of the Milky Way, helping to determine the size of the universe. He did this by comparing the brightness of Cepheid variables in M31 and the Milky Way, finding that they were dimmer in M31 because they were so much farther away.

3 M110 (NGC 205)

⊂⊙ Within ½ degree of M31 is one of its two companion galaxies, M110, glowing at magnitude 8. In a 4 inch (100 mm) scope, M110 appears as an elongated patch of light, brightening toward its core.

M110 is the last object appearing on Charles Messier's list, having been added in 1967.

4 M32 (NGC 221)

⊂⊙ M32 is a compact elliptical galaxy about 1 degree southeast of M110. Also a companion galaxy of M31, M32 appears as an oval patch of light in a 4 inch (100 mm) scope, but for optimum views use a larger telescope.

EG ANDROMEDAE

⊂⊙⊙ Half a degree farther southeast is the cataclysmic variable red giant EG Andromedae. Its magnitude ranges from 7.1 down to 7.8 in a complicated cycle.

M33 (left), the Pinwheel Galaxy, is the biggest and brightest galaxy in the Local Group, after the Milky Way and the Andromeda Galaxy.

5 R Andromedae

⊂○○ Southwest of EG is R Andromedae, a long-period Mira variable well known for its broad-ranging cycle, moving from magnitude 5.3 down to 15 over a period of about 409 days. It is sometimes visible in binoculars, but at minimum is a challenge for an 8 inch (200 mm) telescope. The three stars **24 Theta [θ] Andromedae**, **25 Sigma [σ] Andromedae**, and **27 Rho [ρ] Andromedae** form a triangle west of R, that helps to locate the star when it is faint.

6 Almach
(57 Gamma [γ] Andromedae)

⊂○○ Sweep your scope about 12½ degrees east to Almach, a fine, color-contrast close double star—one of the best doubles for small-telescope observers. The magnitude 2.3 golden primary contrasts with its magnitude 5.1 greenish blue companion, lying 10 arcseconds away.

7 NGC 752

⊂○○ Shift about 5 degrees south of Almach to NGC 752. The 60 stars in this open cluster can be seen with the unaided eye from a dark site. With a finderscope or binoculars, you may be able to see chains and knots of stars forming a twisted X within this rich cluster.

8 The Pinwheel Galaxy (M33, NGC 598)

⊂○○ About 7 degrees southwest of NGC 752 is the beautiful Pinwheel Galaxy, across the border in Triangulum. Although bright, at magnitude 5.5, this spiral galaxy is hard to see because it appears face-on and is spread over a large patch of sky. It can be seen as a fuzzy glow through binoculars in a dark sky, but you will need a scope of 8 inches (200 mm) and a wide-field eyepiece to see more detail of the Pinwheel galaxy, including its diffuse, twisting arms.

NGC 604

⊂○○ The splotch of nebulosity sitting prominently on the northeastern tip of the Pinwheel Galaxy is NGC 604, shining more brightly than other parts of M33's spiral arms. NGC 604 is an oval-shaped emission nebula of glowing hydrogen gas where new stars are born.

9 STRUVE [Σ] 183

About 4 degrees southeast of M33 is the bright yellow multiple star **Caput Trianguli (2 Alpha [α] Tri)**. Use it as a pointer to locate the much dimmer double star Struve 183, about 1 degree southeast. A fine close double, Struve 183 has a magnitude 7.7 light yellow primary and a magnitude 8.4 blue secondary, 6 arcseconds away.

10 6 IOTA [ι] TRI

Four degrees northeast of Struve 183 is the stunning color-contrast double 6 Iota [ι] Tri. The primary is a magnitude 5 yellow star and the secondary is a magnitude 6.5 pale blue star, shining 3.8 arcseconds away.

Take the time to re-explore the highlights of our tour, along with the many other deep-sky objects surrounding them in this area.

Radio Mapping of M31

In 1912, the U.S. astronomer V. M. Slipher made the first spectrogram of M31. The blueshifts and redshifts of the spectrum lines of different parts of the galaxy showed that it was rotating.

This image (below), based on the 21 centimeter wavelength by the Westerbork Synthesis Radio Telescope, also shows that M31 is rotating and that there is a high concentration of cold hydrogen gas in the galaxy's outer arms.

The color enhancement of the radio image uses yellow and red to indicate the areas that are rotating away from us, while green and blue indicate areas that are in systematic motion toward us. From our vantage point, the Andromeda Galaxy is rotating in a clockwise direction.

Clusters around Cassiopeia and Perseus

Unfortunately, the spectacular open clusters in this part of the Milky Way are not visible to stargazers in the mid-southern latitudes or below. For northern observers, however, Cassiopeia is a circumpolar constellation that never disappears from the night sky. The best months to explore this region are September through to February. This area of the sky is especially rewarding for those observing with binoculars.

Cassiopeia, the Queen of Ethiopia, married King Cepheus and had a beautiful daughter, Andromeda. Perseus the Hero rescued her daughter Andromeda from Cetus, the sea monster, and later married her. All four family members share this part of the sky.

Cassiopeia sits on her throne in the form of an easy-to-locate W-shaped asterism of bright stars. To her southeast is the Y-shaped figure of her son-in-law Perseus.

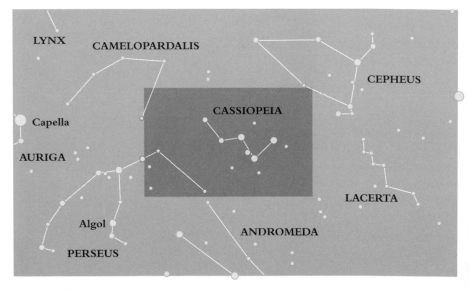

The Double Star Cluster (above)—NGC 869, at right, and NGC 884, at left—is a favorite target for Northern Hemisphere observers. Appearing close in the sky, they are not actually associated.

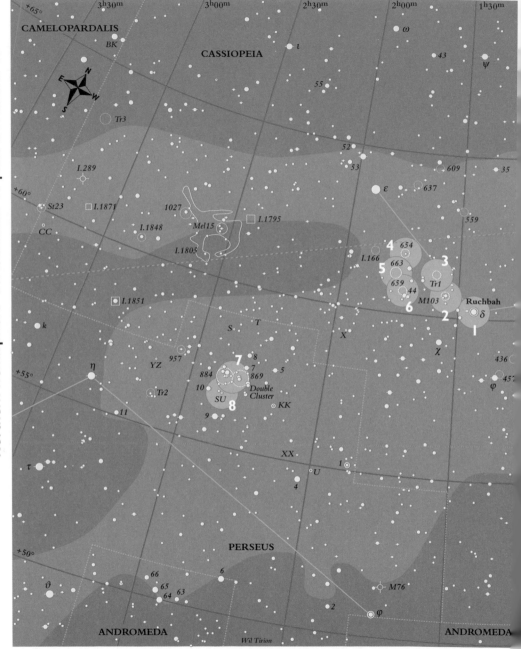

Northern Hemisphere   On meridian 10 p.m. November 10

CAMELOPARDALIS

CASSIOPEIA

PERSEUS

ANDROMEDA

Wil Tirion

ANDROMEDA

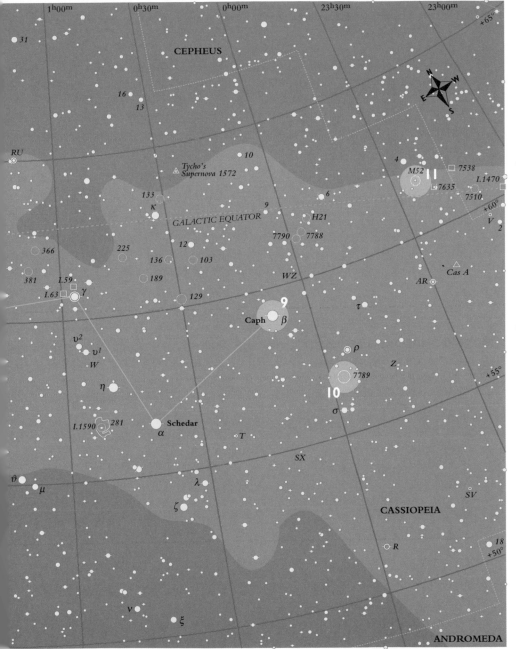

Northern Hemisphere On meridian 10 p.m. November 10

1 Ruchbah
(37 Delta [δ] Cassiopeiae)

👁 Our tour of rich Milky Way open clusters begins at Ruchbah, the magnitude 2.7 blue-white star forming a part of the eastern downstroke of Cassiopeia's highly recognizable W shape. Ruchbah lies 100 light-years from us. This beautiful star is the primary in a multiple system as well as an eclipsing-binary variable. A faint secondary star revolves around Ruchbah, partially eclipsing it, causing Ruchbah's magnitude to dim very slightly over a 760-day period.

Ruchbah's name originates from the Arabic *Al Rukah*, in relation to its position as "the knee" of the woman in the chair.

About ½ degree northeast of Ruchbah, within the same binocular or finder field, is the U-shaped gathering of open clusters: M103, Trumpler 1, NGC 654, NGC 663, and NGC 659.

2 M103 (NGC 581)

🔭 Shift your scope about 1 degree northeast of Ruchbah to locate M103. Pierre Méchain discovered this loose, magnitude 6.2 open star cluster in 1781. The brighter stars within the cluster seem to form the shape of an arrowhead. A 4 inch (100 mm) scope can resolve many of the fainter stars, some of which are colored. M103 may not actually be a star group that is bound by gravity, but simply a grouping of about 60 stars that appear as a scattered cluster from our vantage point.

3 Trumpler 1

🔭 Looking ½ degree farther northeast from M103, you should be able to spot Trumpler 1. This open cluster is a little difficult to pick out from the rich Milky Way star field it appears to be a part of. The small clump of stars seems to have a bright streak running through it that cannot be properly resolved, even with a 6 inch (150 mm) telescope.

4 NGC 654

🔭 About 1 degree northeast from Trumpler 1 is NGC 654. This cluster consists of about 60 stars in a loose association, but is still an easy object to see with binoculars, appearing as a hazy glow of tiny, faintly resolved stars.

5 NGC 663

Nudge ½ degree south of NGC 654 to the open cluster NGC 663. The 80 stars in this cluster give it a roundish look, somewhat like a cross between an open and a globular cluster, through a 6 inch (150 mm) telescope.

6 NGC 659

Some ½ degree southwest of NGC 663 lies NGC 659, an X-shaped cluster of about 40 stars.

The magnitude 5.8 golden-yellow double star **44 Cassiopeiae**, which is probably not a member of the cluster, lies close by.

7 THE DOUBLE STAR CLUSTER (NGC 884 {CHI [χ] PERSEI} AND NGC 869 {H PERSEI})

Return to Ruchbah, then hop about 8 degrees southeast to the Double Star Cluster in Perseus. This magnificent conglomeration

Supernova remnant Cassiopeia A

When Cassiopeia A (3C 461) exploded as a supernova some 9,700 years ago, a gigantic circular shell of gas raced out into space. Today, this still-expanding supernova remnant is too faint to see with amateur equipment, but its powerful energy is detectable at radio wavelengths. The radio output emission is created by high-speed electrons spiraling around magnetic field lines as the expanding cloud collides with thin gas between the stars.

Radio images of the cloud (right), the brightest radio source outside the Solar System, show gas racing away from the spot where the star exploded. By calculating this speed and the distance traveled by the gas since the explosion, astronomers estimate that the light from the explosion reached Earth around 1680, creating a 5th magnitude star. No record exists of anyone noticing this short-lived supernova in Cassiopeia.

In the rich star field (opposite), the Bubble Nebula (NGC 7635) appears at lower right to the open cluster M52, seen at upper left. NGC 7789 (right) is a rich open cluster, slightly larger than M52.

of bright stars has been well known since ancient times. Because of their size, these two 100-plus member clusters are best viewed with binoculars or a wide-field telescope eyepiece. Careful study of each cluster will reveal the many double-, multiple-, and variable-star systems they contain.

8 SU PERSEI

Some ½ degree southeast of the center of NGC 884 is the semi-regular variable SU Persei, which is actually a member of NGC 884. This pulsating red supergiant varies from magnitude 9.4 down to 10.8 during a cycle that lasts about 533 days.

9 CAPH (BETA [β] CASSIOPEIAE)

Sweep some 17 degrees west and slightly north of SU Persei to Caph, a wide double star and a short-period pulsating variable of a rare type known as Delta Scuti. Its variability is hard to detect visually because its magnitude of 2.2 fluctuates very slightly during a cycle that lasts a couple of hours.

10 NGC 7789

Hop 4 degrees southwest to the broad open cluster NGC 7789. This large cluster is located between the yellow semi-regular variable **7 Rho [ρ] Cassiopeiae** and the wide, white multiple-star

system **8 Sigma [σ] Cassiopeiae**. Use binoculars or a wide-field eyepiece to view the cluster, because it covers an area roughly the apparent size of the Moon.

⓫ M52 (NGC 754)

ᴄⲞⲞ Located about 6 degrees northwest from NGC 7789 is M52, an open star cluster. The 200 members of this cluster are located on the western border of Cassiopeia. A fine string of stars extending like an arm in an east-west direction across the cluster is a good test for 4 inch (100 mm) scopes or larger.

In areas filled with relatively easy binocular targets, such as this, it is a pleasure to amble around the many "families" of open clusters.

A Galaxy Feast in the Furnace

Although it can be seen from both hemispheres, this part of the sky is more accessible to skywatchers in the Southern Hemisphere. In the Northern Hemisphere, the region should be viewed during winter evenings, when it is at its highest point.

The constellation of Fornax was introduced by Nicolas Louis de Lacaille, a famous eighteenth-century French astronomer. He originally named it the Fornax Chemica, or Chemical Furnace, but today it is simply known as the Furnace.

Although this patch of sky may appear fairly barren at first, throughout Fornax and in parts of neighboring Eridanus, the River, you are looking toward a region rich in galaxies. The Fornax Galaxy Cluster, a relatively nearby cluster of galaxies, is one of the highlights of this star-hop. You need at least a 4 inch (100 mm) telescope to see many of the star systems in this area.

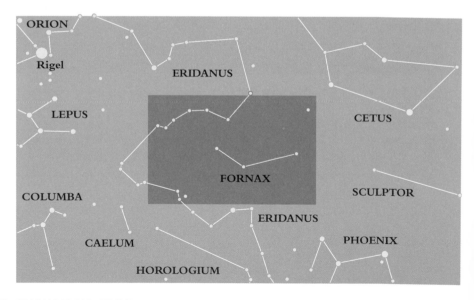

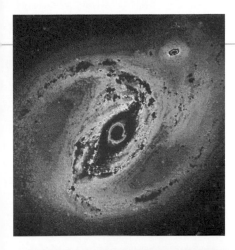

The computer-enhanced image of NGC 1097 (left) shows the galactic core in dark blue and the surrounding region in red. The galaxy's spiral arms are visible in blue and green. Another small galaxy that is interacting with NGC 1097 is shown at top right. A portion of the Fornax Cluster (below).

Northern and Southern Hemisphere On meridian 10 p.m. December 1

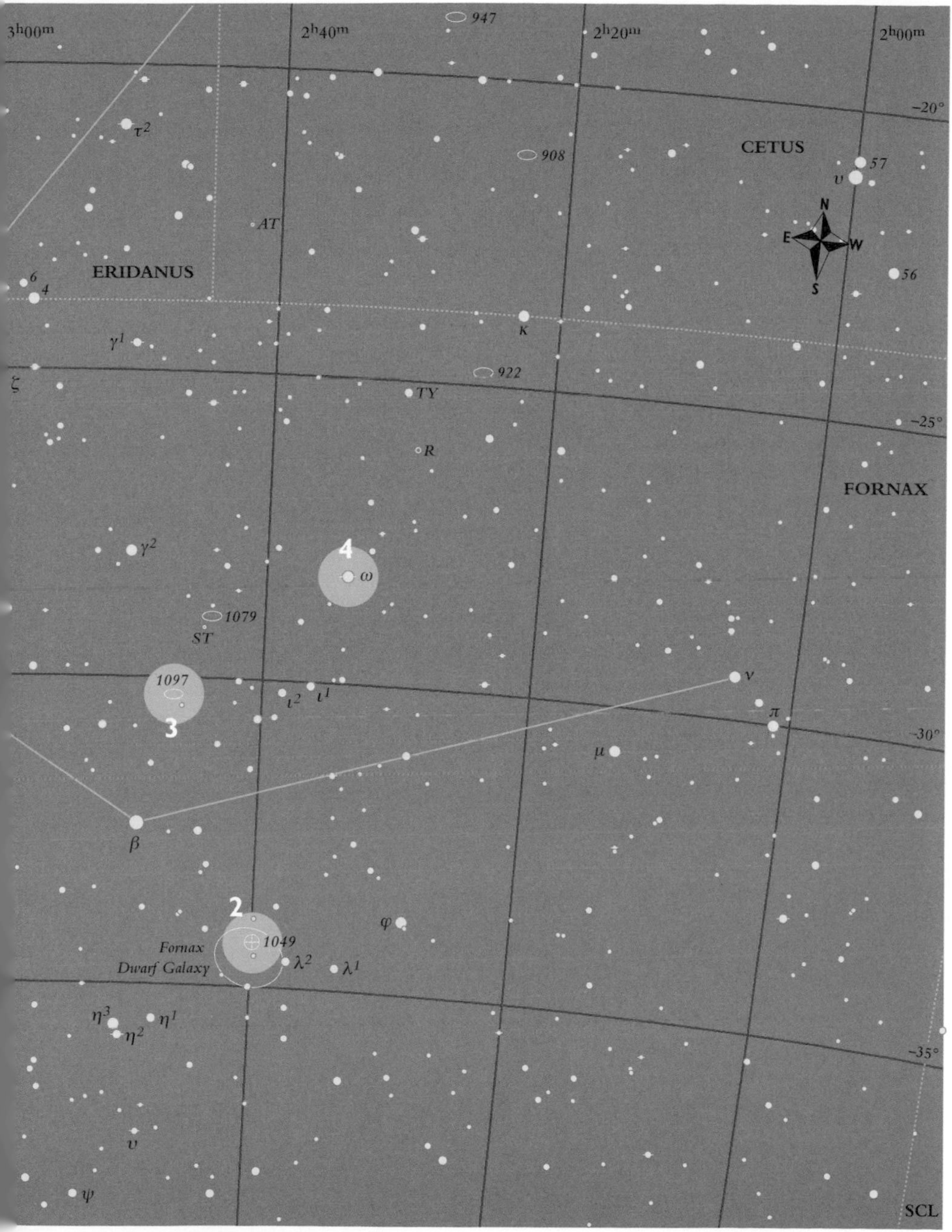

Northern and Southern Hemisphere On meridian 10 p.m. December 1

3ʰ00ᵐ 2ʰ40ᵐ 2ʰ20ᵐ 2ʰ00ᵐ

947

908

CETUS

57
υ

56

AT

N
E W
S

ERIDANUS

6
4

γ¹

ζ

κ

−20°

922
TY

R

−25°

FORNAX

γ²

4
ω

1079
ST

1097
3

ι² ι¹

ν

π

μ

−30°

β

φ

2
1049
Fornax
Dwarf Galaxy

λ² λ¹

η³
η² η¹

−35°

υ

ψ

SCL

1 ALPHA [α] FORNACIS

Our starting point on this journey is the star Alpha Fornacis, the brightest star in Fornax, although at 4th magnitude it is not what you would call prominent. This is an interesting binary star, with its magnitude 7 companion, also a deep yellow color, shining about 5 arcseconds away. The exact period during which the stars orbit each other is not altogether certain, but the currently recognized value is about 314 years.

The difference in brightness between the two components makes this a difficult object

The barred spiral galaxy NGC 1300 (opposite) lies 75 million light-years away in Eridanus. The arms are blue with the light of new young stars.

for small scopes. On a steady night with good seeing, a 3 inch (75 mm) scope should show the secondary fairly easily. The secondary star is also suspected of being variable, possibly fading to as low as magnitude 8 at minimum, when you may have some difficulty seeing it.

2 NGC 1049

About 9 degrees southwest from Alpha, you will find the star **Beta [β] Fornacis**. Use it as a pointer to help locate NGC 1049, 3 degrees farther southwest. This globular cluster calls for a larger aperture because it shines at only magnitude 13. An 8 inch (200 mm) scope may just show it as a fuzzy blob about 20 arcseconds across. It appears faint because it is not a part of our galaxy, belonging instead to the Fornax System, a dim 1 degree wide dwarf galaxy that looms so large it cannot be recognized visually, even though it is within the Local Group—the group that contains our galaxy.

3 NGC 1097

Shift 4 degrees north and a little east to NGC 1097, a barred spiral galaxy that is easy enough to see with a small scope. The galaxy shines at magnitude 9.3 and has a very bright nucleus. Its elongated form is revealed in a scope that is 4 inches (100 mm) or larger.

4 OMEGA [ω] FORNACIS

Just over 3 degrees northwest of NGC 1097 is the double star Omega Fornacis, which is an easy object for any small telescope. Its 5th and 7th magnitude components are easily separated at 11 arcseconds.

5 NGC 1232

To find NGC 1232, hop back to Alpha Fornacis, then move just over 8 degrees north and a little west, across the border into Eridanus, the River. NGC 1232, a large but faint spiral galaxy, is not an easy object for small scopes and its total magnitude of 9.9 is somewhat deceptive. As with many objects on this starhop, an 8 inch (200 mm) telescope will reveal more of the galaxy.

6 NGC 1300

⊄⊙ To locate NGC 1300, nudge your scope 2½ degrees east and a little south of NGC 1232, where you will find the 4th magnitude star **16 Tau⁴ [τ⁴] Eridani**. Just over 2 degrees north of Tau⁴ is the 10th magnitude barred spiral galaxy NGC 1300. This beautiful galaxy has a bright core and is easy to see through a 4 inch (100 mm) scope. In a dark sky, a hint of the spiralling arms can be detected in 12 inch (300 mm) telescopes.

7 NGC 1332

⊄⊙ Return to Tau⁴ before moving 1½ degrees east and a little north to the elongated elliptical galaxy NGC 1332. Shining at magnitude 10.3, this fuzzy patch has a fairly bright nucleus and is not hard to see through a 4 inch (100 mm) telescope.

8 NGC 1360

⊄⊙ About 4½ degrees south and a little east, back in Fornax, is NGC 1360. This planetary nebula, about 6 arcminutes across, offers an interesting change from observing the multitude of galaxies in this region. Its magnitude 11 central star can be distracting, but the nebula is not a difficult object in a 6 inch (150 mm) scope.

9 NGC 1398

⊄⊙ Gently guide your scope 1 degree southeast of NGC 1360 to NGC 1398, glowing at magnitude 9.7. This barred spiral galaxy is not difficult to spot, but is best suited to 6 inch (150 mm) scopes and larger.

10 NGC 1316

⊄⊙ The next hop is quite some distance away. First, shift 10 degrees south to the little triangle of stars **Chi¹,²,³ [χ¹, χ², and χ³] Fornacis**. About 2 degrees southwest of this triangle is the 9th magnitude spiral NGC 1316, the brightest galaxy in the Fornax Cluster. A 3 inch (75 mm) telescope shows it clearly as a fuzzy patch of light. NGC 1316 is also known as the radio source Fornax A. See if you can spot the 11th magnitude galaxy **NGC 1317**, just 6 arcminutes north of NGC 1316.

11 THE GREAT BARRED SPIRAL (NGC 1365)

🔭 Retrace your steps to the Chi[1,2,3] triangle, then hop 1 degree east to find the magnificent NGC 1365, a favorite among deep-sky observers. This 9th magnitude galaxy is the best example of a barred spiral in the southern sky. Easily found in 4 inch (100 mm) telescopes because of its quite prominent central region, NGC 1365 has a bright bar that is visible with an 8 inch (200 mm) telescope.

12 NGC 1399

🔭 Using a wide-field eyepiece, nudge 1 degree northeast of NGC 1365 to the heart of the Fornax Cluster. With a 4 inch (100 mm) scope you should easily be able to see quite a few faint galaxies, the brightest two being NGC 1399 and **NGC 1404**, both ellipticals, lying only a few arcminutes apart.

The Fornax region has the effect of making you feel very small. Several of the galaxies we have seen on this tour belong to the Fornax Cluster, our close neighbor in the universe.

Barred Spiral Galaxies

In a barred spiral galaxy, the spiral arms seem to originate from the ends of a "bar"—composed of stars, gas, and dust—that crosses the nucleus. The bar relates to dynamic conditions within a galaxy. On close examination, many spiral galaxies—including the Milky Way—show the trace of a bar.

The ratio of the mass of the faint halo surrounding a galaxy to that of its disk may play a role, as calculations suggest that galaxies with less massive haloes form bars more quickly. Many barred spirals, such as NGC 1365 (above), have well-defined arms, and there seems little doubt that an explanation of the bar is linked to our understanding of spiral structure.

Venturing into the Far South

This is our southernmost starhop, so unfortunately this region of the sky is probably not visible for skywatchers in the Northern Hemisphere. Even if you were observing within 15 degrees of the equator, you could still only expect to see a few of the objects.

The highlights of this area are the Magellanic Clouds, originally known as the Cape Clouds because they were associated with being as far south as the Cape of Good Hope. Portuguese seamen saw these two large patches of sky during voyages made in the fifteenth century. The famous explorer Ferdinand Magellan later described them and they were duly named in his honor, although no one knew what it was they were looking at.

It took four centuries, but astronomers finally recognized the existence of galaxies other than our own, realizing that the Magellanic Clouds were two of the nearest galaxies to the Milky Way.

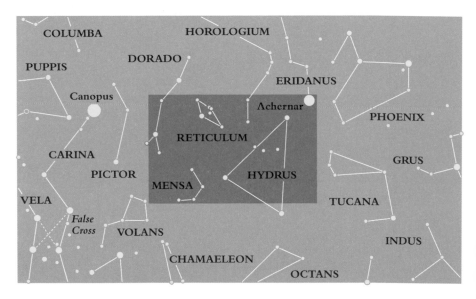

The Large and Small Magellanic Clouds (LMC and SMC) (above, left to right respectively) are classified as irregular galaxies. Brilliant Achernar (left) stands out in an otherwise barren patch of sky at the "mouth" of Eridanus.

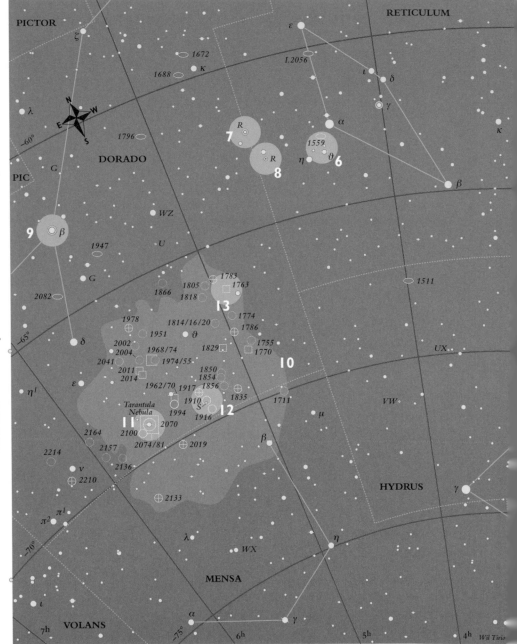

Southern Hemisphere On meridian 10 p.m. December 10

Southern Hemisphere On meridian 10 p.m. December 10

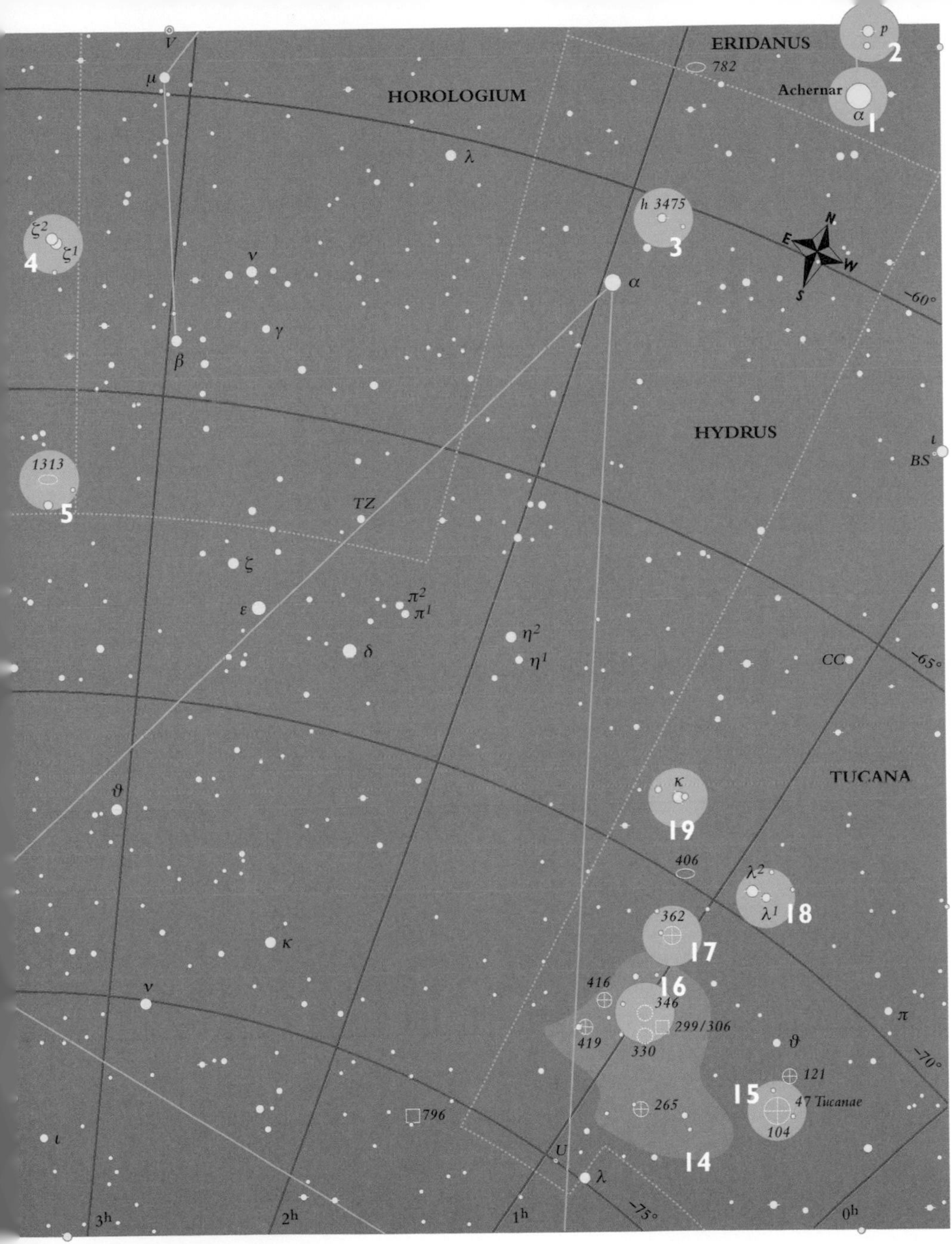

ERIDANUS

HOROLOGIUM

Achernar

p

2

α **1**

782

h 3475

3

α

N

E

S

W

−60°

ζ² ζ¹ **4**

ν

γ

β

μ

V

λ

HYDRUS

ι
BS

1313 **5**

ξ

ε

δ

TZ

π²
π¹

η²
η¹

CC

−65°

ϑ

κ

ν

ι

κ **19**

406

λ² λ¹ **18**

TUCANA

π

−70°

416
419

362 **17**

346 **16**
299/306
330

ϑ

265

121
47 Tucanae
104
15

14

796

U

λ

−75°

3ʰ

2ʰ

1ʰ

0ʰ

1 ACHERNAR (ALPHA [α] ERIDANI)

👁 Our starting point for this starhop is the brilliant magnitude 0.5 bluish white Achernar, the ninth brightest star in the night sky and the brightest in the constellation of Eridanus, the River.

Achernar is the most southerly of the very bright stellar beacons, standing out in an otherwise barren patch of sky. Finding it is easy—it is about as far from the south celestial pole as the Southern Cross is on the opposite side.

The name Achernar comes from the Arabic meaning "the end of the river," and was originally attributed to Theta [θ] Eridani. Theta was so named because it appeared to mark the end of the River for ancient astronomers, whose view of the sky was limited by their Northern Hemisphere locations. We now know Theta as Acamar, which is a corruption of its former name.

2 p ERIDANI (DUNLOP 5)

⊂◯ Aim your scope toward Achernar, before nudging it just over 1 degree north to locate the double star p Eridani, lying upstream from Achernar. This is a wonderful double for any size telescope, and a favorite among many observers. Shining at magnitude 5.8, its yellow-white components are equal in brightness, and lie about 10 arcseconds apart.

3 H 3475

⊂◯ Return to Achernar, then move to a point about two-thirds of the way to **Alpha [α] Hydri** to find h 3475. The stars of this double are much closer together than those of p Eridani, with its two 7th magnitude components being 2.4 arcseconds apart. It is a good test for a 3 inch (75 mm) scope on a still night. This is one of the many double stars discovered by John Herschel during his stay in South Africa in the 1830s.

4 ZETA [ζ] RETICULI

⊂◯ To find Zeta Reticuli, hop to Alpha Hydri, then shift west about 9 degrees along the way to **Alpha [α] Reticuli**. Zeta is a wide double star that is easy to separate with binoculars, its two 5th magnitude component

The wispy tendrils of the Tarantula Nebula are clearly seen in this image, taken just after nearby SN1987A blazed into view.

recommended for viewing this galaxy, but even with a 12 inch (300 mm) telescope, the bar is only vaguely visible.

stars, Zeta¹ and Zeta², lying 5 arcminutes apart. Each is a magnitude 4.7 yellowish star. These stars are remarkably similar to the Sun, a fact that has prompted speculation about the possibility of life existing on orbiting planets, although such planets have not been found yet.

5 NGC 1313

Moving poleward 4 degrees will bring NGC 1313 into view. This is a well-known barred spiral galaxy near the corner of the constellation of Reticulum, the Reticule. It has a total magnitude of 9.4, but appears quite large and faint. An 8 inch (200 mm) scope or larger is

6 THETA [θ] RETICULI

To the northeast of NGC 1313 and just southeast of Alpha Reticuli, Theta Reticuli shines faintly to the unaided eye. Theta is a pleasing double star comprising 6th and 8th magnitude components, separated by about 4 arcseconds. With a 3 inch (75 mm) scope, you should have little difficulty separating them, but the higher the magnification, the better the view.

NGC 1559

In the same field, about ½ degree north of Theta, is the barred spiral galaxy NGC 1559. Although it is about a magnitude fainter in total brightness than NGC 1313, this galaxy is more compact, appearing as a broad, fuzzy line. A 4 inch (100 mm) scope, or possibly even a smaller one, should clearly show the galaxy. The brightening toward its core is easier to see with larger scopes.

7 R DORADUS

Moving toward the border with Dorado, 2 degrees to the northeast of NGC 1559, is the star called R Doradus, which is just inside the constellation of Dorado, the Swordfish. R Doradus is a vivid orange-red color, not unlike a fainter view of the planet Mars. It is a semi-regular variable star with a period that fluctuates from cycle to cycle, averaging out at about 338 days. R Doradus is an easy binocular target because it only varies between magnitudes 4.8 and 6.6.

8 R RETICULI

Moving back about 1 degree southwest is R Reticuli. Unlike R Doradus, this Mira-type variable can drop to magnitude 14 at minimum, so you will not see it with binoculars then. However, at maximum, around every 278 days, it can reach

magnitude 7, which makes checking to see just how bright it is a worthwhile effort. It has a ruddy look that is obvious through binoculars, and it lies about 12 arcminutes south of a 6th magnitude star.

9 BETA [β] DORADUS

Swing 7 degrees east to the Cepheid variable Beta Doradus, which fluctuates between the magnitudes of 3.5 and 4.1 over a period of 9.84 days. It is thought to lie 1,700 light-years away.

10 THE LARGE MAGELLANIC CLOUD

Far more distant, but seen just a few degrees poleward of Beta, lies the Large Magellanic Cloud (LMC). Easily visible to the unaided eye as a "cloud" of light several degrees across, the LMC is a fine sight in binoculars, which help show the elongated, patchy appearance of this irregular galaxy. Lying about 160,000 light-years from the Milky Way, the LMC is the second-closest galaxy to our own. The closest known is the Sagittarius dwarf galaxy, detected in 1994, which is slowly being torn apart by the Milky Way.

11 THE TARANTULA NEBULA (NGC 2070)

👁 Near the eastern end of the the LMC is the wonderful Tarantula Nebula. Being the brightest object in the LMC, the Tarantula Nebula is visible to the unaided eye—a remarkable fact, given that it is in another galaxy. Even through a 3 inch (75 mm) scope, some of its spider-like structure can be seen, while in an 8 inch (200 mm) scope the view is stunning. Within the nebula's dazzling heart is a dense and mysterious cluster of brightly glowing supergiants known as R136. NGC 2070 is more than 1,000 light-years across, making it the largest known diffuse nebula, some 30 times the size of the Great Nebula in Orion.

12 NGC 1910

📷 Sweep your scope through the LMC, heading slowly west for 3 degrees, until you come across NGC 1910. One of the many clusters in the LMC, this compact group contains the bluish white variable star **S Doradus**, which is the proto-type of its class. S Doradus varies irregularly between magnitude 9

Supernova 1987a

Astronomers around the world were excited when a new naked-eye star suddenly appeared within the Large Magellanic Cloud on February 24, 1987. It was the first supernova seen with the unaided eye since 1604, reaching magnitude 2.9 at its peak and remaining visible for several months. The object was originally a massive blue star called Sanduleak −69 202.

The star actually exploded some 165,000 years ago, the light having taken that long to reach us. The light was accompanied by a burst of neutrinos—tiny, elusive particles. Scientists had predicted that these would be produced in very large numbers during a supernova explosion.

The study of SN1987a continues today, with rings of light, shown in the illus-tration of the Hubble Space Telescope image (right), being the most recent surprises in the ongoing tale of the supernova's discovery.

and 11, the variations being the result of the periodic shedding of the star's outer layers.

⑬ NGC 1763
To spot the bright nebula NGC 1763, head northwest, to the edge of the LMC. NGC 1763 is easily seen with binoculars, and a 3 inch (75 mm) scope reveals two bright, seemingly separate areas.

⑭ THE SMALL MAGELLANIC CLOUD
👁 Leaving the LMC and heading some 20 degrees west, you will come across its smaller counterpart—the galaxy called the Small Magellanic Cloud (SMC). Slightly more distant than the LMC and somewhat smaller, the SMC, also an irregular galaxy, is nevertheless an easy naked-eye target. Binoculars will not show nearly as much of the SMC as the LMC. This lesser galaxy has a more irregular form, appearing as a large blob of light, about 3½ degrees across, that fits neatly into a typical binocular field.

⑮ 47 TUCANAE (NGC 104)
👁 A chief item of telescopic interest in this region is the naked-eye spot of light about 3 degrees west of the SMC, 47 Tucanae. A 3 inch (75 mm) telescope shows a "granular" appearance, while a 6 inch (150 mm) reveals a multitude of stars. It is widely accepted that 47 Tucanae is the most brilliant globular after Omega Centauri, although it has a condensed core, giving it quite a different appearance. This is the astronomer Johann Bode's celebrated "ball of suns," also having been referred to as "a stupendous object" by John Herschel. Seemingly leading the SMC around the sky, 47 Tucanae is a superb globular belonging to the Milky Way Galaxy.

16 NGC 346

←◎ Move 3 degrees back to the southeast, into the SMC, to find NGC 346, an open cluster that lies within the SMC. About 5 arcminutes across, it is embedded in a region of nebulosity and appears as an easy-to-see fuzzy spot in a 3 inch (75 mm) scope. Its total brightness is close to that of a 10th magnitude star. See if you can pick out the nearby cluster **NGC 330**, which is visible in the same low-power field, about ½ degree southwest of NGC 346.

17 NGC 362

←◎◎ Edge your scope 1 degree north of NGC 346 to NGC 362. Seen as a round patch of light through binoculars, this is a conspicuous globular cluster. It is hard to resolve through a 4 inch (100 mm) telescope, which shows only a hint of its starry nature, but a 6 inch (150 mm) telescope will show it reasonably well.

In the sky, the fabulous globular cluster 47 Tucanae (left), a highlight of the Southern Hemisphere skies, appears to lie close to the much more distant SMC.

18 Lambda¹ [λ¹] Tucanae (Dunlop-2)

←◎ One and a half degrees farther north lies a little pair of naked-eye stars. The fainter of the two is Lambda¹ Tucanae. This star is a wide double that is easy to resolve in any size telescope. The 6th and 8th magnitude yellow-white components of Lambda¹ are separated by 20 arcseconds.

19 Kappa [κ] Tucanae

←◎ The final object on our hop is another double star, Kappa Tucanae, 2 degrees east and a little north of Lambda¹. Kappa is an easy pair in a 3 inch (75 mm) scope, especially on high power. Its 5th and 7th magnitude stars lie 5.4 arcseconds apart. Look for another 7th magnitude star, shining just a few arcminutes away in the same field.

Southern Hemisphere observers really are the envy of northerners for having the Magellanic Clouds all to themselves. It is a rewarding pastime simply to spend an evening browsing around this region with anything from the unaided eye to a large telescope.

Taurus and the Seven Sisters

The zodiac constellation of Taurus, the Bull, is clearly visible from both the Northern and Southern hemispheres, from February through April.

According to legend, the red eye of mighty Taurus glares at Orion, the Hunter, as the bull guards the Pleiades (opposite), the Seven Sisters, from Orion's advances. Orion's heart is set on making Merope, one of the Pleiades, his wife. Her parents, the Titan Atlas and the Oceanid Pleione, watch closely from the edge of the Pleiades Cluster. Of the seven young sapphire-blue Pleiade sisters, only Merope married a mortal, the King of Corinth, so she hides her shame at this behind a wispy reflection nebula.

The Pleiades' half-sisters form the nearby Hyades Cluster, another fantastic naked-eye and binocular object on this starhop.

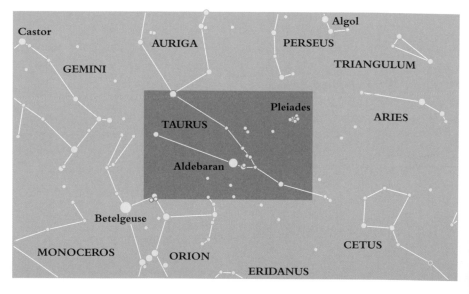

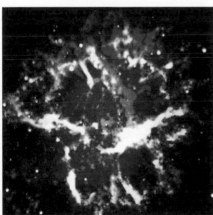

The Pleiades (above) is a highlight in Taurus. Merope is the 3rd star from the left, hiding behind her reflection nebula. The Crab Nebula (left) contains the first pulsar to be detected visually at its core.

Northern and Southern Hemisphere On meridian 10 p.m. March 10

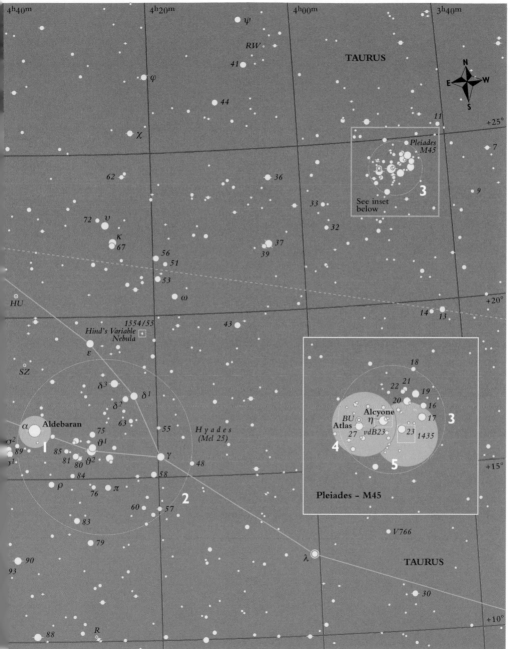

Northern and Southern Hemisphere On meridian 10 p.m. March 10

1 ALDEBARAN
(87 ALPHA [α] TAURI)

👁 This tour of Taurus and the Seven Sisters begins at the 1st magnitude orange giant Aldebaran, the 13th brightest star in the sky. Although it seems to form the eastern tip of the Hyades Cluster, Aldebaran, just 65 light-years distant, is actually much closer to us. Like many other orange giants, it is possible that this star is also slightly variable. Aldebaran has five close star companions, but they are faint and extremely difficult to observe through amateur equipment.

At about 40 times larger than the Sun and intrinsically some 125 times brighter, Aldebaran would fill most of the area inside Earth's orbit.

The name Aldebaran is derived from the Arabic *Al Dabaran*,

The Pleiades, at upper right, and the Hyades, beside Aldebaran at left (opposite), are nearby clusters appearing large in the sky.

meaning "the follower," probably because this star follows the Pleiades through the night sky.

2 THE HYADES (MEL 25)

👁 This large (more than 4 degrees in diameter), rich, distinctly V-shaped open star cluster consists of a mixture of about 100 bright stars and many faint ones, including dozens of double and variable stars. The cluster, which is 150 light-years away, marks the head of the bull. It is named for the half-sisters of the Pleiades, being the daughters of Atlas and Aethra. The Hyades' distance to us provides a crucial step in measuring distances in the universe, as it is one of the closest clusters to us.

3 THE PLEIADES (M45, MEL 22)

👁 About 14 degrees northwest of Aldebaran is M45—the Seven Sisters—the brightest and most famous star cluster in the sky. M45 is a young open cluster

dominated by youthful hot blue stars and enveloping nebulosity. The brightest part of the nebula surrounding the Pleiades is around the magnitude 4.1 star **Merope (23 Tauri)**. The Pleiades star nursery has been known since ancient times. Seven bright stars are visible to the naked eye from a dark site, although the cluster shows best through binoculars or a low-power telescope eyepiece, since it covers an area about four times the size of the Full Moon. It is essential to use high power when studying the fainter stars and patches of nebulosity.

4 ALCYONE (25 ETA [ε] TAURI)

⊂◯ The brightest member of the Pleiades is magnitude 2.9 Alcyone, a wide quadruple-star system embedded within the reflection nebula **van den Bergh 23**. The individual components of Alcyone's system are easy to separate with a small telescope.

ATLAS (27 TAURI)

⊂◯ This young blue giant star is a close double that usually requires a 10 inch (250 mm) telescope at least and good seeing conditions to separate its magnitude 3.6 and 6.8 components, which lie only 0.4 arcseconds away from each other.

⑤ TEMPEL'S NEBULA (NGC 1435)

☊ This is the reflection nebulosity in which blue-white Merope is embedded. The nebula appears to be nearly transparent so is quite hard to detect, but once you "see" it you might think that it looks as if someone has smeared white shoe polish on a pane of glass. This nebula is part of a series of small nebulas extending over much of the western side of the Pleiades.

⑥ NGC 1647 (MEL 26)

☊ Return to Aldebaran, then hop about 3½ degrees northeast to NGC 1647. This open star cluster contains about 25 uniformly bright 8th magnitude stars gathered in a loose grouping along the line of the western horn of the bull. More than 200 additional fainter stars are part of this rich cluster. As you study the individual stars, try to pick out some of the many close double stars.

⑦ NGC 1746 (MEL 28)

☊ Look for the open star cluster NGC 1746, which lies about 5½ degrees northeast of NGC 1647 and just 1 degree southwest of the magnitude 5.5 blue-white double star **103 Tauri**. NGC 1746 has a dense central region of about 20 stars, along with about 30 more in knots scattered about the cluster's core.

⑧ 123 ZETA [ζ] TAURI

👁 Shift your scope about 8 degrees southeast to Zeta Tauri, the last bright star in the southern horn of the bull. Zeta is an extremely close binary star whose components cannot be separated with amateur scopes. It is also a variable, belonging to the rare Gamma Cassiopeiae-type class. Zeta lies about 420 light-years away from us.

⑨ THE CRAB NEBULA (M1, NGC 1952)

☊ Nudge about 1 degree northwest of Zeta to the famous Crab Nebula, lying 6,500 light-years from us. The nebula is visible with small telescopes but can be somewhat disappointing. Details in the cloud can be detected in 10 inch (250 mm) scopes or larger. First discovered by British amateur astronomer John Bevis in 1731, M1 is the gaseous supernova remnant of the explosion of a star witnessed and recorded by Chinese astronomers in AD 1054. The explosion was so bright that the star was visible in daylight for a period of 23 days.

In the core of the Crab Nebula, a tiny spinning neutron star flashes a beam of energy on and off 30 times a second. This "star," called a pulsar, is all that remains of the original star that exploded as a supernova so long ago. This was the first pulsar to be detected visually.

This patch of sky has intrigued and entranced skywatchers since ancient times because its highlights, the Pleiades and Hyades, are so big and bright, as well as being rich in mythology.

M45, The Seven Sisters

The ancient Greeks were not the only people to develop myths and legends about the origins of the cluster they named the Pleiades. The Australian Aborigines also integrated the skies they observed into a heritage of stories, known as the Dreamtime. The bark painting (below), by Wongu, a member of the Yolngu tribe in Arnhem Land, depicts the Seven Sisters inside a

wooden canoe. The three stars of Orion's belt are shown in a line at the head of the canoe, to the right of the image, with the seven prominent stars in the middle representing the Pleiades, their wives. The lone fish inside the canoe, at center top, represents the nearby Hyades Cluster, while the fish swimming in the water are bright stars in the Milky Way.

Riding with the Charioteer

The rich star fields of the Milky Way in the pentagon-shaped constellation of Auriga, the Charioteer, hug the galactic equator, forming the centerpiece of this area of sky. It is visible to skywatchers in both the Northern and Southern hemispheres.

The route of this hop includes some of the finest open star clusters in the northern half of the sky. Cutting diagonally across Auriga is a string of open star clusters, including M36, M37, and M38. In addition to these highlights, many other star clusters lie among a variety of objects.

To the ancient Greeks and Romans, the constellation of Auriga represented either a charioteer or a herd of goats. In the herd, bright, white Capella, the Goat Star, is the mother of the flock and her three starry "kids" graze close by.

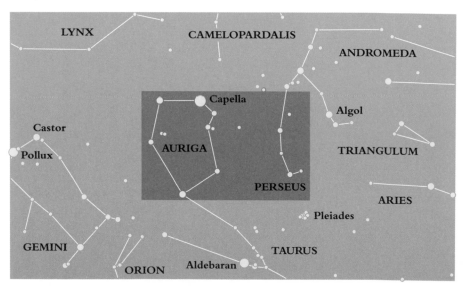

M37, M36, and M38 (left to right, below) lie within the Milky Way in the constellation of Auriga (left).

Northern and Southern Hemisphere On meridian 10 p.m. January 1

Northern and Southern Hemisphere On meridian 10 p.m. January 1

1 Capella
(13 Alpha [α] Aurigae)

👁 This starhop begins with the
sixth brightest star in the sky, the
magnitude 0.08 golden-yellow
giant Capella. This brilliant
spectroscopic multiple star lies
only 42 light-years from Earth.
Capella's four components are
too close together to be separated
through conventional telescopes.

Capella A and Capella B are
binary yellow companions that
form one of the star systems
making up Capella. The A and
B stars are estimated to be 90
and 70 times more luminous than
the Sun, respectively. The other

The California Nebula (opposite) is a large, faint cloud of gas amid the bright stars of the constellation of Perseus, including 4th magnitude Minkib at center bottom.

binary star completing this multiple system is Capella H, consisting of a pair of red dwarf stars.

In many ancient myths, Capella, the Goat Star, is represented as a she-goat, carried over the shoulder of the charioteer. It is also sometimes referred to as the Little She-goat.

2 ALMAAZ (EPSILON [ε] AURIGAE)

👁 About 3½ degrees southwest of Capella is Almaaz, an eclipsing binary. Intrinsically, this magnitude 3.8 white star is one of the most luminous individual stars we know of. It is partially eclipsed by a mysterious companion object every 27 years, the eclipse itself lasting about 2 years. The next eclipse will begin in 2009. During the eclipse, Almaaz's brightness drops by about ⅔ magnitude. Many theories have been posed as to the nature of the eclipsing object.

One theory holds that it is an almost transparent infrared supergiant star that is so large it would fill most of the area inside the orbit of Saturn. It is also possible that it may be simply a cloud of dust and gas.

3 NGC 1664

⊂◉ Nudge 2 degrees west of Almaaz to the faint open star cluster NGC 1664. Use low power for this rather sparse 30-member cluster, which looks like a string of tiny jewels on a chain, or an elongated hollow diamond. The brightest star, of about 7th magnitude, is located near the southern end of the chain.

4 M38 (NGC 1912)

⊂◍◐ Scanning some 10 degrees to the southeast along the galactic equator you will find M38, the dimmest of the three Messier objects in the center of Auriga. This cross-like open cluster, consisting of about 160 stars of magnitude 10 or fainter, was discovered by the Italian astronomer Giovanni Hodierna in the seventeenth century. He also discovered the open clusters M36 and M37.

5 STRUVE [Σ] 698

◖◉ The double star Struve 698 lies about 1 degree southwest of M38. This beautiful little double star consists of two red stars of magnitudes 6.6 and 8.7, separated by 31 arcseconds. They were first measured by the German astronomer F. G. W. Struve in 1831. Struve discovered over 2,000 double stars during his career as an astronomer in Germany and Russia. The components of Struve 698 should be easy enough to resolve through a 4 inch (100 mm) telescope.

6 NGC 1893

◖◉◖ Another 1½ degrees farther southwest is NGC 1893, an elongated open star cluster comprised of between 40 and 60 members. Most of the component stars of the cluster are faint, but they still stand out in the foreground of the surrounding star fields.

7 M36 (NGC 1960)

◖◉◖ Sweeping some 3 degrees east of NGC 1893 is M36, an open star cluster of about 60 young blue and white stars, with a slight condensation of stars near its center. Search through the cluster to find the numerous double stars within it.

8 M37 (NGC 2099)

◖◉◖ Moving on about 4 degrees southeast from M36 lies M37. This very rich, magnitude 6.2 open star cluster, the best in the constellation of Auriga, contains about 170 bright stars, as well as hundreds of much fainter stars scattered throughout. The majority of the stars are young blue-white giants and super-giants. The brighter members form a rough trapezoid shape with a belt of fainter stars cutting across the geometric figure.

9 45 EPSILON [ε] PERSEI

◖◉ Return to M38, then sweep about 17 degrees west and a little north to Epsilon Persei. The primary for this double-star system is a magnitude 2.9 blue-white giant. The greenish magnitude 8.1 secondary is about 9 arcseconds away and can be seen through scopes of 6 inches (150 mm) or larger. The large difference in brightness between the two components means they are difficult to separate.

10 THE CALIFORNIA NEBULA (NGC 1499)

CO Hop 4 degrees due south from Epsilon Persei to **Minkib (46 Xi [ξ] Persei)**, the 4th magnitude blue-white star located on the southwestern fringe of the California Nebula. Minkib is the illuminating power for the nebula, the last object on our starhop. The California Nebula, an elusive and faint reflection nebula, appears as a huge, elongated patch of grayish wispy reflection nebulosity. It is named for its vague resemblance to the U.S. state of California, but you need to use your imagination to see the similarity to its namesake. The nebula has a very low surface brightness, and is best seen with a nebula filter. Using low power and a wide-field eyepiece at a dark site is also a great help to observers.

Ride with the Charioteer, scanning the depths of the Milky Way Galaxy for the many other star clusters and double stars to be found in this rich star region.

Stellar evolution: Capella and the Sun

The life of a star can last from a few million to more than a hundred billion Earth years. Its life span is directly related to the amount of hydrogen fuel it contains and the rate at which it converts this fuel to helium. Part of our Sun's life cycle is detailed in the illustration below.

Currently about five billion years old (shown at top), the Sun will grow to become a yellow giant (shown at right), Capella's present size. The Sun is expected to use up the hydrogen fuel in its core in about another five billion years, before swelling up as a red giant (shown at left), then fading away to become a white dwarf star.

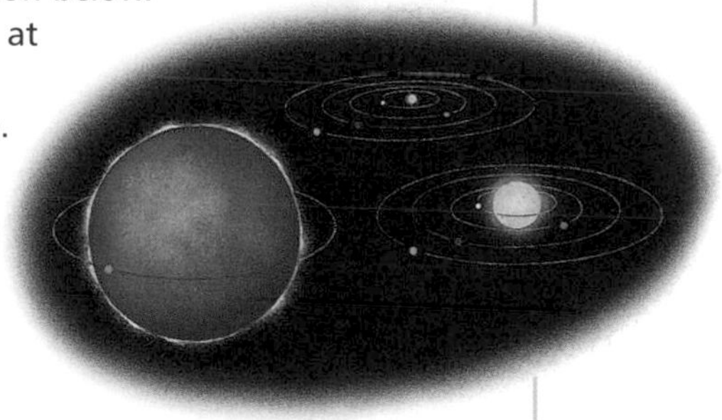

Capella is 13 times larger than the Sun. It is already well on the way to becoming a red giant star.

The Stellar Nursery of Orion

Orion straddles the celestial equator, making its star nursery visible to observers in both the Northern and Southern hemispheres. With his mighty club raised, Orion, the Hunter, dominates the night sky early in the year as he prepares to battle Taurus, the Bull. Behind Orion's back is the mystical Monoceros, the Unicorn, partly obscured by a maze of Milky Way star fields. His two hunting dogs, Canis Major and Canis Minor, keep him company.

The Hunter's starry sword dangles from his three-star belt. The sword contains the Great Nebula (the Orion Nebula), where gas covering the sky throughout the constellation is unmasked by the blazing light of young, hot blue-white stars. Even younger stars lie hidden within the gas clouds around it, only revealed by their infrared glow.

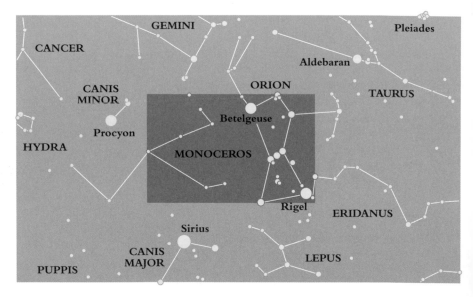

M42 and M43 (above)
form the pink glow in
the sword of the Orion
constellation (right).

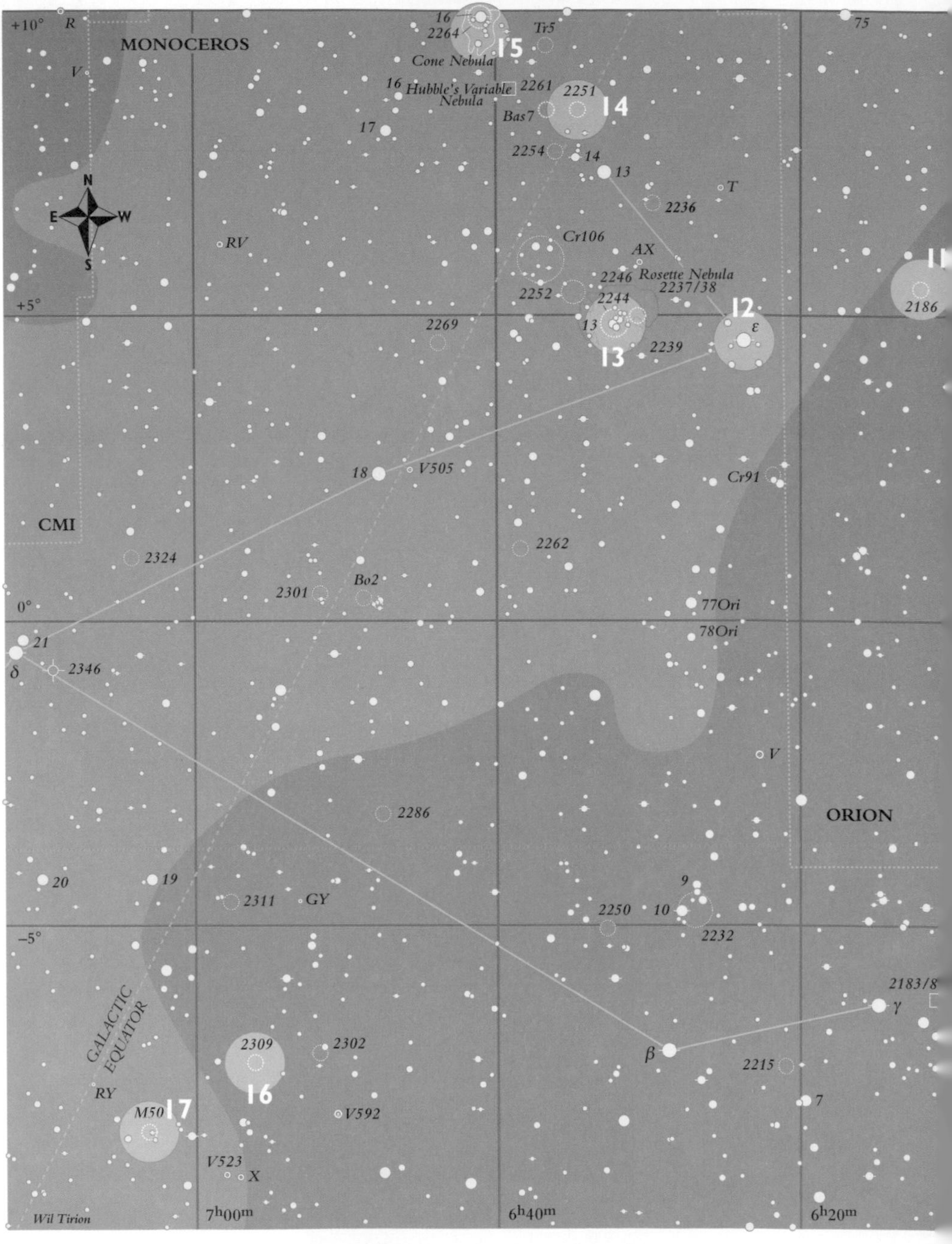

Northern and Southern Hemisphere   On meridian 10 p.m. January 20

MONOCEROS

CMI

ORION

16
2264
Cone Nebula
15
Tr5
75

16 Hubble's Variable 2261
Nebula
Bas7
2251
14

17
2254
14
13
T
2236

RV
Cr106
AX
Rosette Nebula
2246
2237/38
11
2186

2252
2244
13
12
ε

2269
13
2239

18
V505
Cr91

2324
2262

Bo2
2301
77Ori

78Ori

21
δ
2346
V

2286
ORION

20
19
2311
GY
9
2250
10
2232

2183/8
γ

GALACTIC
EQUATOR
2309
2302
β
2215

RY
17
16
V592
7

M50
V523
X

Wil Tirion
7h00m
6h40m
6h20m

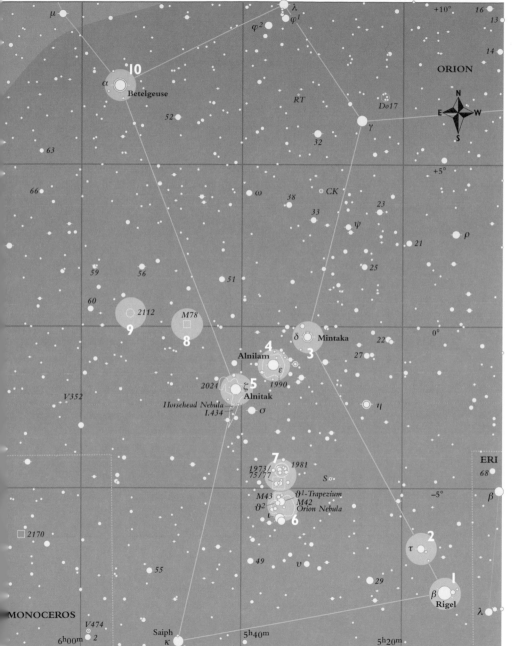

Northern and Southern Hemisphere On meridian 10 p.m. January 20

The Rosette Nebula surrounds the star cluster NGC 2244 (above). They lie near the red supergiant Betelgeuse (below).

Although Rigel is clearly visible to the naked eye, a 6 inch (150 mm) telescope is needed to separate the magnitude 6.7 bluish companion from the primary star.

Rigel's name is derived from the Arabic *Rijl Jauzah al Yusra*, meaning "left leg of the giant." It has been said that honors and splendor would befall those who were born under this star.

1 RIGEL (19 BETA [β] ORIONIS)

⊂⊙ Our journey around the stellar nursery in Orion begins at Rigel, the seventh brightest star in the sky, marking Orion's left (western) foot. Rigel is a brilliant magnitude 0.1 bluish white supergiant. Estimated to lie some 775 light-years away, Rigel is about 40 times the size of the Sun and its actual luminosity is about 40,000 times greater. It would fill most of the area inside the orbit of Mercury.

2 20 TAU [τ] ORIONIS

⊂⊙ About 2 degrees northeast of Rigel is the magnitude 3.6 double star Tau Orionis. This is an easy-to-observe, wide double, with its magnitude 3.6 blue primary shining 35 arcseconds from the much fainter secondary.

3 MINTAKA (34 DELTA [δ] ORIONIS)

⊂⊙ Follow Orion's left leg north to the westernmost of the three bright belt stars—Mintaka. This is a magnitude 2.2 white double star shining just south of the celestial equator. In telescopes of 4 inches (100 mm) or more, Mintaka's bluish magnitude 6.7 companion is visible at a very easily separated 52 arcseconds directly north of it.

4 ALNILAM
(46 EPSILON [ε] ORIONIS)
👁 Follow the line of the belt east from Mintaka to Alnilam, enveloped in the faint emission/reflection nebula **NGC 1990**. Alnilam is a magnitude 1.7 blue-white young supergiant with an intrinsic luminosity about 40,000 times that of the Sun. Alnilam's name comes from the Arabic *Al Nitham*, meaning "the string of pearls."

5 ALNITAK
(50 ZETA [ζ] ORIONIS)
👁 The third of the belt stars, Alnitak is a double star, shining at magnitude 1.8 and illuminating much of this region. The elusive Horsehead Nebula (see Box, p. 439) is within the long stretch of nebulosity IC 434, located about ½ degree south of Alnitak.

6 THE GREAT NEBULA
(M42, NGC 1976)
👁 Shift about 4 degrees southward, following the stars that mark Orion's sword, to discover the wonderful Great Nebula (or Orion Nebula) in Orion. This glowing, irregular cloud is one of the most impressive sights for skywatchers, as more astonishing details unfold with every increase in aperture. The Great Nebula was first seen telescopically by the Italian astronomer Nicholas Peiresc in 1611. M42 is a large emission nebula visible to the naked eye in dark skies, and appears as a soft fuzzy spot in the middle of Orion's sword. It is about 30 light-years in diameter, and estimated to be some 1,600 to 1,900 light-years away from us. There are dozens of variable stars within it.

The vibrant red colors of the nebula show up beautifully in photographs, but are too faint to be seen with telescopes. However, some observers have reported seeing a slight pale-green tint to it through an 8 inch (200 mm) scope.

The turbulent appearance of M42 is borne out by spectroscopic studies of the cloud, which show that gas is racing in different directions within it, indicating the localized areas where gas is condensing into new stars.

M42 is considered to be one of the most beautiful objects in the heavens, full of wreaths of swirling gas. It is a sight you will undoubtedly want to return to many times.

THE TRAPEZIUM (41 THETA¹ [θ] ORIONIS)

◁O The Trapezium is a group of four young, bright, hot white stars at magnitudes 5.1, 6.7, 6.7, and 8.0. Theta¹ is the main source of the strong ultraviolet light that causes the abundant hydrogen gas in M42 to glow. It is only possible to separate Theta's four additional faint, magnitude 11 to 16 components in telescopes of 15 inches (375 mm) or larger.

M43 (NGC 1982)

◁O Slightly northeast of the Trapezium is the diffuse nebula M43. This circular emission nebula appears to be attached to the northern side of M42, although it is not actually a part of it. An 8th magnitude star is the source of the light that makes M43 visible to us. The dark patch lying between M42 and M43 is also commonly known as the Fishmouth.

◻7 NGC 1973, 1975, AND 1977

◁O About ½ degree north of M43 is the triple nebula of NGC 1973, 1975, and 1977. This glowing triangle of nebulosity consists of three separate emission or reflection nebulas that appear to be connected. Most of the energy exciting these wispy nebulas to glow is sourced from the multiple star 42 Orionis.

NGC 1981

◁O Move on about 25 arc-minutes north from NGC 1973, 1975, and 1977 to find the star cluster NGC 1981. This loose open star cluster consists of about twenty magnitude 8 to 10 stars. Most of the members of the cluster are young white stars.

◻8 M78 (NGC 2068)

◁O Return to Alnitak then hop about 2½ degrees northeast to M78. This small, circular nebula softly glows at magnitude 8.3 in reflected light from two young, hot blue-white stars embedded within it. M78 is a small, illuminated portion of a large, dark nebula that partly encircles much of Orion's belt and sword area. Other illuminated patches form an arc known as Barnard's Loop, after the American pioneer of astrophotography Edward Emerson Barnard (1857–1923).

9 NGC 2112

⊂⊙ Two degrees east of M78 is the small open star cluster NGC 2112. The 50 members of this compressed open cluster shine at a combined magnitude of 9.1. It is a challenge to pick out the open cluster from the surrounding star fields.

10 BETELGEUSE (58 ALPHA [α] ORIONIS)

👁 This cool red supergiant lies 7 degrees north of NGC 2112, and is quite possibly the largest star in our part of the Milky Way. Betelgeuse is the only 1st magnitude star known to vary greatly in brightness, with an irregular period lasting about 6 years. Estimates indicate that at its normal size, it would fill the area within the orbit of Mars, and that when it swells up, its diameter would equal Jupiter's orbit. Betelgeuse is also the only star, besides the Sun, with surface features that have been seen by astronomers.

11 NGC 2186

⊂⊙ The open star cluster NGC 2186 lies about 4 degrees southeast of Betelgeuse. This is

The Horsehead Nebula (B33)

An interesting, but exceedingly difficult, object to observe is the famous Horsehead Nebula (below). The Horsehead is a thick black cloud of dust and gas that can be seen only because it blots out some of the light coming from the faintly glowing streamers of the diffuse emission nebula IC 434. The Horsehead is estimated to be 1 light-year across and composed of a thin haze of dust in non-luminous gas.

You need a clear dark sky to have any chance of observing this elusive object—probably the most challenging you will encounter. To locate the nebula, scan the area about halfway between Alnitak and the 11th and 12th magnitude stars directly south of it. An H-beta filter that screws into your eyepiece may help you to observe it.

a large, loose open star cluster enveloped in a rich Milky Way star field. Most of the 30 members of the cluster are 9th to 11th magnitude and can be seen with small scopes.

🔟 8 EPSILON [ε] MONOCEROTIS

◖🔭 The 4th magnitude star about 3 degrees east of NGC 2186 is Epsilon Monocerotis, our next target. Epsilon is a triple-star system in which the three pale yellow-white to bluish white components are easy to separate through a small telescope. The A star shines at magnitude 4.3, the B star at magnitude 6.7, 13 arcseconds away, and the C star at magnitude 12.7.

🔟 THE ROSETTE NEBULA (NGC 2237)

◖🔭 The faint circular mass of gas 2 degrees east of Epsilon is our next stop. This doughnut-like emission nebula includes the open star cluster NGC 2244. The nebula is very large at about 80 arcminutes in diameter. As it is so diffuse, it can be difficult to locate in telescopes smaller than 8 inches (200 mm). The Rosette

Nebula is estimated to be at a distance of about 2,600 light-years from us. This would make it some 55 light-years in diameter —almost twice the size of M42.

NGC 2244

◖🔭 This open star cluster, which is enveloped by the Rosette Nebula, appears in the hole of the doughnut. Its brightest apparent member is the 6th magnitude yellow giant 12 Monocerotis. Some astronomers think that this star is a foreground object and not actually part of the cluster, since the other members appear to be mostly young white stars.

🔟 NGC 2251

◖🔭 Hop about 4 degrees north to NGC 2251. This elongated open star cluster contains about 30 stars located mostly in a twisted string. The cluster shines with a combined magnitude of about 7.3, but most of the stars are fainter than magnitude 12.

🔟 THE CHRISTMAS TREE CLUSTER (NGC 2264)

◖🔭 Slide about 2 degrees northeast to the open star cluster NGC 2264. The triangular shape of this open star cluster strongly suggests its common name, given by Lowell Observatory astronomer Carl Otto Lampland. There is a faint nebula surrounding the cluster, and the black **Cone Nebula** intrudes visually into this at the southern end. This effect is too faint to be seen in telescopes smaller than 12 inches (300 mm). The brightest star in the cluster, S Monocerotis, is an intensely luminous, magnitude 4.6 blue-white double.

The glimmering nebula NGC 1977 is another illuminated portion of the gas that envelops the constellation of Orion.

16 NGC 2309

Take a long hop, about 17 degrees south, to NGC 2309. About 40 stars make up this magnitude 10.5 compact open star cluster. It appears to be centered on a magnitude 11.5 star, in front of a very attractive star field.

17 M50 (NGC 2323)

About 2 degrees southeast of NGC 2309 is the last object on our starhop, the easy-to-find, rich open star cluster M50. This beautiful magnitude 6.3 cluster contains about 50 stars, appearing as a mottled patch of light barely visible to the unaided eye in dark skies. The cluster is roughly diamond shaped and is best viewed with binoculars or a low-power telescope eyepiece. A bright yellow-orange star holds center stage slightly southwest of the core. Two parallel arms of stars extend out from the core.

The Orion area is another patch of the night sky that you could spend years exploring and yet still not see all of the objects that are to be found. Our tour has only touched on some of the amazing highlights.

The Dog Star and Surrounds

The best views of the constellation of Canis Major, the Great Dog, are to be had during the evenings of the early months of the year. This prominent, easy-to-find constellation lies on the southwestern side of the Milky Way. Although visible from both hemispheres, southern observers will have a better view of it.

Farther north of this sky chart is the constellation of Canis Minor—which, as you might suspect, is the Little Dog. In classical mythology, the two dogs are said to have accompanied the great Orion as he hunted. They were placed in the sky to keep him company after his death.

Moving into the band of the Milky Way near Canis Major, we cross the border into neighboring Puppis, the stern of the ship Argo. This region contains many interesting objects for binoculars and small telescopes.

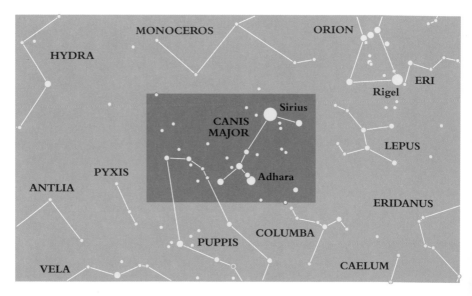

M46 (above), on the left, M47 (above),
on the right, and M93 (left) are the
highlights of northern Puppis.

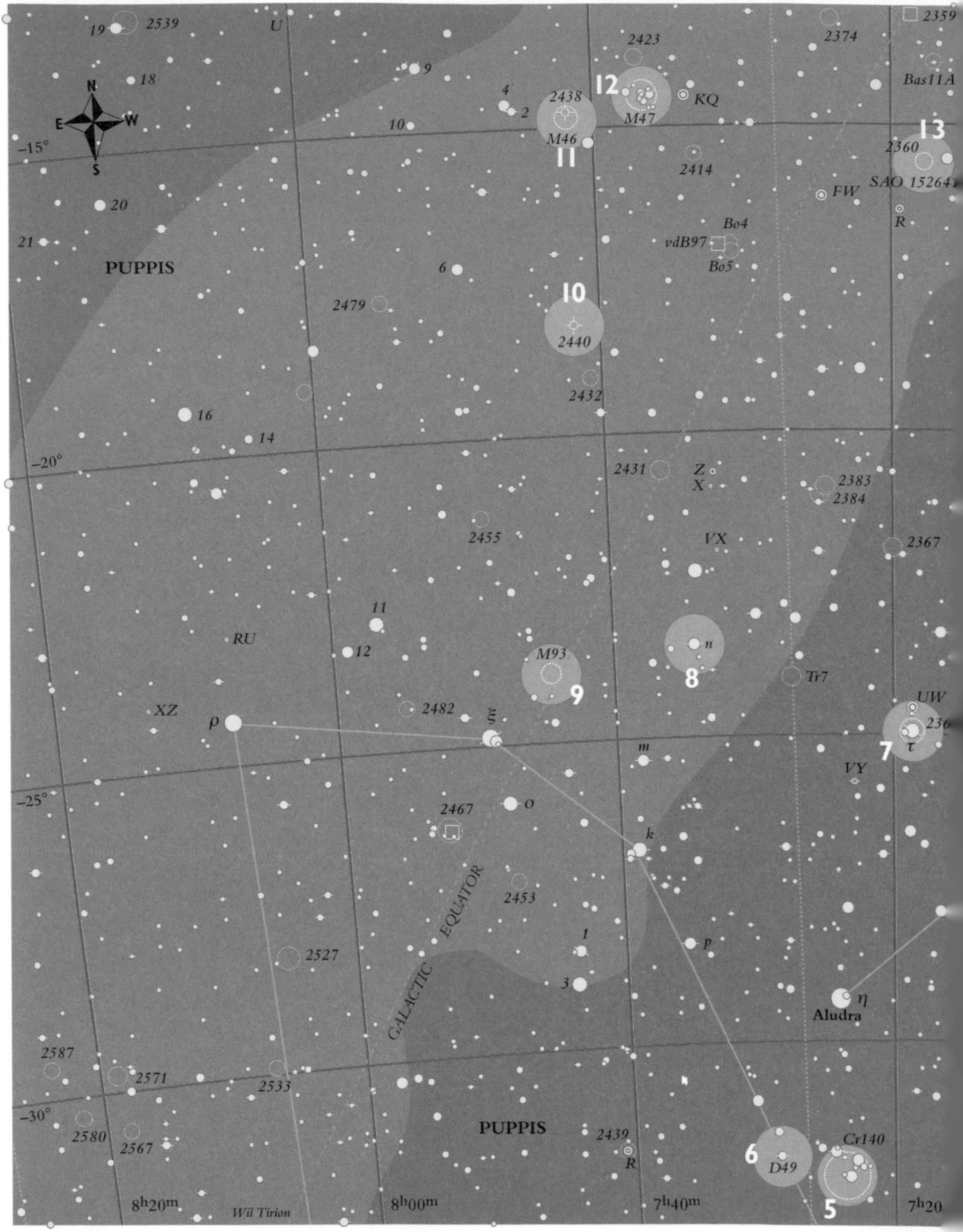

Northern and Southern Hemisphere On meridian 10 p.m. February 10

PUPPIS

PUPPIS

Aludra

Wil Tirion

8ʰ20ᵐ   8ʰ00ᵐ   7ʰ40ᵐ   7ʰ20

−15°

−20°

−25°

−30°

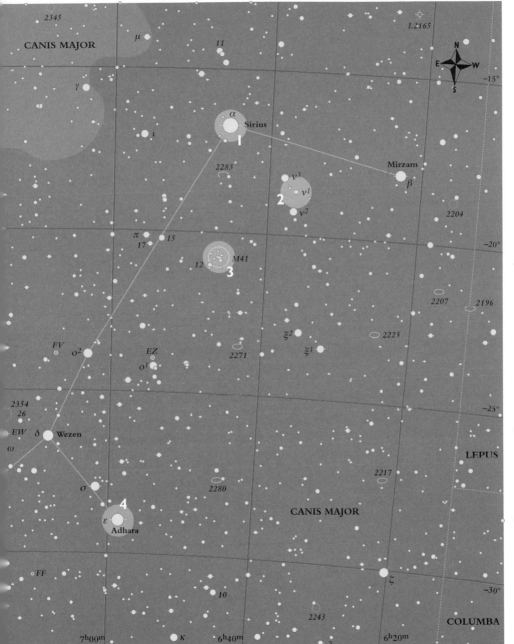

Northern and Southern Hemisphere On meridian 10 p.m. February 10

1 Sirius (9 Alpha [α] Canis Majoris)

👁 The three stars of Orion's belt point toward Sirius, the Dog Star—the brightest star in the sky, at magnitude −1.4. Sirius has a magnitude 8.4 companion, Sirius B, that orbits it every 50 years. Sirius B, or "the Pup," as it is often called, currently lies only about 4 arcseconds away, and is very difficult to see even with large amateur scopes. Sirius B is a famous example of a white dwarf star, which is only a little bigger than Earth and extremely dense. Just one cubic inch of its material would weigh about 2 tons.

The brilliance of Sirius has given rise to countless stories through the ages. In ancient Egypt, Sirius was known as the Nile Star because at the time of

The constellations of Canis Major and Puppis span much of this slice of the Milky Way (opposite). Sirius glows brightly on the left.

year when it rose just before dawn, it heralded the annual flooding of the Nile River, an important event in Egyptian life.

2 6 NU¹ [ν¹] CANIS MAJORIS

To find Nu¹ Canis Majoris, nudge your scope 3 degrees southwest from Sirius. Nu¹ is the middle of a group of three stars— the others, predictably, are Nu² and Nu³. Nu¹ is a fine double that is easy to separate in any size scope. Its components, at magnitudes 5.8 and 8.5, lie 17.5 arcseconds apart.

3 M41 (NGC 2287)

A 3 degree hop southeast brings us to the brilliant star cluster M41. This magnificent star cluster is visible to the unaided eye as a patch of light 4 degrees almost due south from Sirius. Many of its stars can be seen with binoculars, but a wide-field telescope eyepiece is best, as the cluster covers more than 1/2 degree.

4 ADHARA (21 EPSILON [ε] CANIS MAJORIS)

Swing your scope 8 degrees south and a little east from our last stop to find the bright double star Epsilon Canis Majoris. Epsilon is, curiously, the second brightest star in Canis Major. At magnitude 1.5, it is a half magnitude brighter than Beta. Epsilon can be resolved using high magnification in 3 inch (75 mm) scopes and larger. Its magnitude 7.4 companion lies 7.5 arcseconds away.

5 COLLINDER 140

This cluster, about 6 degrees southeast of Epsilon, can be seen with the naked eye and is a fine binocular object. Collinder 140 contains about 30 stars, the brightest being magnitude 5.4.

6 DUNLOP 49 PUPPIS

Adjust your scope about 1 degree east and slightly north of our last stop at Collinder 140 to find the star called Dunlop 49, across the border in Puppis. This is a superb double star for any small scope, because its magnitude 6.5 and 7.2 stars are almost 9 arcseconds apart.

7 NGC 2362

⊂⊙ The star **30 Tau [τ] Canis Majoris**, 7 degrees northwest of Dunlop 49, lies at the heart of tightly packed NGC 2362. At magnitude 4, the cluster is one of the real gems of the sky for all size telescopes. At about 8 arcminutes across, this cluster contains some 60 stars, many of which pop into view when using averted vision.

8 N PUPPIS (HN19)

⊂⊙ A few degrees northeast of NGC 2362 is the star n Puppis, a fine double for any size telescope to separate. Its magnitude 6 components are almost equal in brightness, separated by 9.6 arcseconds.

9 M93 (NGC 2447)

⊂⊙ Shift your gaze 2½ degrees east from our last position to the star cluster M93. Covering about ⅓ degree, this cluster is easy to see with binoculars, its brightest members forming a compact group near the middle. With a 3 inch (75 mm) telescope, you should be able to see a number of stars of around magnitude 8 and fainter.

10 NGC 2440

⊂⊙ About 5½ degrees north and a little west of M93 lies NGC 2440, a planetary nebula shining at magnitude 10.8. A 3 inch (75 mm) scope reveals its somewhat irregular shape. NGC 2440 covers an area of about 14 x 32 arcseconds. Its bluish color is quite obvious, especially in larger telescopes.

11 M46 (NGC 2437)

⊂⊙ Hop 3½ degrees farther north to the open star cluster M46. Discovered by Messier in 1771, M46 contains a large number of fairly faint stars, which Messier thought were a nebulous patch. Switch to high magnification to view the magnitude 10 planetary nebula **NGC 2438**, which is seen against the backdrop of the northern part of M46. NGC 2438 measures about 1 arcminute across.

12 M47 (NGC 2422)

⊙ Switch back to low magnification to observe M47, lying about 1½ degrees west of M46. Unlike M46, this open cluster is visible to the naked eye, although it is best viewed using binoculars. It contains several stars of around magnitudes 6 and 7, as well as many others that are fainter.

🔟 NGC 2360

Lying 4½ degrees west of M47 is NGC 2360, the last object on our starhop. It is located just east of the magnitude 5 star **SAO 152641**. Visible as a small patch of light through binoculars, NGC 2360 is a cluster comprising about 80 stars of magnitude 10 and fainter. A beautiful object through a 4 inch (100 mm) telescope, the cluster looks somewhat like crystals of spilt table salt.

Tonight's tour of the Dog Star and surrounds has brought us back almost to Sirius, shining like a welcoming beacon. This part of the Milky Way Galaxy has revealed an interesting variety of objects, most notably the many star clusters.

White Dwarf Stars

Sirius B, Sirius A's companion (below), was the first white dwarf to be identified. Incredibly, Sirius B has a mass almost equal to that of our Sun, but a diameter of only about 19,000 miles (30,500 km)—less than three times that of Earth.

We now know that a white dwarf is the collapsed core of a star—the last stage in the evolution of a star that was originally up to about eight times as massive as the Sun. In 1931, it was discovered that a white dwarf star cannot contain more than 1.4 solar masses. However, stars lose a great deal of mass during their lives by shedding material, most visibly in the form of planetary nebulas late in their life cycle.

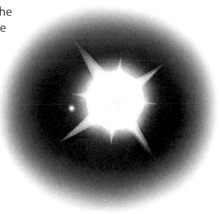

Jewels in Cancer and Gemini

The constellations on this hop along the zodiac are clearly visible from both the Northern and Southern hemispheres.

The legends of Cancer, the Crab, and Gemini, the Twins, come from Greek mythology. The goddess Hera sent Cancer to distract her enemy Hercules who was engaged in battle with Hydra, a sea serpent with many heads. Cancer nipped at Hercules' ankles, but was crushed to death.

Saddened, Hera placed the crab among the stars to honor its valiant but ill-fated efforts.

Gemini represents the twin sons of Leda, the Queen of Sparta. One was fathered by her husband, King Tyndareus, and the other by Zeus while in the form of a swan (represented by Cygnus). The twins, Castor and Pollux, served aboard Jason's ship, the Argo, in the legendary voyage of the Argonauts.

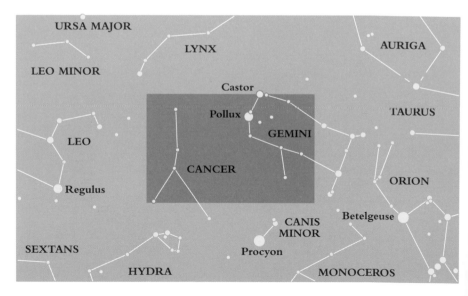

The Eskimo Nebula (below) and the Praesepe (left) are opposites in terms of the level of magnification that reveals them best.

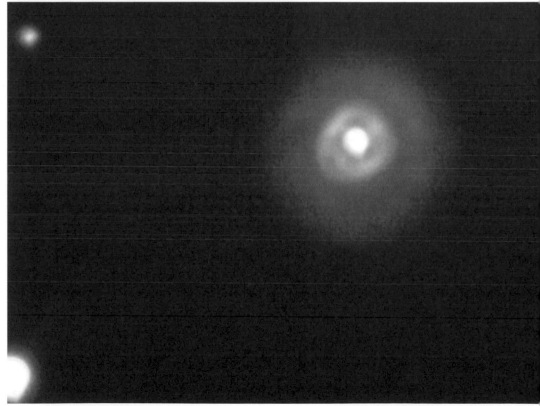

Northern and Southern Hemisphere On meridian 10 p.m. February 20

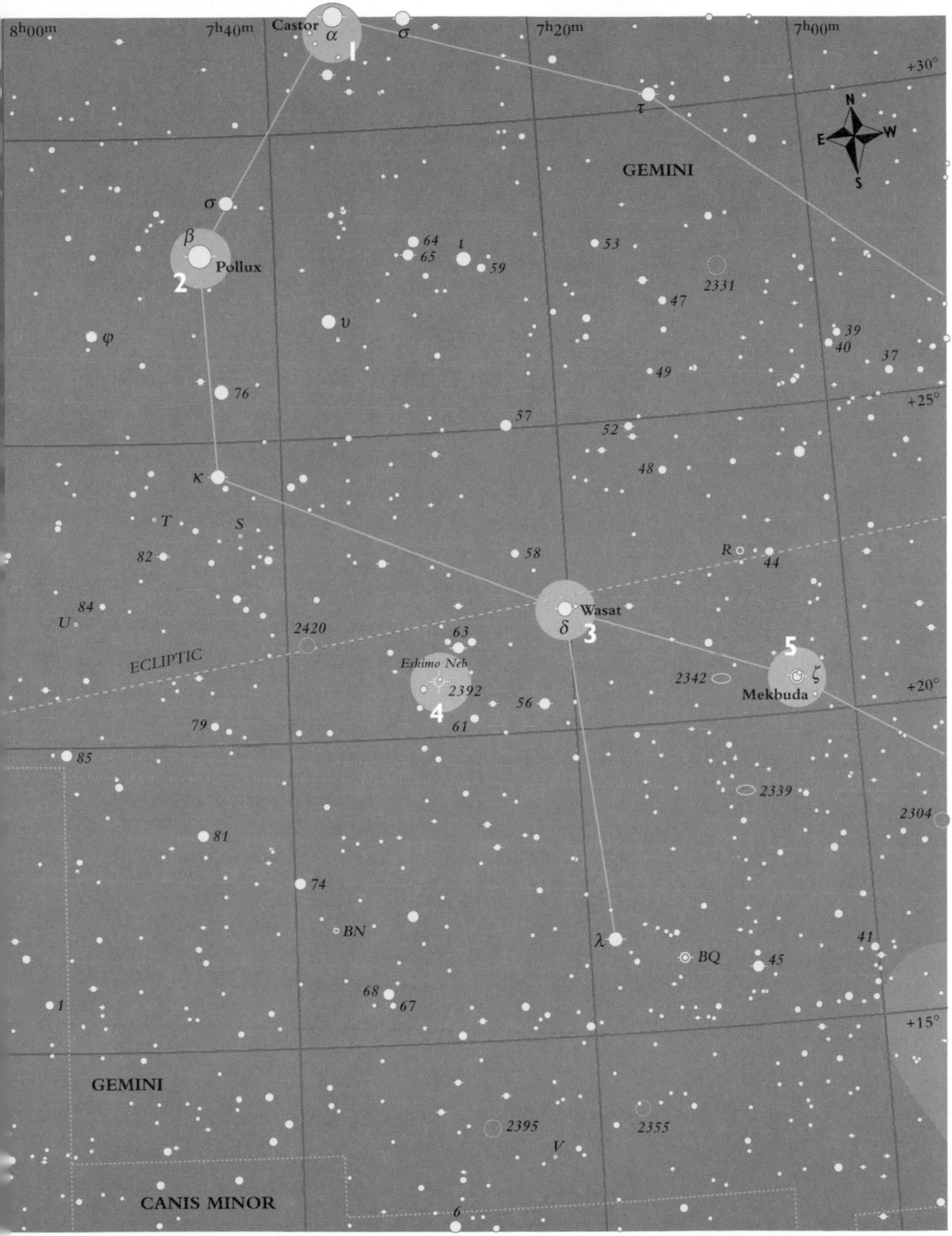
8h00m
7h40m
7h20m
7h00m
+30°
+25°
+20°
+15°
Castor
Pollux
Wasat
Mekbuda
GEMINI
GEMINI
CANIS MINOR
ECLIPTIC
Eskimo Neb
2331
2420
2392
2342
2339
2304
2395
2355
N
S
E
W

1 CASTOR
(66 ALPHA [α] GEMINORUM)

Our tour begins at one of the best-known and brightest doubles, the 1st magnitude yellowish star, Castor, the Horseman, at the eastern end of the constellation of Gemini. In fact, Castor is a multiple star shining with a combined visual magnitude of 1.6.

The magnitude 1.9 A and magnitude 2.9 B stars, themselves both spectroscopic binaries, currently lie 3 arcseconds apart and can be separated in scopes of 10 inches (250 mm) or larger. The B star orbits the A star over a period of about 400 years. The faint red dwarf C star (designated YY Geminorum), also a spectroscopic binary, completes the entire Castor system.

A spectacular bright shower of meteors, called the Geminid meteors, emanates from a point near Castor each year, reaching its maximum around 14 December (see also p. 78).

2 POLLUX
(78 BETA [β] GEMINORUM)

Four and a half degrees southeast of Castor is the other twin, Pollux. This is the sky's 17th brightest star, shining as a magnitude 1.2 golden-yellow giant. Pollux is about 34 light-years from Earth and intrinsically 35 times brighter than the Sun.

3 WASAT
(55 DELTA [δ] GEMINORUM)

Move your telescope about 8 degrees southwest to the double star Wasat, a magnitude 3.5 yellow star with a faint red dwarf companion at magnitude 8.2. This star system lies some 60 light-years away with an orbital period believed to be more than 1,000 years long. In 1930, Clyde Tombaugh found Pluto near this binary system.

4 THE ESKIMO NEBULA
(NGC 2392)

About 2 degrees southeast of Wasat is the bright planetary nebula NGC 2392, discovered by William Herschel in 1787. It is intense and compact, looking somewhat like a large, fuzzy bluish green star, making an attractive contrast to the magnitude 8.3 orange star nearby, which has a similar brightness. As with most planetary nebulas,

Extrasolar Planets

Only recently have astronomers detected clear evidence of planets orbiting distant Sun-like stars. One of the first of a handful of extrasolar planets to be discovered was the planet-size companion of 55 Rho[1] [ρ] Cancri, found by a team from the universities of California and San Francisco. The illustration below compares the orbit of Mercury around the Sun (top) with Rho[1] Cancri and its planet (bottom). Rho[1] is a magnitude 5.9 yellow star with a planetary companion, about 0.8 times the mass of Jupiter, that orbits Rho[1] over just 14.7 days.

Extrasolar planets are far too faint to be seen visually, even by the HST, but they reveal their presence by the tiny wobbles their gravity induces in the motions of each star.

high magnification is essential for good viewing. You can only expect to see the eskimo's "face" in photographs taken through large scopes.

5 MEKBUDA (43 ZETA [ζ] GEMINORUM)

👁 Sweep some 6 degrees west of NGC 2392 to Mekbuda, one of the brightest variable stars. This yellow pulsating Cepheid variable has a period of 10.16 days during which its magnitude fluctuates between 3.6 and 4.2. With binoculars, you might also note a magnitude 7.6 companion star nearby, which is actually unrelated to Zeta.

6 TEGMENI (16 ZETA [ζ] CANCRI)

Hop about 16 degrees east and slightly south of Mekbuda to the binary star called Tegmeni, across the border in Cancer. The B component of this system orbits the A star over a period of about 59 years. Both components are yellowish main-sequence stars with nearly equal magnitudes of 5.6 and 5.9.

7 V Cancri

 This red giant Mira-type variable lies 2 degrees east of Tegmeni. This is one of many variables whose full cycle can be followed in scopes of less than 8 inches (200 mm). The normal magnitude range of V Cancri is 7.9 to 12.8, during a period of 125 days. At maximum, it would fill the volume of Mars's orbit.

8 The Praesepe/Beehive Cluster (M44, NGC 2632)

 Shift your scope 5 degrees northeast to the Praesepe, a large, naked-eye open star cluster that has been known since ancient

times. It covers about 1½ degrees of sky and is some 520 light-years distant. The cluster's several hundred scattered stars show best through binoculars or a finderscope because the cluster is quite broad. At high magnification it is quite disappointing because the view is too close.

9 ASELLUS AUSTRALIS (47 DELTA [δ] CANCRI)

👁 Nudge 2 degrees southeast of the center of the Praesepe to Asellus Australis, a magnitude 4.3 yellow optical double star. The Romans gave this star its name, the Southern Donkey. Asellus Australis and **Asellus Borealis (43 Gamma [γ] Cancri)** are known collectively as the Donkeys.

10 ACUBENS (65 ALPHA [α] CANCRI)

About 6 degrees southeast of Asellus Australis is the magnitude 4.3 white wide double star Acubens, about 170 light-years

The open star cluster M67 (opposite) is often overlooked in favor of its larger cousin, the Praesepe.

away. Its name is derived from the Arabic *Al Zubanah*, meaning "the claw," because it marks one of the crab's claws. The secondary star in this system shines at magnitude 11.8 and is visible through 3 inch (75 mm) telescopes or larger.

11 M67 (NGC 2682)

Use the bright stars Asellus Australis and Acubens to help locate M67, about 2 degrees west of Acubens. This cluster, the last object on our tour, was discovered by the German astronomer Johann Gottfried Koehler between 1772 and 1779. In dark skies, this densely packed magnitude 6.1 open cluster can be seen with the naked eye, but it needs a small scope or binoculars to really appreciate it. M67 contains some 500 stars of magnitudes 10 to 16 and many more fainter ones. M67 is estimated to be four to five billion years old— one of the oldest open star clusters known.

Cancer and Gemini include some interesting star fields, beckoning you to mine their collection of clusters and double and variable stars.

Gems in the Great Ship Argo

Northern Hemisphere skywatchers are disadvantaged here because many objects in this patch of sky are not seen at all from latitudes above about 30 degrees north.

Carina, the Keel, and Vela, the Sails, were two of the four constellations formed when the huge constellation of Argo Navis was subdivided by the French astronomer Nicolas Louis de Lacaille in the eighteenth century.

The other two are Puppis, the Stern; and Pyxis, the Compass. Straddling the constellations of Carina and Vela is the so-called False Cross, which newcomers to the southern skies can easily confuse with the Southern Cross.

With binoculars or a telescope, you can expect to see many fine objects within this part of the Milky Way Galaxy, including several of the best star clusters in the entire night sky.

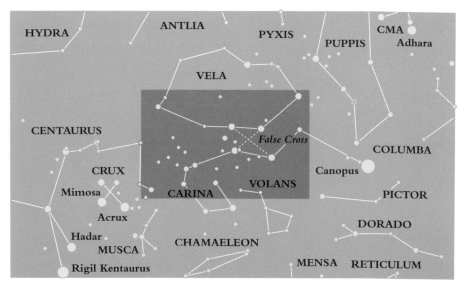

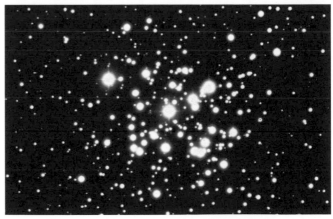

Eta Carinae Nebula (above) and NGC 3293 (right) are two of the highlights of the Milky Way in the constellation of Carina.

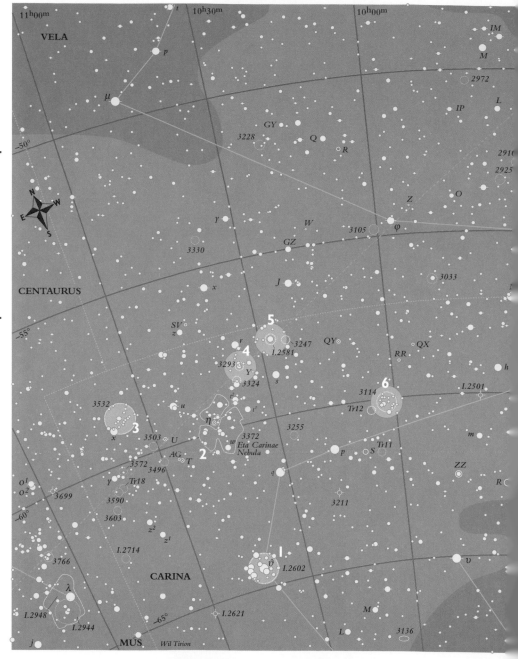

Southern Hemisphere On meridian 10 p.m. March 10

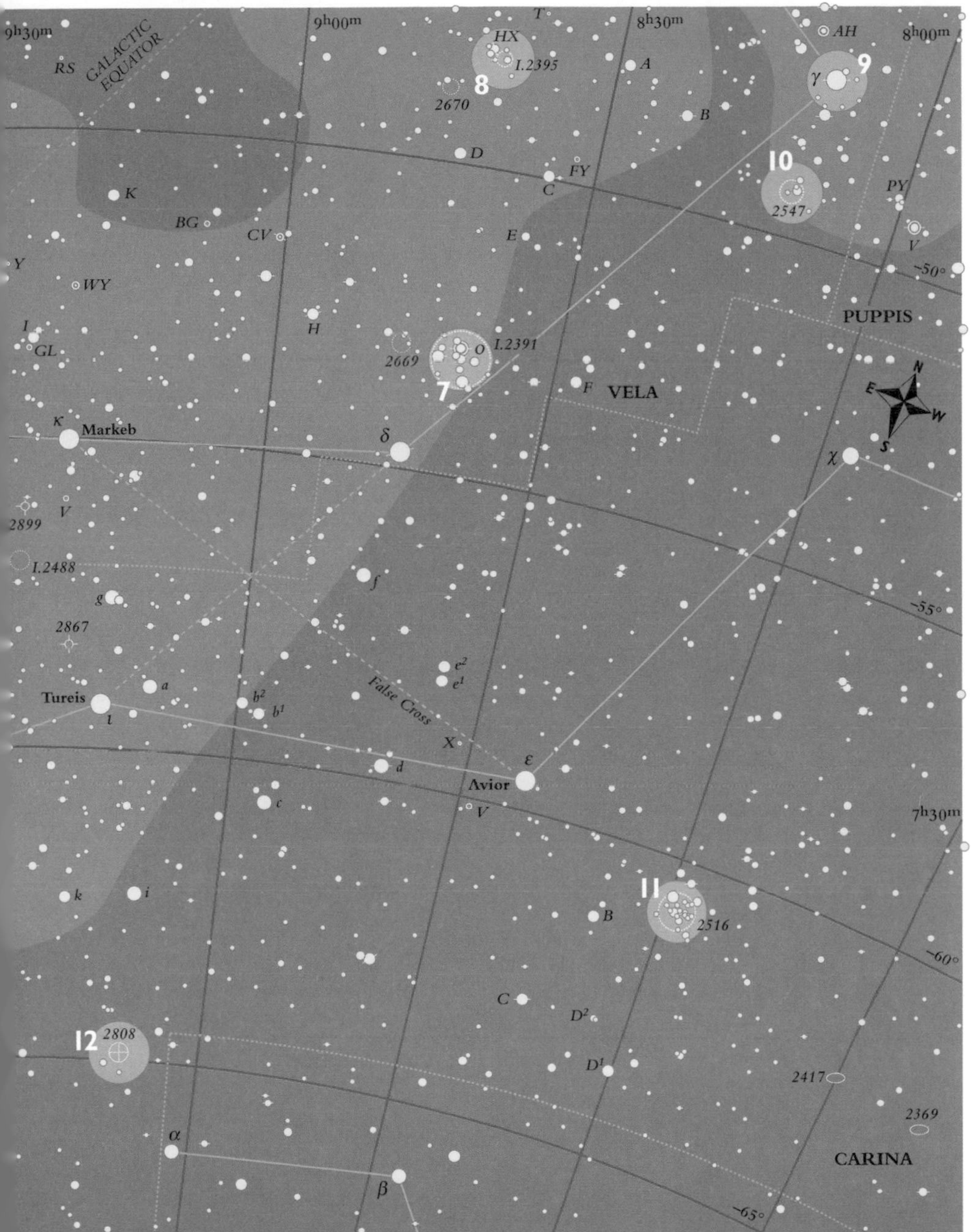

Southern Hemisphere On meridian 10 p.m. March 10

9h30m
9h00m
8h30m
8h00m
7h30m

GALACTIC EQUATOR

RS

K

BG

CV

Y

WY

I

GL

H

κ Markeb

δ

V

2899

I.2488

g

2867

Tureis

ι

a

b²

b¹

False Cross

f

e²

e¹

X

d

V

Avior

ε

c

k

i

12 2808

α

β

CARINA

11 B

2516

C

D²

D¹

2417

2369

–50°

–55°

–60°

–65°

PUPPIS

VELA

χ

F

O I.2391

2669

7

E

C FY

D

2670

8

HX

I.2395

T

A

B

9 γ

AH

10

2547

PY

V

N E S W

1 THETA [θ] CARINAE AND IC 2602

👁 Our starting point on this starhop through the Great Ship Argo is the 3rd magnitude star Theta Carinae. Even with the unaided eye, you can easily see that Theta is more than just a single star. With binoculars, you are afforded a superb view, and this closer inspection allows you to put the character of the object into perspective. It is a central star surrounded by a number of scattered 5th magnitude and fainter stars forming the open star cluster IC 2602.

Theta Carinae, which covers a full degree of sky, has also been called the Southern Pleiades by

NGC 3532 (opposite), just above Eta Carinae in the sky, is one of the finest open clusters, lying about 1,300 light-years away from us.

some Southern Hemisphere observers.

To find the next stop on this starhop, the star Eta Carinae, shift your scope about 4½ degrees due north of IC 2602. Eta is enveloped in the dramatic and beautiful Eta Carinae Nebula.

2 ETA [η] CARINAE

⊂◯◯ This is the brightest star in a field that is truly beautiful, even in scopes of less than 3 inches (75 mm). The star appears orange-red and is embedded in the superb **Eta Carinae Nebula**. Eta is a variable star—one of the most luminous in the Milky Way. In 1843, it outshone every star in the night sky except Sirius. A 4 inch (100 mm) scope will show Eta surrounded by a small "blob" of red light—the nebulous patch called the Homunculus (see Box, p. 464).

3 NGC 3532

👁 Turning about 3 degrees east and slightly north of Eta,

the open cluster NGC 3532 is revealed. John Herschel, who cataloged thousands of celestial objects when observing from South Africa in the 1830s, considered NGC 3532 to be the finest cluster he had ever seen. It appears as a fuzzy patch to the naked eye and is a superb object with binoculars. Any size scope will resolve a large number of stars, which are best viewed using low power.

4 NGC 3293

⊂◯◯ The compact cluster NGC 3293 is 4 degrees west and a little north of NGC 3532. Through binoculars, this cluster appears as a tiny bright spot, but a telescope view reveals a stunning group of several dozen stars of different colors. A 3 inch (75 mm) scope with moderate magnification gives a fantastic view. An orange star near one edge of the cluster is especially attractive.

5 IC 2581

⊂◯◉ Nudge your scope about 1 degree west and slightly north to bring IC 2581 into view. Gathered around quite a distract-ing magnitude 5 star, IC 2581 is a cluster of some 25 stars that are much more obvious with high magnification. You should be able to resolve this cluster well with a 4 inch (100 mm) telescope.

6 NGC 3114

👓 Shift your focus 4 degrees southeast to locate the next cluster, NGC 3114. Binoculars do a fine job of revealing this magnificent cluster of 7th magnitude stars and fainter covering an area of more than ½ degree. To the naked eye, it appears as a 4th magnitude patch of light. Low magnification is essential when viewing this cluster through a telescope.

7 IC 2391

👓 Almost 2 degrees north and a little west of **Delta [δ] Velorum** is IC 2391, also known

The Eta Carinae Nebula (NGC 3372)

The Eta Carinae Nebula is one of the finest areas of nebulosity in the southern sky—a visually stunning object whose complex structure is an impressive sight. Photographs show that the nebula is very detailed and extensive, covering some 4 square degrees of sky. This nebula is carved into two glowing halves by a dark dust lane, one of many that seem to divide the nebulosity into a number of areas of glowing light. The brightest of these "islands" of light contains the dark, irregular, and elongated mass that is the Keyhole Nebula (right). It covers quite a small area and appears close to the star Eta.

The star Eta (seen at lower left) is surrounded by a bright patch of nebulosity known as the Homunculus. It gets its name from the fact that, close up, its peanut shape appears to vaguely resemble the body of a man. This gas was ejected during the 1843 outburst.

as the Omicron Velorum cluster. Its members are loosely packed around the magnitude 3 bluish white **Omicron [O] Velorum**. It is a better subject for binoculars than for a scope.

8 IC 2395

Head north about 5 degrees from IC 2391 to IC 2395. You can spot this cluster in binoculars, but it is better suited to a telescope. It is not exactly a rich group, but still one worthy of attention, and a 3 inch (75 mm) scope, or even smaller, provides a good view.

9 GAMMA [γ] VELORUM

A little more than 6 degrees west of IC 2395 is Gamma Velorum. This is a spectacular double star whose 2nd and 4th magnitude components are 41 arcseconds apart and can be separated with binoculars. Any small scope will show two other stars, of magnitudes 8 and 9, about 90 arcseconds away.

10 NGC 2547

This attractive open cluster, about 2 degrees south of Gamma, contains stars with a moderate range in brightness. A 4 inch (100 mm) scope provides a good view of the cluster, which covers about 1/3 degree.

11 NGC 2516

Eleven degrees farther south of NGC 2547 is NGC 2516. This cluster is a fine sight in binoculars. The long axis of the False Cross points toward it, as if to draw attention to it, and it is easily located a few degrees southwest of **Epsilon [ε] Carinae**. The 1/2 degree wide cluster contains a number of stars of magnitude 7 and fainter.

12 NGC 2808

A little south of the halfway point between NGC 2516 and Theta Carinae is NGC 2808. This globular cluster shows up well as a glowing spot of light in binoculars. A 6 inch (150 mm) scope or larger is needed to start to resolve it well, but a hint of its stellar nature can be obtained with smaller telescopes.

Whenever you fix your gaze toward the starry sky, you will always remember the fine objects in this area—especially the great star clusters.

Roaming around the Lion

Like all the ancient zodiac constellations, Leo, the Lion, lies on the Sun's path through the sky, the ecliptic. It is easily visible from both the Northern and Southern hemispheres. There are plenty of bright galaxies, double stars, and variables in this region. Leo is easy to locate because this part of the sky is dominated by the backward-question-mark, or sickle, asterism that marks the lion's head and chest, and the triangle of stars that marks its hindquarters.

According to ancient Greek legend, Leo was the cave-dwelling Nemean Lion choked to death by the mighty Hercules. Because no weapon could penetrate Leo's skin, Hercules used the lion's own razor-sharp claw to remove its pelt. He made the pelt into a cloak to protect himself and carried it with him into the heavens.

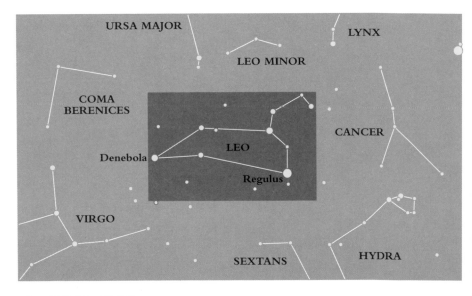

Several galaxies in Messier's list, including M65 (left), are found in Leo (below).

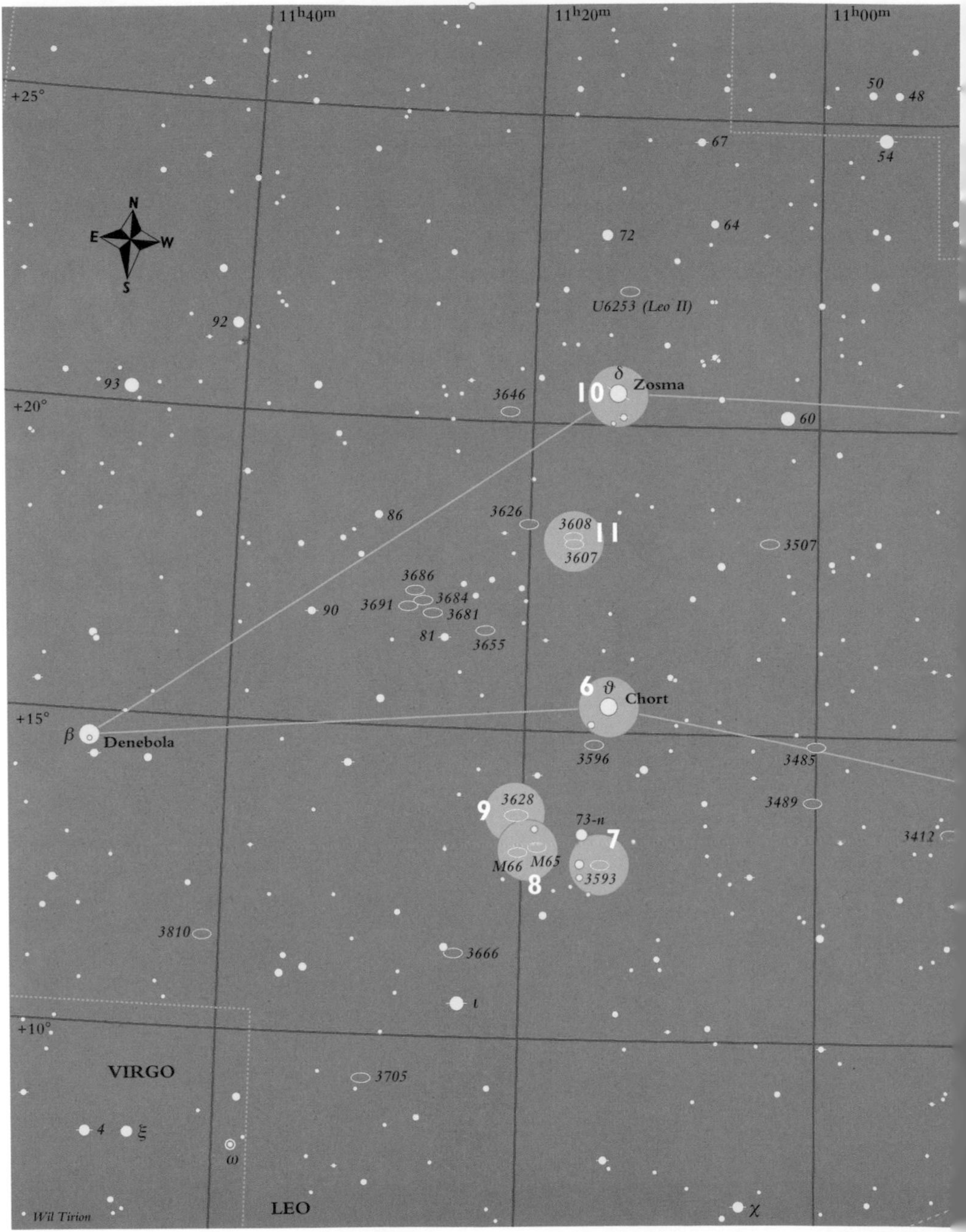

Northern and Southern Hemisphere   On meridian 10 p.m. April 1

11h40m   11h20m   11h00m

+25°

50
48

67
54

N
E — W
S

72
64

U6253 (Leo II)

92

δ Zosma
93   +20°   3646   10   60

86   3626   3608   11   3507
3607

3686
90   3691   3684
3681
81   3655

6 ϑ Chort
+15°
β   Denebola   3596   3485
3489
3412

9 3628
73-π
7

M66 M65   3593
8

3810
3666

ι

+10°

VIRGO
3705

4 ξ
ω

LEO   χ

Wil Tirion

Northern and Southern Hemisphere On meridian 10 p.m. April 1

1 REGULUS
(32 ALPHA [α] LEONIS)

👁 This starhop begins at Regulus, the blue-white heart of Leo, and the 21st brightest star in the sky. It is located at the base of the sickle-shaped asterism that marks the lion's chest and mane and, at magnitude 1.3, is the primary of a very close multiple-star system. Regulus is 5 times the diameter of our Sun and 160 times as luminous.

The Polish astronomer Nicolaus Copernicus gave Regulus its Latin name, which means "little king," referring to the belief that this star ruled the heavens. This celestial imagery shares an apt symmetry with the commonly held notion of the lion as king of the beasts on Earth.

Hop about 5 degrees west to the magnitude 5.6 reddish star **18 Leonis** and magnitude 6.4 yellow-white **19 Leonis**.

The barred spiral galaxy M95 (opposite) is 63,000 light-years away. Even with a 10-inch (250-mm) telescope it is difficult to resolve its spiral structure.

Use these two stars to locate R Leonis in the same low-power eyepiece view.

2 R LEONIS

🔭 In 1782, the Polish astronomer J. A. Koch first recorded the variability of this pulsating red giant Mira-type variable, one of the earliest to be discovered. The magnitude of R Leonis cycles from 5.8 down to fainter than 11th magnitude. Although it is normally a sharp red star, R Leonis can appear to be a deep shade of purple during its 312-day cycle.

3 M105 (NGC 3379)

🔭 Return to Regulus, then hop about 10 degrees east to find **52 Leonis**, a magnitude 5.4 yellowish star. About 1½ degrees south of 52 Leonis is a triangle of hazy light formed by three galaxies—M105, and NGC 3384 and 3389. At magnitude 9.2, M105 is the brightest and largest of the three. Typical of elliptical galaxies, M105 appears as a fuzzy ball that you cannot focus into a sharp point of light.

NGC 3384

🔭 The second galaxy in the group is NGC 3384, also an elliptical, which appears as an elongated oval with a bright nucleus.

NGC 3389

🔭 The third galaxy, NGC 3389, is fainter and harder to find. Appearing as a pale, thin streak of light, it is a magnitude 11.8 spiral that seems to glow evenly from edge to edge.

4 M96 (NGC 3368)

🔭 About 1 degree south of M105 is the spiral galaxy M96. This silver-gray beauty appears in a relatively starless field, so it is easy to spot. The intense core of the galaxy is much sharper and brighter than the wispy wreath of its arms.

5 M95 (NGC 3351)

🔭 This magnitude 9.7 barred spiral galaxy, adjacent to M96, has a fairly bright core surrounded by wispy arms. Its nucleus appears almost stellar, with a fuzzy fringe around it. M95 is not as big or as bright as M96. Even in scopes larger than 10 inches (250 mm), it is difficult to see the faint arms of the galaxy, but a 4 inch (100 mm) telescope shows the gradual brightening toward the core.

6 CHORT (70 THETA [θ] LEONIS)

👁 Sweep about 8 degrees northeast of M95 to blue-white Chort. This stunning jewel marks the hips of the Lion and is the western apex of the triangle of stars marking the rear haunches of Leo.

7 NGC 3593

Nudge about 3 degrees south of Chort to find NGC 3593, a magnitude 11.3 spiral galaxy with a bright and elongated core. The outline of the galaxy's arms is quite diffuse, blending into the background at the edges.

8 M65 (NGC 3623)

This beautiful magnitude 9.9 spiral galaxy is at least 200,000 light-years distant from M66, although the famous pair appears in the same low-power eyepiece view.

M66 (NGC 3727)

At magnitude 9.9, M66 is brighter and a bit shorter than M65. M66 is another spiral galaxy, with a finger of light extending from its southern tip. Many of its dark areas can be seen with a 4 inch (100 mm) telescope.

9 NGC 3628

This elongated, pencil-slim spiral galaxy is at the northern apex of the richly studded triangle that includes M65 and M66. The edges are quite grainy on this magnitude 9.9 object. It is halfway between two 10th magnitude stars to the north and south, but because of its low surface brightness and being seen edge-on, it is not easy to locate.

10 ZOSMA (DELTA [δ] LEONIS)

Sweep about 7 degrees northwest of NGC 3628 to blue-white Zosma, a magnitude 2.6 main-sequence star at the heart of a very open multiple system. These stars are easy to separate in any size scope because the magnitude 8.6 companion is located 191 arcseconds from the primary.

🔟 NGC 3607

🔭 Move back some 2½ degrees south of our last stop to find the elliptical galaxy NGC 3607, a magnitude 10.9 object that looks like an out-of-focus star through a telescope.

NGC 3608

🔭 At about a magnitude fainter than NGC 3607, the elliptical galaxy NGC 3608 appears smaller, although astronomers believe that these galaxies are actually about the same size. NGC 3608 is roundish with a faint stellar core.

This is just a sampling of the night-sky wonders to be found in Leo. Additional faint galaxies, shown on the main sky chart, are within the body of the celestial king of beasts, waiting for you to explore them.

The Messier Marathon

In the Northern Hemisphere, a window of opportunity opens around the time of the vernal equinox, every March, when all 110 Messier objects can be observed on one night.

French astronomer Charles Messier and his collaborator, Pierre Méchain, were engaged in a quest to discover comets and, in the process, listed many other wonderful celestial objects in order to avoid confusing them with comets.

To complete a Messier Marathon, begin with the spiral galaxy M74 in Pisces, in the western sky at dusk. During the night, sweep from one Messier object to the next, ending with M30 in Capricornus, shortly before the onset of morning twilight.

The beautiful spiral galaxy M66 (left) is just one of the marathon objects to aim for while you are in Leo.

A Hop around the Big Dipper

One of the first star patterns that Northern Hemisphere skywatchers usually learn to recognize is the Big Dipper, in the constellation of Ursa Major, the Great Bear. Unfortunately for observers in mid-southern latitudes, this famous asterism is not visible. The seven bright stars of the circumpolar bowl and handle are part of what is known as the Ursa Major Moving Group, the closest open star cluster to us.

The Dipper stars are rich in mythology and have been known by various names throughout history. The lore that many cultures have created for this distinctive constellation is based on that of a bear. However, the ancient Egyptians considered the asterism to be either a hippopotamus or a Nile River boat to carry the god Osiris. Ancient Romans saw the Big Dipper as seven oxen pulling a plough.

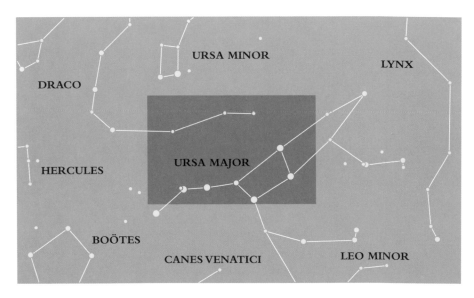

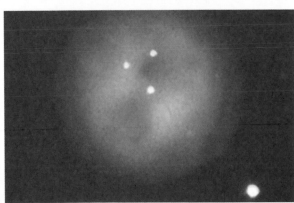

The Big Dipper (above) is home to a variety of unique objects including the Owl Nebula (left), a very large planetary nebula.

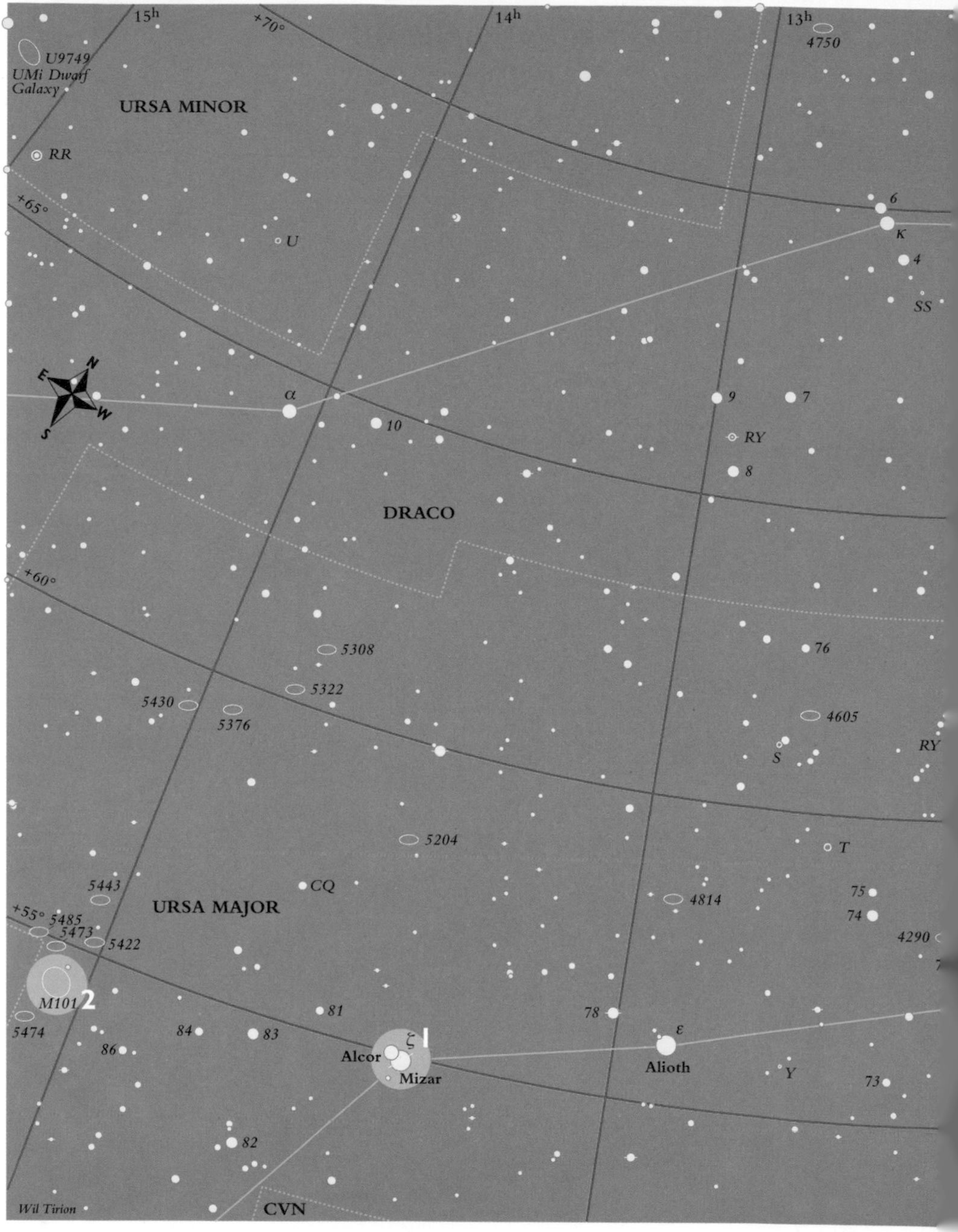

Northern Hemisphere On meridian 10 p.m. April 20

U9749
UMi Dwarf
Galaxy

URSA MINOR

RR

U

13ʰ

4750

6
K
4
SS

14ʰ

15ʰ

+70°

+65°

+60°

α

10

9   7

RY

8

DRACO

76

5308

5322

5430

5376

4605

RY

S

5204

T

CQ

4814

75
74

4290
7

5443

+55° 5485
      5473
      5422

URSA MAJOR

M101

5474

86   84   83

81

Alcor ξ

Mizar

78

ε

Alioth

Y

73

82

Wil Tirion

CVN

N
E   W
S

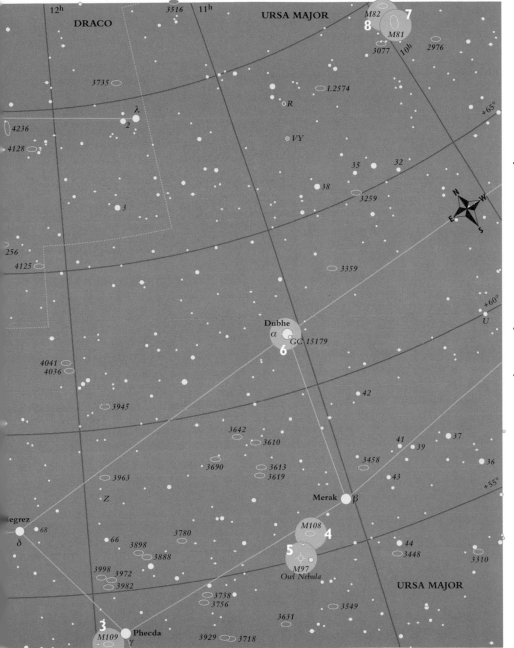

Northern Hemisphere   On meridian 10 p.m. April 20

Star Outburst in M82

M82 is now thought to be a nearby example of a starburst galaxy. Astronomers attribute the burst of star formation in M82 to a possible encounter with M81, its companion spiral galaxy, approximately 100 million years ago. This may have severely disrupted M82's gas clouds, igniting the starburst that involved a mass of material equal to several million Suns. The massive young stars that formed within the galaxy's nucleus gave rise to raging winds of hot gas, which, combined, made a powerful galactic wind. This wind created the filamentary structures (above) that were once thought to be products of an explosion.

▮ MIZAR (79 ZETA [ζ] URSAE MAJORIS) AND ALCOR (80 URSAE MAJORIS)

👁 This tour begins at Mizar and Alcor, the famous pair that makes up the apparent wide double star in the middle of the Dipper handle. If your eyesight is sharp, you can separate the components with the naked eye, since they are 12 arcminutes apart. A pair of binoculars provides a great view of Mizar and Alcor, and with a small telescope, you can see that Mizar is actually a double star itself. Its 4th magnitude companion, known as Mizar B, lies about 14 arcseconds away. In 1650, Italian astronomer Giovanni Riccioli identified Mizar's two stars as the first true binary-star system.

M101, our next target on this starhop, is one of three Messier objects commonly known as the Pinwheel Galaxy. The other two "Pinwheels" are M99 (see p. 486) and M33 (see p. 388).

2 The Pinwheel Galaxy (M101, NGC 5457)

This gem of a spiral galaxy lies about 5 degrees east of Mizar and Alcor. M101 is one of the largest and finest face-on spirals visible, and although it is fairly bright, at around magnitude 9, it is also diffuse, making it hard to spot, even with a 10 inch (250 mm) scope. It is best viewed in a dark sky using low magnification and a wide field in order to detect the knotty arms loosely extending outward from the core.

Pierre Méchain discovered M101 in 1781. He also found an object sometimes listed as M102, considered to be a missing Messier object. However, in a letter dated 1783, Méchain wrote that he thought M102 was just a re-sighting of M101.

3 M109 (NGC 3992)

Hop over to the southeastern corner of the Dipper's bowl to **Phecda (64 Gamma [γ] Ursae Majoris)** and use this magnitude 2.4 white star, "the thigh of the Bear," to locate the barred spiral M109 about ¼ degree east of it. The arms, visible through the extended grayish nebulous haze

of the galaxy, are best seen on a very dark night using a 10 inch (250 mm) telescope or larger.

4 M108 (NGC 3556)

To find M108, hop first to the bright, white **Merak (48 Beta [β] Ursae Majoris)**. If you draw an imaginary line between Merak and Phecda, then M108 is about 1½ degrees southeast from Merak along this line. M108 is a milky-white, edge-on spiral galaxy that appears flat, with no sign of the central bulge typical of most other spiral galaxies. M108 glows at magnitude 10.1. It has a mottled texture with about four bright spots visible within its arms. Visible through a 10 inch (250 mm) telescope, an elongated dust lane runs through the long axis of the galaxy.

5 The Owl Nebula (M97, NGC 3587)

The Owl Nebula is found about ½ degree farther southeast from M108. This large, but quite diffuse, magnitude 12 planetary nebula was discovered by Pierre Méchain in March 1781. Although the nebula appears to us about the same size as Jupiter, it is estimated to be 3 light-years in diameter, making it one of the largest planetary nebulas. You should be able to see it through a 4 inch (100 mm) scope in a dark sky, but because of its low surface brightness you need a 10 inch (250 mm) telescope or larger to gain even a hint of the owl's dark eyes.

6 Dubhe (50 Alpha [α] Ursae Majoris)

⫷ To the Arabs, this magnitude 1.8 golden-yellow close double star was *Thar al Dubb al Akbar*, meaning "the back of the Great Bear." Dubhe and Merak form the western end of the Dipper's bowl and point the way to Polaris, the North Star. Dubhe also has a magnitude 7 bluish companion, **GC 15179**, lying 6.3 arcminutes from the primary, which is easily separated in small scopes. A line between Phecda and Dubhe will point you toward our next targets, the galaxies M81 and M82, which are located about 10 degrees northwest of Dubhe.

7 M81 (NGC 3031)

⫷ The bright core of M81 appears distinctly elliptical, at the center of a strikingly symmetrical overall structure that is easily visible with binoculars. Lurking within the bright core are most of the galaxy's 250 billion stars. The two spiral arms of the galaxy appear to be quite diffuse because they have fewer stars tracing them out.

M81 and M82 lie about 38 arcminutes apart, easily appearing in the same low-power telescope or binocular field. They are considered by many to be one of the finest pairs for observers.

8 M82 (NGC 3034)

⫷ Smaller and dimmer than M81, M82 is classified as a peculiar galaxy (see Box, p. 478). In scopes smaller than 15 inches (380 mm), M82 looks like an unusually amorphous, edge-on spiral, although a spiral structure has not been confirmed, even in photographs taken at the largest Earth-bound telescopes or with the Hubble Space Telescope.

Sweep your scope in and around the bowl of the Big Dipper to observe and enjoy the many other faint galaxies waiting to be found.

This CCD image of M81 (opposite) clearly reveals the galaxy's classic spiral arms, which surround a bright central nucleus.

The Virgo–Coma Cluster of Galaxies

From April through June, skywatchers are afforded the best opportunity to observe about 250 of the 3,000 "island universes" located within the Virgo Cluster of Galaxies. This cluster extends north and south through much of the constellations of Virgo, the Virgin, and Coma Berenices, the Hair of Berenice. This region is clearly visible from both the Northern and Southern hemispheres.

The majority of galaxies in the Virgo Cluster are some 65 million light-years from us. This means that the light from these distant multitudes of stars has been traveling, uninterrupted, through space for about 65 million years. Throughout this sky tour, you will be looking back into time and seeing what these galaxies were like about the time the dinosaurs died off on Earth— an amazing thought.

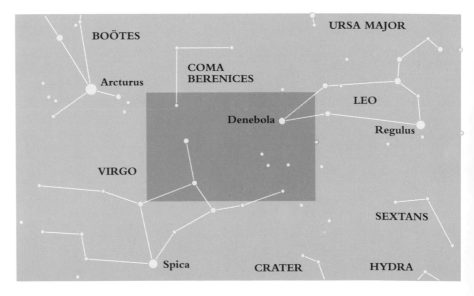

The center of the Virgo Cluster (below) includes M86 and M84. M100 (left) lies just a few degrees north of the center.

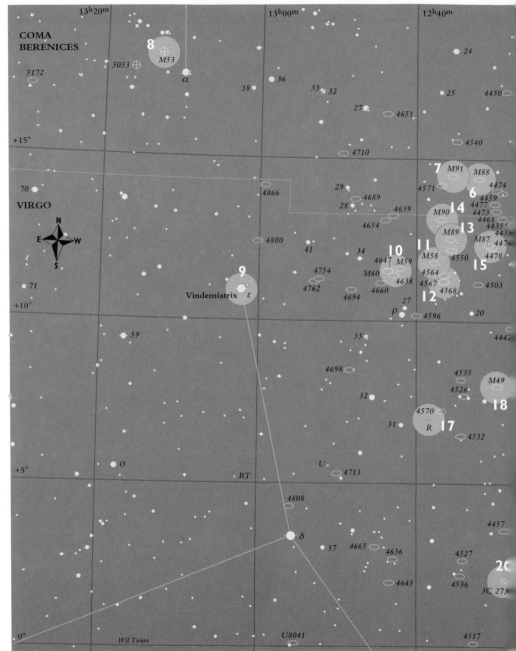

Northern and Southern Hemisphere On meridian 10 p.m. April 30

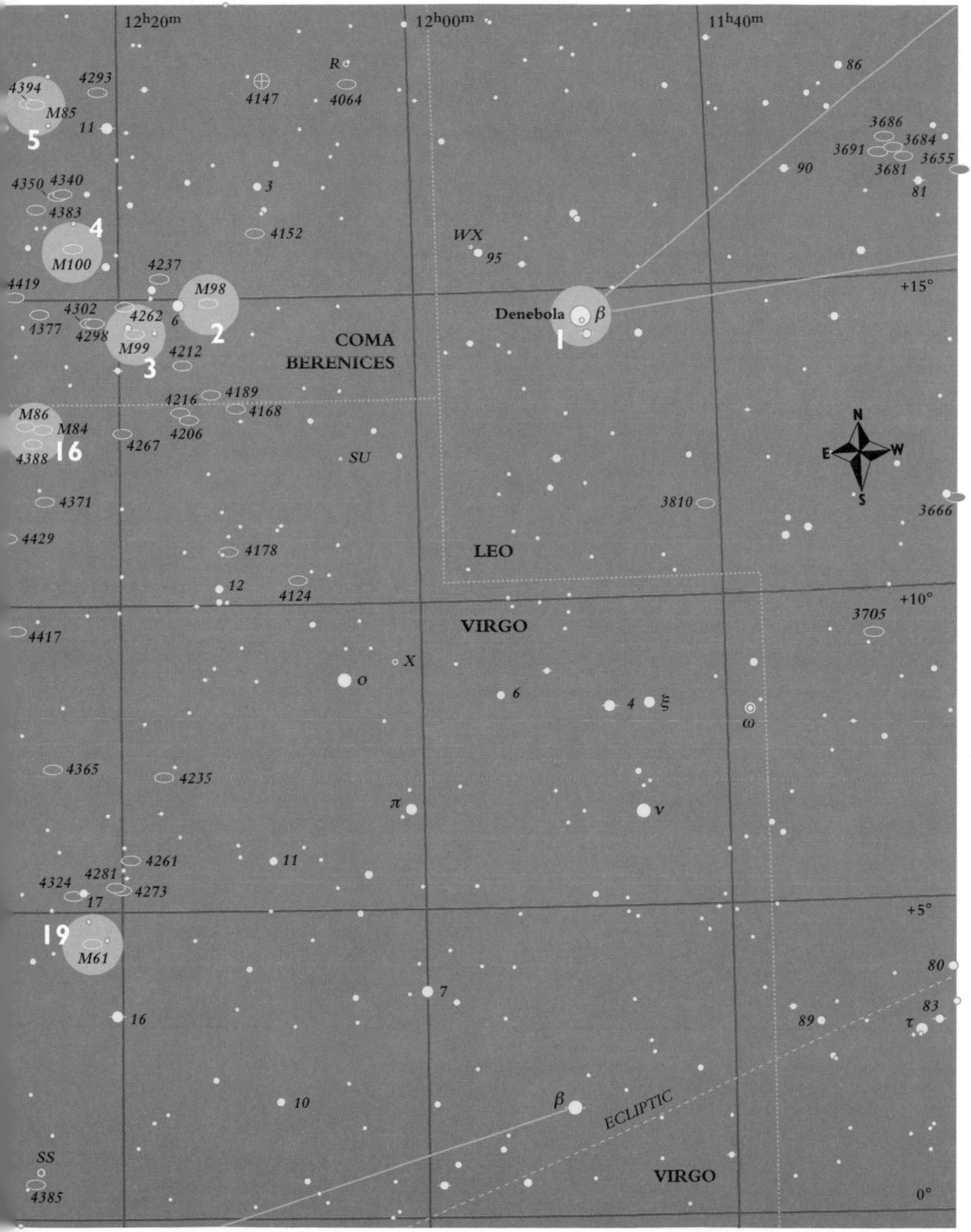

12h20m 12h00m 11h40m

86

4394 4293
M85 11
5

3686
3691 3684
4147 4064 3681 3655
R 90 81

4350 4340
4383 WX +15°
4419 95
M100 3 4152
4 4237
M98 Denebola β
4302 6 **2** **1**
4262 4212 COMA
4377 4298 BERENICES
M99 **3**

N
4216 4189 E W
M86 4168 S
M84 4206 4267 SU
4388 **16** 3810
4371 3666

4429 4178
12 LEO 3705 +10°
4124
4417 VIRGO

X
4365 o
4235 6 4 ξ
π ω
ν
4261
4281 11
4324 4273
17

19 7 80
M61
16 89 83
τ

10 β
ECLIPTIC 0°

SS
4385 VIRGO

The Coma Berenices Cluster is much more distant than M53 (left) in the Milky Way or M99 (below) in the Virgo Cluster.

observation of objects located millions of light-years beyond our galaxy's bounds.

To early Arab astronomers, Denebola was called *Al Dhanab al Asad*, which denoted its position as the tuft of hair on the lion's tail and from which its modern name is derived.

From Denebola, hop about 6½ degrees east to the 5th magnitude whitish star **6 Comae**, to help you find the spiral galaxies M98 and M99, which all appear within the same finder view.

1 DENEBOLA (94 BETA [β] LEONIS)

👁 To locate the galaxies on the northwestern side of Virgo and Coma Berenices, aim your scope toward our starting point, the easy-to-locate Denebola, a magnitude 2.1 blue-white giant on the eastern edge of Leo. On this starhop, we will be looking directly out of the disk of the Milky Way Galaxy, where the lack of stars, dust, and gas allows

2 M98 (NGC 4192)

On the evening of March 15, 1781, the French astronomer Pierre Méchain discovered M98, M99, and M100. The edge-on spiral galaxy M98 appears as a thin patch of light with a slight bulge visible near its nucleus. Although M98 may appear to be a member of the Virgo Cluster of Galaxies, it is actually located about halfway between the Sun and the cluster itself.

3 THE PINWHEEL GALAXY (M99, NGC 4254)

Nudge your scope 1 degree southeast of 6 Comae to bring the

galaxy M99 into view. In a 4 inch (100 mm) scope or larger, the sweeping arms in this roundish face-on galaxy will be able to be distinguished. At 50,000 light-years in diameter, M99 is roughly about half the size of the Milky Way Galaxy.

4 M100 (NGC 4321)

◖◗ Return to 6 Comae, then hop about 2 degrees northeast. Two 5th magnitude stars heading in the same direction will point you toward M100—a large, face-on spiral galaxy glowing at magnitude 9.6.

At 7 arcminutes across, it presents the largest apparent size of any galaxy in the Virgo Cluster. In 8 inch (200 mm) telescopes or smaller, it can resemble a dim globular cluster, appearing circular with very faint arms. It is relatively easy to see because of its brilliant star-like core.

5 M85 (NGC 4382)

◖◗ Almost 2 degrees north of M100 is the magnitude 4.7 yellow double star, **11 Comae**. Use it to direct you to M85, about 1 degree northeast. A circular patch of

light glowing at magnitude 9.2, M85 is estimated to be 100 to 400 billion times more massive than the Sun.

NGC 4394

◖◗ In the same low-power telescope eyepiece as our previous stop—M85—is the magnitude 10.9 barred spiral galaxy NGC 4394. This small, round spiral galaxy is about 3.9 arcminutes across with a brightly shining nucleus that appears almost stellar.

6 M88 (NGC 4501)

◖◗ The easiest way to find M88 is to return to 6 Comae then hop back to M99. M88 and our next target, M91, are at the same declination as M99, so with an equatorially mounted telescope, center M99 in your eyepiece, then turn off the motor drive, if your scope is equipped with one, and wait 14 minutes or so for M88 to drift into your eyepiece field of view.

M88 appears to be elongated because we are looking at a spiral galaxy tilted to our line of sight. Its core seems almost stellar, shining brightly for such a distant object.

7 M91 (NGC 4548)

⊂⊙ Leave your scope fixed for three more minutes after sighting M88, and the barred spiral galaxy M91 will also make an appearance, slipping quietly into your 1 degree field. The slightly fainter M91 has low surface brightness, so it is more difficult to see than M88. The thin bar of its barred spiral structure is only visible in 12 inch (300 mm) telescopes or larger.

8 M53 (NGC 5024)

⊂⊙ Shift almost 9 degrees northeast of M91 to **42 Alpha [α] Comae**. One degree farther northeast is the magnitude 7.7 globular cluster M53, lying 65,000 light-years from us. In February 1775, German astronomer Johann Bode discovered this small, roundish globular cluster, describing it as "a new nebula, appearing through the telescope as round and pretty lively." At about 3 arcminutes in diameter, M53 is a relatively easy target for any size telescope. The glowing halo of stars encircling the tightly compacted core of the cluster is a delight through a 4 inch (100 mm) telescope.

9 VINDEMIATRIX (47 EPSILON [ε] VIRGINIS)

👁 About 8 degrees south of M53 lies the easy-to-locate magnitude 3 star Vindemiatrix. This yellow-white giant glows as a bright light in the night sky. From ancient Roman times, the early morning rising of Vindemiatrix in late August marked the time to commence harvesting the grapes. Its name is derived from the Latin word *Vindemitor*, which means "grape gatherer."

10 M60 (NGC 4649)

⊂⊙ Shift about 4½ degrees west and slightly north of Vindemiatrix to locate M60, one of the largest elliptical galaxies known. A halo seems to surround the bright core of this magnitude 8.8 galaxy. The mass of M60 is estimated to be equal to an amazing 1 trillion Suns, making it comparable in mass to M49.

NGC 4647

⊂⊙ This spiral galaxy and M60 appear to be interacting even though NGC 4647 is moving away from the Sun, while M60 is in approach. Although faint, at magnitude 12, NGC 4647 has a bright core and appears roundish and slightly smaller than M60.

M59 (NGC 4621)

⊂◉ Also in the same low-power eyepiece view is M59, a magnitude 9.8 elliptical galaxy that appears oval with a bright core.

⑪ M58 (NGC 4579)

⊂◉ Swing about 1 degree west of M59 to M58, a magnitude 9.8 barred spiral galaxy. In an 8 inch (200 mm) scope, it appears elongated and faint, due to its low surface brightness. M58 is almost a twin, in terms of its size and mass, to the Milky Way Galaxy.

⑫ THE SIAMESE TWINS (NGC 4567/68)

⊂◉ Nudge your scope about ½ degree southwest of M58 to the Siamese Twins. This unusual pair consists of two seemingly attached galaxies, though at magnitude 10.8, NGC 4568 is slightly brighter than its "twin" and appears larger.

⑬ M89 (NGC 4552)

⊂◉ M89 is an elliptical galaxy almost 1½ degrees north of the Siamese Twins. It appears as a round, glowing patch with a

M87 (above), a giant elliptical galaxy surrounded by thousands of globular clusters, lies near the heart of the Virgo Cluster of Galaxies.

bright center through an 8 inch (200 mm) scope.

⑭ M90 (NGC 4569)

⊂◉ Continuing about ½ degree northeast of M89 is the graceful M90, appearing as an elongated oval with a bright core. This beautiful magnitude 9.5 spiral galaxy is about 80,000 light-years in diameter. You should also be able to see M90's dust lanes through a 10 inch (250 mm) telescope or larger.

15 M87 (NGC 4486, 3C 274)
⊂◯◯ Hop 1½ degrees southwest of M90 to bring M87 into view. This is a giant elliptical galaxy surrounded by more than 4,000 globular clusters. It is estimated to contain more than 1 trillion solar masses. We see it glow at magnitude 9.6, as a bright, fuzzy patch of light.

What you see is not all you get with this monster in the sky. Images taken by the Hubble Space Telescope reveal evidence of a black hole in the core of M87, surrounded by a mass of stars packed hundreds of times more tightly than in a normal elliptical galaxy. This galaxy is also known as Virgo A, because it is one of the earliest sources of radio waves discovered in the sky.

16 M86 (NGC 4406)
⊂◯◯ Located a little more than 1 degree northwest of M87 is M86, at magnitude 9.8. This slightly oval galaxy brightens a little toward its core. M86 may be as close to us as 20 million light-years, or as far away as 42 million. Despite the general expansion of the universe and

Virgo's Big Heart, M87

Among more than 1,000 systems within the vast Virgo Cluster of Galaxies is the giant elliptical galaxy M87, one of the largest known. It covers an area of about 4 x 3 arcminutes and is surrounded by an extraordinary collection of more than 4,000 globular clusters. In a 6 inch (150 mm) scope, you will see it clearly as a magnitude 9 glow with a definite nucleus, but in photographs taken with professional equipment, it is possible to see a jet of very hot gas emanating from the nucleus. This was discovered by Heber Curtis at the Lick Observatory, California, in 1918. The jet is about 4,000 light-years long and is now known to emit strong radio waves (right) and X-rays. Today, the jet is believed to be a high-speed beam of particles, probably associated with a central black hole.

unlike the majority of galaxies in the Virgo Cluster, which are moving away from us, M86 is moving toward us.

M84 (NGC 4374)

⊂◯◯ Within the same telescope-eyepiece view and lying directly west of M86 is another elliptical galaxy—M84. It may be located on the western edge of the core of the Virgo Cluster. At magnitude 9.9, M84 appears to be near-circular and, like M86, has a noticeable brightening toward its nucleus.

17 R VIRGINIS

⊂◯◯ Swing your scope some 4½ degrees southeast of M86 and M84 toward the red giant Mira type variable R Virginis. The magnitude of R Virginis ranges from 6.2 down to 12 over a period of about 145 days. It was discovered to be a variable star in 1809.

18 M49 (NGC 4472)

⊂◯◯ Our next stop is the giant elliptical galaxy M49, which lies about 2 degrees northwest of R Virginis. From our distant perspective it appears to be a 9th magnitude oval shape with an almost even luminosity across most of its surface.

19 M61 (NGC 4303)

⊂◯◯ Moving on about 3 degrees southwest of M49, we come to the wide, yellow double star **17 Virginis**. About ½ degree farther south from 17 Virginis is the large, magnitude 9.7 face-on spiral galaxy M61. The arms and dust lanes of this galaxy are visible through a 10 inch (250 mm) telescope.

20 3C 273

⊂◯◯ Coming to the end of our journey through the Virgo Cluster is the amazing object, 3C 273, about 2½ degrees southeast of M61. This is the brightest known quasar and probably the most distant object visible in an 8 inch (200 mm) telescope. It appears to be just one of many faint stars through a telescope eyepiece.

There are many more interesting galaxies to observe in the Virgo-Coma area, dozens more than we could possibly cover here, so, chart in hand, move on to enjoy discovering for yourself some of the other "island universes."

A Stroll around the Sombrero

Although visible from both hemispheres, this part of the sky is in the southern half of the celestial sphere, so is a little better suited to Southern Hemisphere observers. However, fine views can be had in the evenings from April to June from most parts of the world.

Some 30 degrees south of the Virgo Cluster of Galaxies is the point where the Virgin meets the eastern end of the long constel-lation of Hydra, the Sea Serpent. Hydra and Virgo are the two largest constellations in the celestial sphere, but the third constellation on our chart for this starhop is one of the smallest—Corvus, the Crow. In mythology, Corvus was sent by Apollo to collect water with a cup. Instead, it returned with a watersnake. All three were banished to the sky, with the cup becoming the nearby constellation of Crater.

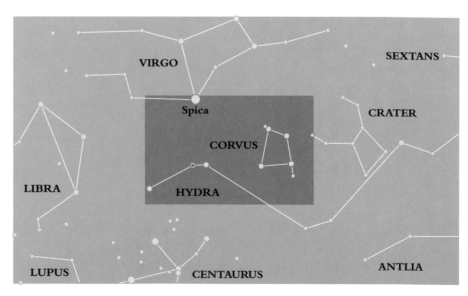

This patch of sky (above) shows Corvus at right, and Spica to the upper left. M83 (right) is a classic spiral galaxy lying in Hydra.

Northern and Southern Hemisphere On meridian 10 p.m. May 1

Wil Tirion

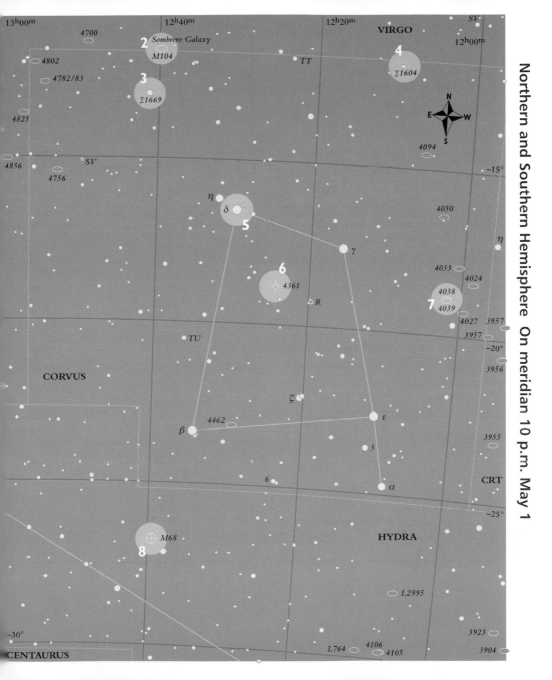

The Sombrero Galaxy is the brightest of the
Virgo galaxies, with a distinctive dust band
crossing its middle.

1 SPICA
(67 ALPHA [α] VIRGINIS)
👁 Attention is drawn to this region of the sky by the brilliant, magnitude 1 bluish white Spica, which is where we begin this starhop. Spica is a double star but, unfortunately, you will not have the chance of separating the components with a telescope or binoculars, since Spica can only be separated by analysis with a spectroscope. The two stars lie less than 20 million miles (32 million km) apart.

These stars also form an eclipsing-binary system, in which one star slightly eclipses the other, resulting in small variations in the brightness of Spica. The two components revolve around each other every 4 days.

Surprisingly, Spica does not form a part of the figure of Virgo. In some legends, Virgo becomes Demeter, the Corn Goddess, and Spica is depicted as an ear of wheat she is holding.

2 THE SOMBRERO GALAXY
(M104, NGC 4549)
📷 Aim your scope at Spica, before heading 11 degrees due west to find M104. This famous 8th magnitude spiral galaxy is easily visible, appearing as a fuzzy patch of light through a 3 inch (75 mm) scope.

With larger telescopes of 6 inches (150 mm) or more, it is not difficult to see how it came by its common name. The tightly coiled spiral arms result in a strong resemblance to the brim of that famous Mexican hat. Look for the prominent dark lane that runs along the length of the galaxy.

3 STRUVE 1669 [Σ 1669]
📷 Heading 1½ degrees to the south and just a little east of the Sombrero Galaxy, we come to Struve 1669, in Corvus. This double star is listed in the star catalog of Frederich von Struve, a prolific discoverer of such objects in the early 1800s. Its 6th magnitude yellowish components are almost equal in brightness at magnitudes 6 and 6.1, and, with a separation of 5 arcseconds, the object is a fine but fairly close double for small scopes. A 10th magnitude star can be seen about 1 arc-minute from Struve 1669.

4 STRUVE 1604 [Σ 1604]

To find Struve 1604, another of Struve's doubles, first return to M104, then shift your scope just over 7 degrees in a due westerly direction. The brightest component is of 7th magnitude, with a 9th magnitude attendant 9 arcseconds away. There is another 9th magnitude star lying some 19 arcseconds farther, making the grouping an attractive sight for any small telescope.

5 ALGORAB
(7 DELTA [δ] CORVI)

Head almost 7 degrees southeast to the relatively bright star Delta Corvi. Shining at magnitude 3, Delta Corvi has a 9th magnitude companion that is fortunately 24 arcseconds away, making it easily visible in a 3 inch (75 mm) scope. Delta lies at the northeastern corner of the deformed rectangle that forms the main pattern in Corvus.

Interacting Galaxies

As galaxies drift through space, there are times when two or more of them can approach so closely that they exert a strong gravitational pull on each other, with the resulting tidal forces causing interesting effects. The pair NGC 4038 and NGC 4039 is a superb example of this (right). Named the Ring-Tail Galaxy because of its shape, it is also known as the Antennae since the material has been expelled in two directions as a result of the interaction.

Many other examples of interacting galaxies are known; for example, in Canes Venatici, the galaxy NGC 5195 appears to have brushed past the Whirlpool Galaxy (M51, NGC 5194). Even our own Milky Way Galaxy is suffering from the tidal effects of an interacting system— the nearby Magellanic Clouds have slightly distorted its shape.

6 NGC 4361

⊂O Try heading into the rectangle's interior, moving your scope southwest 2½ degrees, to find the 10th magnitude planetary nebula NGC 4361. This needs a 4 inch (100 mm) scope or larger to be seen well. It has a distinctly irregular disk shape and covers a total of about 45 x 110 arcseconds. NGC 4361 was discovered by William Herschel in 1785.

7 THE RING-TAIL GALAXY (NGC 4038/9)

⊂O Cross northwest to **Gamma [γ] Corvi**. Use this magnitude 2.5 star as a midway point to help find NGC 4038/9 (see Box). Nudge your scope about 3½ degrees farther southwest from Gamma to find a patch of light in the field. These interacting galaxies shine at magnitude 10.7. The pair takes the form of the letter C. The best size scope for revealing detail is an 8 inch (200 mm) telescope.

8 M68 (NGC 4590)

⊂O Moving on to **Beta [β] Corvi**, about 9 degrees southeast, head 3½ degrees farther south and slightly east to find M68, across the border into Hydra. This magnitude 8 globular cluster was discovered by Messier in 1780. A 4 inch (100 mm) scope is necessary to begin to resolve the cluster into stars.

9 M83 (NGC 5236)

⊂O Head 13 degrees southeast to locate M83, an 8th magnitude spiral galaxy—one of the easiest to see with a small scope and visible in 7 x 50 binoculars. A 6 inch (150 mm) scope reveals it as a fuzzy elliptical patch of light with a small, very bright core.

10 R HYDRAE

⊂O Moving 6½ degrees north and a little west we come to star R Hydrae, just over 2 degrees east of **Gamma [γ] Hydrae**. This is one of the easiest long-period Mira-type variables to locate. It varies between magnitudes 4 and 10 over 390 days, making it fairly easy to see, even at minimum.

This starhop includes two of the best galaxies for large and small scopes—the Sombrero and M83—along with many other faint galaxies that seem to form a path between them.

Closing in on Crux

This part of the sky is far more accessible to observers in the Southern Hemisphere. However, those living south of about 20 degrees north can still catch a glimpse of these objects, low in the sky, during the evenings from May through July.

In 1517, Andrea Corsali described a group of stars he saw in the southern sky as "a marveylous crosse in the myddest of fyve notable starres." Today, we know it as the Southern Cross, and although it is the smallest of all the constellations, it is a prominent group of stars. The Southern Cross is famous, among other things, for its appearance on the flags of several countries.

Crux, the Southern Cross, and parts of nearby Centaurus, the Centaur, contain a number of interesting and visually stunning objects for one of our most southerly starhops.

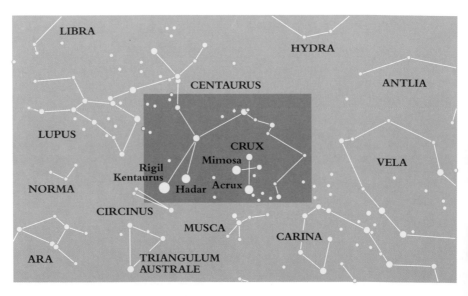

Alpha Centauri (left) is one of the two stars pointing to Crux in the Milky Way (below).

Southern Hemisphere On meridian 10 p.m. May 1

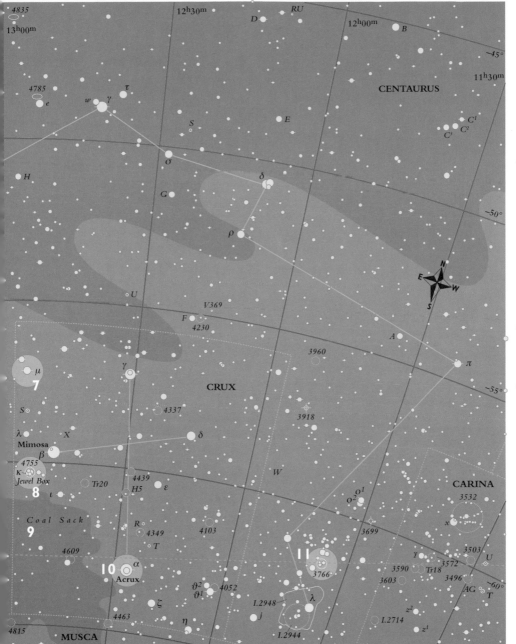

Southern Hemisphere On meridian 10 p.m. May 1

1 Alpha [α] Centauri (Rigel Kentaurus)

⊂⊏⊙ Our starting point for this starhop is the famous Alpha Centauri, the brightest star in Centaurus and, indeed, the third brightest in the entire sky. This is a spectacular double star for any size telescope. The two component stars, of magnitudes 0.0 and 1.2, are yellow and yellow-orange respectively, the brighter of the two being quite similar to our Sun. They orbit their common center of gravity every 80.1 years, varying in apparent separation from about 2 to 22 arcseconds. Currently, they are 16 arcseconds apart. Just 4.4 light-years distant, Alpha Centauri is the nearest star system to the Sun.

To make things really easy, the Southern Cross is clearly identified by the two Pointer stars, Alpha and **Hadar (Beta [β] Centauri)**, forming a line toward Crux in a westerly direction.

A Star Attraction

Omega Centauri appeared as a star in Ptolemy's catalog nearly 2,000 years ago. We now know it as the most spectacular globular cluster in the entire sky, containing about a million stars of 11th magnitude and fainter. Omega Centauri's stars are packed so tightly that, near the center, they are typically only 1/10 of a light-year apart. At some 17,000 light-years away, it is also among the nearest globular clusters to Earth.

An interesting observation about Omega Centauri is that its stars vary significantly in their content of elements heavier than hydrogen and helium, suggesting that the stars differ in age and are not all about the same age, as was previously thought. The reasons for these variations remain unclear.

2 NGC 5617

⊂OO Move your scope just over 1 degree west of Alpha, in the direction of the blue giant Beta (β) Centauri, the other pointer, to locate NGC 5617. Shining at magnitude 6, this open cluster is visible with binoculars, and is also a good subject for small telescopes. A 4 inch (100 mm) scope on low power provides a good view of the cluster, which is about 10 arcminutes across.

3 R CENTAURI

⊂OO Aim your scope to a point two-thirds of the way from Alpha to Beta Centauri, and then shift its position ½ degree north, to locate R Centauri. This is a Mira-type variable star whose magnitude ranges between 5.3 and 11.8 over 546 days. At maximum, it can be seen with the unaided eye. A small scope will show the star's beautiful red color at its brightest.

4 NGC 5316

⊂OO Direct your scope toward Beta Centauri, before hopping 2 degrees southwest to NGC 5316. This open cluster looks similar to NGC 5617 in binoculars,

appearing as a patch of light. A small scope provides a good view of its attractive field, with a 4 inch (100 mm) resolving quite a number of stars.

5 OMEGA [ω] CENTAURI (NGC 5139)

👁 To find our next target, first follow a line about 7½ degrees from Beta to **Epsilon [ε] Centauri**. Extend it another 6½ degrees to locate Omega Centauri. This is the finest of all the globular clusters in the sky (see Box). It can be seen with the unaided eye as a 4th magnitude spot of light, and stands out well in binoculars. A 3 inch (75 mm) scope begins to resolve it, and the view through an 8 inch (200 mm) is stunning.

6 NGC 4945

⊂O From Omega, adjust your telescope's position just over 4 degrees to the southwest to locate NGC 4945. This 9th magnitude edge-on barred spiral galaxy appears as a slender streak of light about 20 arcminutes long, less than ½ degree east of the star **Xi¹ [ξ¹] Centauri**. A wide-field eyepiece will capture the galaxy, along with Xi¹ and the brighter

Xi² [ξ²] Centauri, an easy double
star. NGC 4945 is visible through
a 4 inch (100 mm) scope, even
though it has low surface brightness, but is better suited to larger
telescopes.

7 MU [μ] CRUCIS

Swing your telescope just
over 7 degrees to the south and
a little west, to close in on the
star Mu Crucis, a showpiece
wide double. Its bluish white
4th and 5th magnitude stars
are separated by 35 arcseconds.
Even a steadily held pair of
7 x 50 binoculars will separate
them, but the view through a
telescope is an opportunity not
to be missed.

The Jewel Box (opposite) is justly famous for its attractive contrasting colors formed into a compact, A-shaped cluster.

8 THE JEWEL BOX (NGC 4755)

Three degrees south of Mu is another showpiece object, the Jewel Box. A small scope will show many separate stars in the cluster. However, it is quite compact, so moderate magnification is a help. The cluster is shaped roughly like the letter A, with one of its brightest stars, a red supergiant, being very obvious in a field of contrasting colors.

9 THE COAL SACK

Continuing south a few more degrees, you will enter the south-eastern corner of Crux, where you should be able to see the Milky Way looking very dark. This is the area known as the Coal Sack. The most famous of the dark nebulas, the Coal Sack is a cloud of gas and dust, about 6 degrees across, which obscures the stars beyond it. Even in light-polluted skies, the Milky Way star field appears fairly barren in this area, but fine views of the Coal Sack can be obtained from dark, country sites where it stands out wonderfully.

10 ACRUX (ALPHA [α] CRUCIS)

Heading 2 degrees west of the Coal Sack, Alpha Crucis pops into view—the star at the foot of the Southern Cross. This is a celebrated double star, whose components, at magnitudes 1.4 and 1.9, lie 4.4 arcseconds apart and form a very long-period binary system. A 3 inch (75 mm) telescope with high magnification shows them well.

11 NGC 3766

Just over 6 degrees west of Alpha lies NGC 3766. In binoculars, this open cluster appears as an obvious fuzzy spot of light in a field very rich in stars. The view through a 4 inch (100 mm) scope is quite beautiful. Two of its brightest stars are a very distinctive reddish orange.

There is little to outshine the view of this part of the night sky, especially on a moonless night away from bright city lights.

Exploring the Scorpion

Scorpius is at its best when high in the sky during the evenings of June, July, and August. At this time, binocular and telescope observers are treated to a view of many fine celestial objects spotted throughout a very rich part of the Milky Way Galaxy.

One of the ancient legends tells us that Orion, the Hunter, died after being stung by a scorpion, and that the two were turned into constellations on opposite sides of the sky. Orion must flee the scorpion for eternity, so as Scorpius rises in the east, Orion sets in the west.

For those less familiar with the night sky, Scorpius is one of the easiest constellations to locate. Simply look for the bright, reddish orange star Antares that marks the Scorpion's heart, and the distinctive curving shape of Scorpius's body.

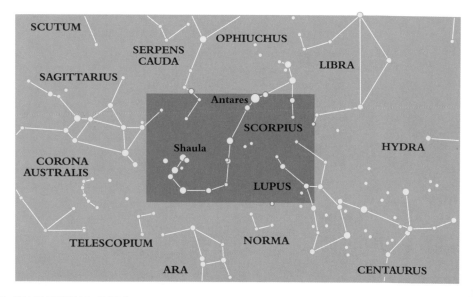

A spectacular view of the constellation of Scorpius (above). The nebulosity surrounding Antares (right).

Northern and Southern Hemisphere On meridian 10 p.m. July 1

SAGITTARIUS

−25°

17h40m   17h20m   31 28   17h00m

6355   36   6293   M19

18h00m

GALACTIC EQUATOR

X

−30°

OPHIUCHUS

43   6316

45   6304

M62

RR

SS

27

RV

ε

SCORPIUS

6425   11

6416   M6
             Butterfly
             Cluster   6383

6404

Ti27

RY

10

6453

M7

9

G

6441

6400

Shaula

λ

H16

υ

κ

Q

6380

Ti29

ι²   ι¹

6337

6302
Bug Nebula   RT

6281   8

6337   6318

6268

7

h 488

μ²

μ¹

6

6242

Cr316

V861   5

6231

4

ξ²   ξ¹

CORONA
AUSTRALIS

−40°

−35°

RU

6322

ϑ   η

6259   6249

−45°

RS

Wil Tirion   6541   6494   6388

Northern and Southern Hemisphere On meridian 10 p.m. July 1

A number of impressive globular clusters, including M4, lie within the field around brilliant Antares, shown on the left.

1 ANTARES (ALPHA [α] SCORPII)

The name Antares means "rival to Mars" and it is easy to see how the name came about. Antares shines at 1st magnitude and looks remarkably like a slightly fainter version of the planet Mars. Antares is a red supergiant star at a very late stage of its evolution. It is immense, with a diameter close to 300 times that of our Sun and is enveloped in a haze of nebulosity. Antares is also a famous, but difficult to separate, double star. The magnitudes of the two components are 1.2 and 5.4, with the secondary often reported as appearing greenish. This is due to a contrast effect; it is actually a star of spectral class B, so that by itself it would appear bluish white. Antares's components lie almost 3 arcseconds apart, so you need at least a 6 inch (150 mm) telescope to separate them.

2 AL NIYAT (20 SIGMA [σ] SCORPII)

⊂⊙ Move about 2 degrees northwest to look at 20 Sigma Scorpii, an easy but unequal double star, whose 3rd and 8th magnitude components are 20 arcseconds apart. They are easy to separate in a 3 inch (75 mm) telescope.

3 M4 (NGC 6121)

⊂⊙⊙ Shift 1 degree south and a little back toward Antares to bring M4 into view. This is one of the great globular clusters in the sky. Easily seen in binoculars, it is nearly ½ degree in diameter. A 4 inch (100 mm) scope begins to resolve individual stars in the cluster, although larger telescopes will reveal many more stars.

4 NGC 6231

⊂⊙⊙ The best way to exit the Antares area is by running southeast along the scorpion's body until you reach the bend in its tail, where NGC 6231 is located, some 17 degrees from M4. It contains a number of blue-white supergiant stars. The cluster covers about ¼ degree, but its brightest members form a more compact group. This is a fine open cluster for small scopes, being clearly visible to the naked eye as a bright spot of light just north of the star pair **Zeta[1,2] [ζ¹, ζ²] Scorpii**. Zeta¹, an orange star, and bluish white Zeta² are not a physical pair but are worth a quick look for their contrasting colors.

5 V861 SCORPII

⊂⊙⊙ From NGC 6231 adjust your scope 1 degree north and about ½ degree east to encounter v861 Scorpii. Lying within the scattered 1 degree wide cluster **Collinder 316**, v861 Scorpii is a bluish star that varies in magnitude between 6.1 and 6.7 every 7.8 days. In mid-1978, the star was found to be an X-ray source and is now a well-known X-ray binary variable.

6 NGC 6242

Nudge your scope just under 1½ degrees north and a little west through this very rich field to find NGC 6242. This open cluster is a pleasing binocular target in addition to being a rewarding sight through a 3 inch (75 mm) telescope. Its brightest star, near the southern end of the cluster, is an attractive orange-red color.

7 H 4889

One and a half degrees northwest of NGC 6242 is the brilliant, wide pair **Mu^{1,2} [μ^1, μ^2] Scorpii**. Another ½ degree farther is h 4889. This is a double whose 6th and 8th magnitude stars lie 7 arcseconds apart. Mu^1 and Mu^2 themselves are a fine naked-eye pair of stars that may be physically associated.

In Polynesian legend, they were called "the inseparable ones."

8 NGC 6281

Sweep your telescope about 3 degrees east for a look at NGC 6281. Easily visible in binoculars, this is a 5th magnitude open cluster similar in size to NGC 6242, but containing fewer stars. It is also well worth a look in any size telescope.

9 NGC 6441

Hop just over 9 degrees east, past **Lambda [λ] Scorpii**, in search of NGC 6441. Although by no means bright, this globular cluster is quite easy to locate, being only a few arcminutes east of yellow-orange **G Scorpii**, a 3rd magnitude star. The cluster requires quite a large scope to resolve its stars. A 10 inch (250 mm) scope reveals its granular appearance.

10 M7 (NGC 6475)

Shift 2 degrees to the north and a little east to find M7. Easily seen as a 1 degree wide, hazy patch of light with the naked eye, M7 is one of the best open clusters for binoculars, which reveal many of its stars. A wide-field eyepiece is essential for a good view through a telescope.

11 THE BUTTERFLY CLUSTER (M6, NGC 6405)

Four degrees northwest of M7 we come to another gem, the open cluster M6. It is just possible to see it with the naked eye, but binoculars or a small telescope provide a far better view. The view through a telescope reveals its main stars arranged in a pattern resembling the body and wings of a butterfly, hence its common name.

BM SCORPII

Near the eastern end of M6, and marking the trailing end of the butterfly's left wing, lies the orange semi-regular variable star BM Scorpii. It varies between magnitude 6.8 and 8.7 over a period of about 850 days.

The grouping of stars and star clusters around Scorpius in a dark sky is an unforgettable sight. It is easy to lose track of time while sweeping your binoculars through this fascinating area.

M7, an Ancient Open Cluster

M7 is the southernmost object in Charles Messier's famous catalog of non-stellar objects. It is also one of the brightest. However, Messier observed it from Paris, where its maximum altitude of only about 6 degrees would have meant that he could not see it in its true splendor. The cluster contains about 80 stars scattered over more than 1 degree of sky. Studies of M7 show that it is about 220 million years old. This compares with only about 50 million years for its nearby companion M6 and 70 million years for the Pleiades in Taurus. There are few open clusters much older than M7, because as clusters age, they are dispersed by gravitational effects and encounters with interstellar clouds.

Toward the Heart of Our Galaxy

Being at a moderate southerly declination, this region passes overhead for those living in the Southern Hemisphere. However, northern skywatchers can spot many of the objects in this patch of sky during the evenings from late June through September.

There is no finer naked-eye view of the night sky than one that includes the constellation of Sagittarius, the Archer, high above the horizon, for it is in this direction that we look toward the center of the Milky Way Galaxy.

The region just east of the tail of Scorpius, the Scorpion, is especially rich in interesting clusters and nebulas. In the adjacent constellation of Ophiuchus, we find some of the famous dark, obscuring dust clouds that stand out so well on clear nights for observers away from the pollution of city lights.

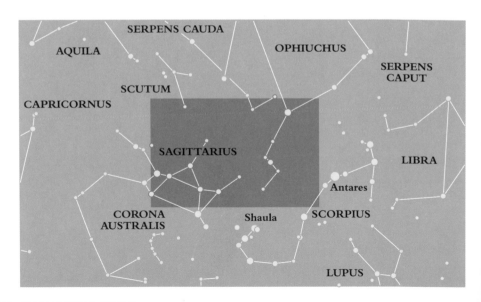

1 NUNKI
(34 SIGMA [σ] SAGITTARII)

👁 While the brightest stars of Sagittarius have the distinctive appearance of a teapot, a familiar part of the asterism is the shape of the so-called Milk Dipper— the handle and part of the lid of the teapot. The Milk Dipper is formed by the stars **Zeta [ζ]**, Tau [τ], Sigma [σ], Phi [φ], and **Lambda [λ] Sagittarii**. Shining at magnitude 2, the blue-white star Sigma forms one end of the base of the dipper and, surprisingly, is the second brightest star in Sagittarius.

Sigma's common name, Nunki, is thought to be derived from the Babylonian *Tablet of the Thirty Stars*. It is said to represent "the star of the proclamation of the sea," the "sea" being the quarter of sky occupied by the water constellations, including nearby Capricornus and Aquarius.

2 M54 (NGC 6715)

🔭 Center your telescope on Nunki and head about 4 degrees due south to M54, an 8th magnitude globular cluster that seems

M20, the Trifid Nebula (above), lies at center bottom of the view of the Milky Way Galaxy (top) which includes M17 at the top.

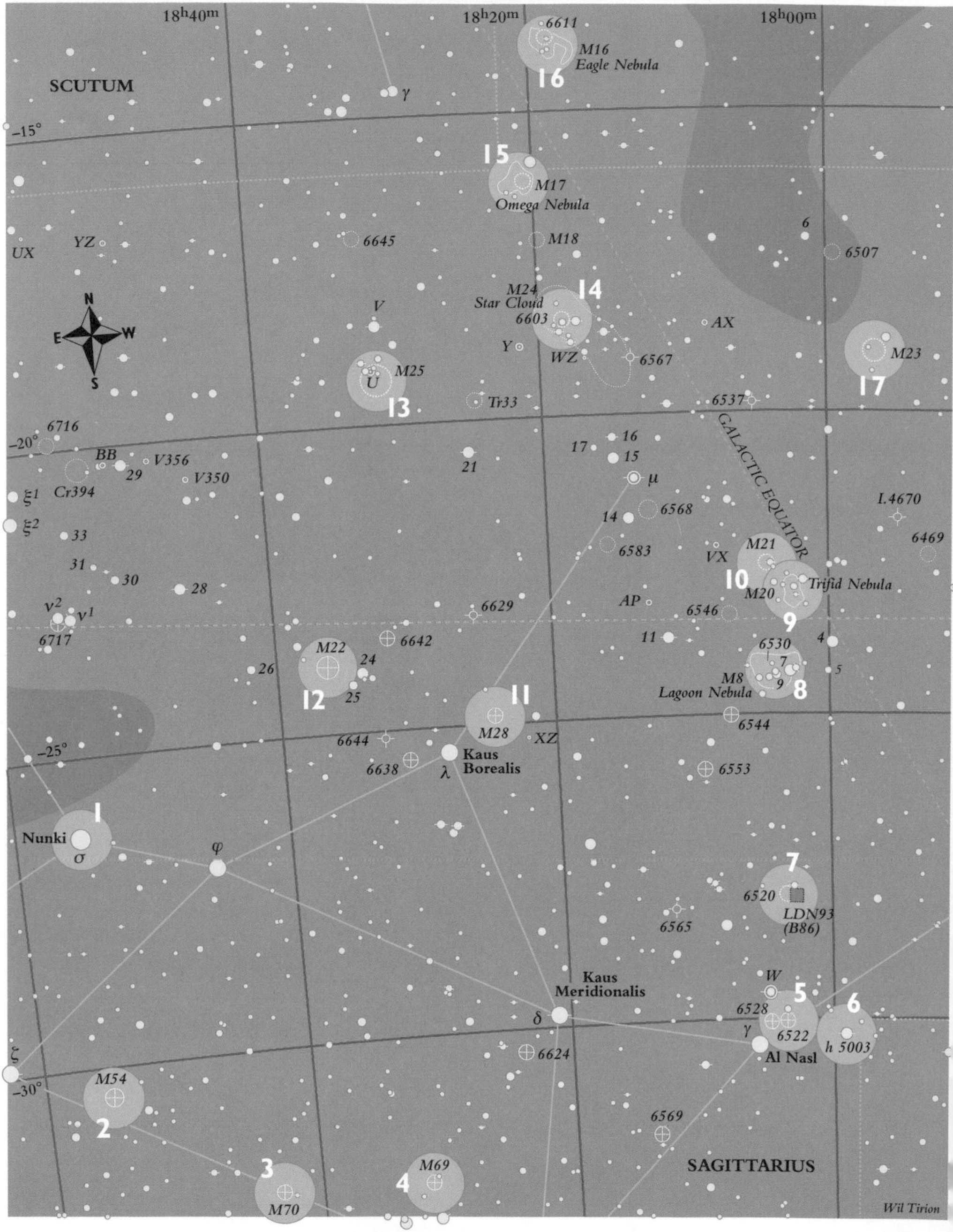

Northern and Southern Hemisphere On meridian 10 p.m. July 20

SCUTUM

18h40m   18h20m   18h00m

6611
M16
Eagle Nebula
16

−15°

γ

15
M17
Omega Nebula

UX   YZ   6645   M18   6507

6
M24
Star Cloud
6603
14

V   Y   WZ   6567   AX   M23
17

U   M25   6537   GALACTIC EQUATOR
13   Tr33

−20°   6716   16   I.4670
BB   V356   17   15   6469
ξ¹   Cr394   29   V350   21   μ   VX   M21
ξ²   33   14   6568   M20   Trifid Nebula
31   30   28   6583   10   9
ν²   ν¹   6629   AP   6546   6530
6717   26   M22   24   6642   11   7   M8   4
12   25   8   Lagoon Nebula   9   5
M28   XZ   6544
11   Kaus
6644   Borealis
6638   λ   6553

−25°

I
Nunki   φ   7
σ   6520
LDN93
(B86)
6565

Kaus
Meridionalis   W
5
6528   6
δ   6522   h 5003
ζ   6624   γ
Al Nasl

−30°   M54
2
6569

3   M69   SAGITTARIUS
M70   4   Wil Tirion

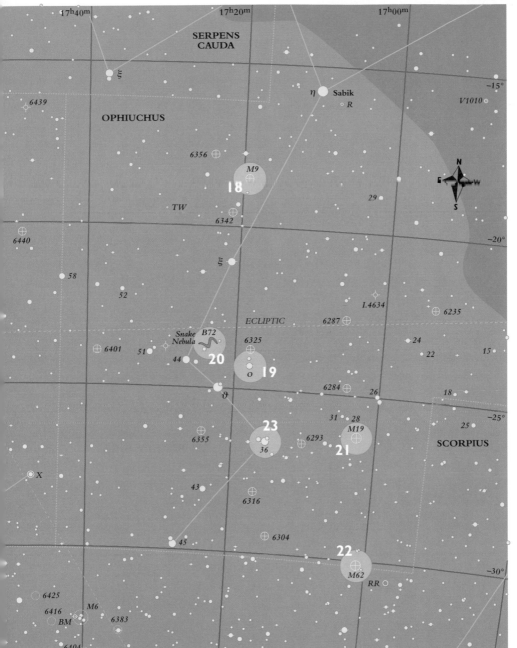

Dark dust lanes create different and dramatic effects in B72, the Snake Nebula (above), and M16, the Eagle Nebula (right).

to have fallen out of the dipper's bowl. It can be seen in binoculars, but is extremely difficult to resolve. Even a 12 inch (300 mm) telescope shows it only as somewhat granular.

3 M70 (NGC 6681)

About 3 degrees southwest lies another globular cluster, M70. This is also an 8th magnitude object, but it can be resolved a little more easily than M54, with a 6 inch (150 mm) scope showing some of its stars. M70 became famous in 1995 when astronomers Alan Hale and Thomas

Bopp, observing the cluster from different locations, discovered Comet Hale-Bopp, the Great Comet of 1997, in the same telescope field as the cluster.

4 M69 (NGC 6637)

The globular cluster M69 lies 2½ degrees due west of M70 and appears virtually as its twin. It requires a 6 inch (150 mm) telescope to begin to resolve it properly into individual stars. Unlike the previous two globulars, which were discovered by Charles Messier, M69 was first seen by astronomer Nicolas Louis de Lacaille in 1752.

5 NGC 6522

Almost 6½ degrees northwest of M69 lies **10 Gamma [γ] Sagittarii**, a bright star. Move across to it, and place brilliant Gamma in the southeastern corner of a wide-field view. You should also be able to see the 9th magnitude globular cluster NGC 6522. Some of the cluster's stars are visible through an 8 inch (200 mm) telescope.

NGC 6528

⊂⊙ The magnitude 10 globular cluster, NGC 6528, is too difficult to resolve even with a 12 inch (300 mm) telescope.

6 H 5003

⊂⊙ Hop 1 degree west of our last stop to h 5003. This delightful double star is a great object for any size scope. A 3 inch (75 mm) telescope, or one even smaller, will show this orange and yellow pair of stars, at magnitudes 5 and 7, separated by 5.5 arcseconds.

7 NGC 6520

⊂⊙ Return to NGC 6522 and NGC 6528, then shift 2 degrees due north to locate NGC 6520. This compact open cluster, visible in binoculars, is worth seeing in a 3 inch (75 mm) scope or larger. Between NGC 6520 and a 7th magnitude star a few

arcminutes northwest lies the dark nebula **Barnard 86**, also known as LDN 93. A 4 inch (100 mm) telescope should reveal the nebula as an apparent gap in the star field around it.

8 THE LAGOON NEBULA (M8, NGC 6523)

👁 Ease your scope 3½ degrees north to find the wonderful Lagoon Nebula. One of the few bright nebulas visible to the unaided eye, this can be seen as a milky-white spot of light against the backdrop of the Milky Way. Although it is one of the finest nebulas for a small telescope, binoculars can also provide a superb view.

9 THE TRIFID NEBULA (M20, NGC 6514)

⊂⊙ Try your hand at the Trifid Nebula, 1½ degrees north and just a little west of M8. This famous nebula is much fainter than the Lagoon Nebula and is best observed in a dark sky. There is always a feeling of delight to see the three dark lanes that give the Trifid Nebula its prominent shape. These dust lanes are visible in a 6 inch

(150 mm) scope. It is helpful to use averted vision when viewing this nebula.

⑩ M21 (NGC 6531)

⬚◯◯ Nudge your scope just over ½ degree northeast of the Trifid to spot M21. Covering almost ¼ degree, M21 is easily resolved in a 3 inch (75 mm) telescope, with its brightest stars being of 8th magnitude.

⑪ M28 (NGC 6626)

⬚◯◯ Moving on about 6 degrees southeast, hop to the star Lambda [λ] Sagittarii, then backtrack 1 degree to pinpoint M28. Although visible in binoculars, it takes a 6 inch (150 mm) scope to begin to resolve the stars of this globular cluster. In smaller telescopes, M28 appears as a round, fuzzy glow.

⑫ M22 (NGC 6656)

👁 About 3 degrees northeast of M28 lies one of the few globular clusters clearly visible with the unaided eye—M22, a spectacular object at magnitude 5.1. A 3 inch (75 mm) telescope will show some of its brightest members, and the view through a 6 inch

(150 mm) is unforgettable. You may be able to detect its slightly elliptical shape. The cluster has a diameter of more than 20 arc-minutes and, at a distance of only about 10,000 light-years, is one of the closest of its type to us.

⑬ M25 (IC 4725)

⬚◯◯ Move 5 degrees north and 1 degree west of M22 to take a look at M25. This scattered open cluster, about ½ degree across, is an easy object for binoculars and small telescopes. Near the center of M25 is the yellowish Cepheid variable **U Sagittarii**, which varies from magnitude 6.3 to 7.1 over 6.75 days.

⑭ M24

👁 To locate the next object on our hop, scan your eye 3 degrees west of M25. M24 is unique among Messier objects because it is a huge star cloud about 1 degree wide and 2 degrees long. Sweeping your scope through it will reveal a very rich region, including open cluster **NGC 6603** near the northeastern end. The cluster is visible with a 4 inch (100 mm) scope, but can be resolved in larger telescopes.

M17, the Omega Nebula, lies on the border of Sagittarius.

⓯ THE OMEGA NEBULA (THE SWAN NEBULA, M17, NGC 6618)

ⵕ If you look another 2½ degrees farther north and a little east, M17 comes into view. This bright nebula is easy to see in binoculars, appearing as a small streak of light. In a 4 inch (100 mm) scope, its unusual shape looks a bit like the figure 2 with an extended baseline. Because of this pattern, M17 is called both the Swan Nebula and the Omega Nebula.

⓰ THE EAGLE NEBULA (M16, NGC 6611)

ⵕ Across the border into Serpens, about 2½ degrees north of M17, the combination of hazy star cluster and nebula, M16, appears. The cluster is obvious enough with binoculars, but you need a 6 inch (150 mm) scope and a dark sky to clearly see that it is actually immersed in a region of nebulosity called the Eagle Nebula (see Box, p. 525). In larger scopes, the whole field is beautiful.

⓱ M23 (NGC 6494)

ⵕ Head 7½ degrees southwest of M16, back into Sagittarius, for a view of M23. This open star cluster is nearly ½ degree across. It is a fine sight in a 4 inch (100 mm) scope, which resolves quite a few stars.

The straight and curved lines of stars within the cluster provide a delightful detail.

18 M9 (NGC 6333)

⊂⊙⊃ Shift your scope 9 degrees farther west to find 8th magnitude M9, a globular cluster about 2½ degrees north of the star **Xi [ξ] Ophiuchi**. It appears fairly condensed and is visible in binoculars, although a 6 inch (150 mm) scope is needed to see some of its multitude of stars clearly.

19 39 OMICRON [o] OPHIUCHI

⊂⊙⊃ About 3 degrees south of Xi lies a small triangle of stars, the westernmost and faintest of the three being our next target. A beautiful double star for any small telescope, Omicron's colorful 5th and 7th magnitude orange and yellowish components are an easy 10 arcseconds apart, so they should be no problem to visually separate with most telescopes.

20 THE SNAKE NEBULA (BARNARD 72)

⊂⊙⊃ The next challenge lies about 1½ degrees northeast of Omicron. A familiar sight in photographs of the Ophiuchus Milky Way, the dark Snake Nebula takes the form of the letter S and is about ½ degree from end to end. It is not exactly an easy object to discern, but if you use moderate aperture and a low magnification, you might be able to find it in a dark sky.

21 M19 (NGC 6273)

⊂⊙⊃ Aiming your scope just over 5 degrees southwest of the Snake Nebula, you should be able to spy the globular cluster M19. At magnitude 7, M19 is an object that is easy to see with binoculars, appearing as a round, fuzzy spot. A 4 inch (100 mm) telescope will begin to show a granular appearance.

22 M62 (NGC 6266)

⊂⊙⊃ Our next stop, the globular cluster M62, is about 4 degrees due south of M19. A little brighter but somewhat more difficult to resolve than M19, M62 appears as a more uniform haze of stars requiring an 8 inch (200 mm) telescope for a good view. However, a number of individual stars can just be resolved when using a 6 inch (150 mm) telescope or larger.

23 36 OPHIUCHI

Returning to the northeast, two-thirds of the way to **Theta [θ] Ophiuchi** is the double star 36 Ophiuchi. Shining like a pair of distant orange headlights, the magnitude 5 stars of 36 Ophiuchi are equal in brightness and color, separated by about 5 arcseconds.

The two form a binary system, moving around each other about every 550 years.

A dark night, away from city lights, and a pair of dark-adapted eyes are the perfect formula for gazing in the direction of our galaxy's center. With its superb collection of objects and delicate dust lanes, many would say that it is the most interesting part of the night sky.

The Stellar Nursery in M16

In 1995, the Hubble Space Telescope returned an eerie picture of the nebulosity of M16, showing huge columns of gas that are several light-years in length (left). A close look at the surfaces of the giant pillars shows what scientists have called evaporating gaseous globules, or EGGs. Ultraviolet light from nearby stars is stripping some of the gas from the columns and exposing the EGGS, in which stars are forming. We see the globules because they are more dense than the rest of the nebula, and so are not "blown away" as easily. However, the gradual loss of material feeding the developing stars is thought to play an important role in limiting their size. We can only wonder how many more stars are forming deep within these huge columns, gathering material in private and becoming larger and larger.

Hunting with the Eagle and the Fox

This part of the night sky is visible to skywatchers in both hemispheres from July through September. The starhop zooms in on parts of the constellations of Aquila, Vulpecula, and Delphinus, the Dolphin, and includes the third smallest constellation of all—Sagitta, the Arrow.

Aquila's name is derived from the Arabic *Al Nasr al Tair*, meaning "the Flying Eagle."

Today, it is simply known as the Eagle, while Vulpecula is generally referred to as the Fox.

This region features rich fields containing thousands of sparkling bright stars, and coal-black dark nebulas. Wide swaths of dust clouds, known as the Great Rift, divide the Milky Way into two parallel bands of stars through the center of this starhop, as they do through nearby Cygnus, the Swan (see p. 534).

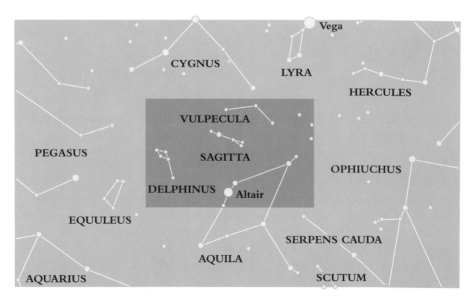

B142 and B143 (above), M27 (right), and NGC 6820 and NGC 6823 (below) all lie within the same patch of the northern Milky Way.

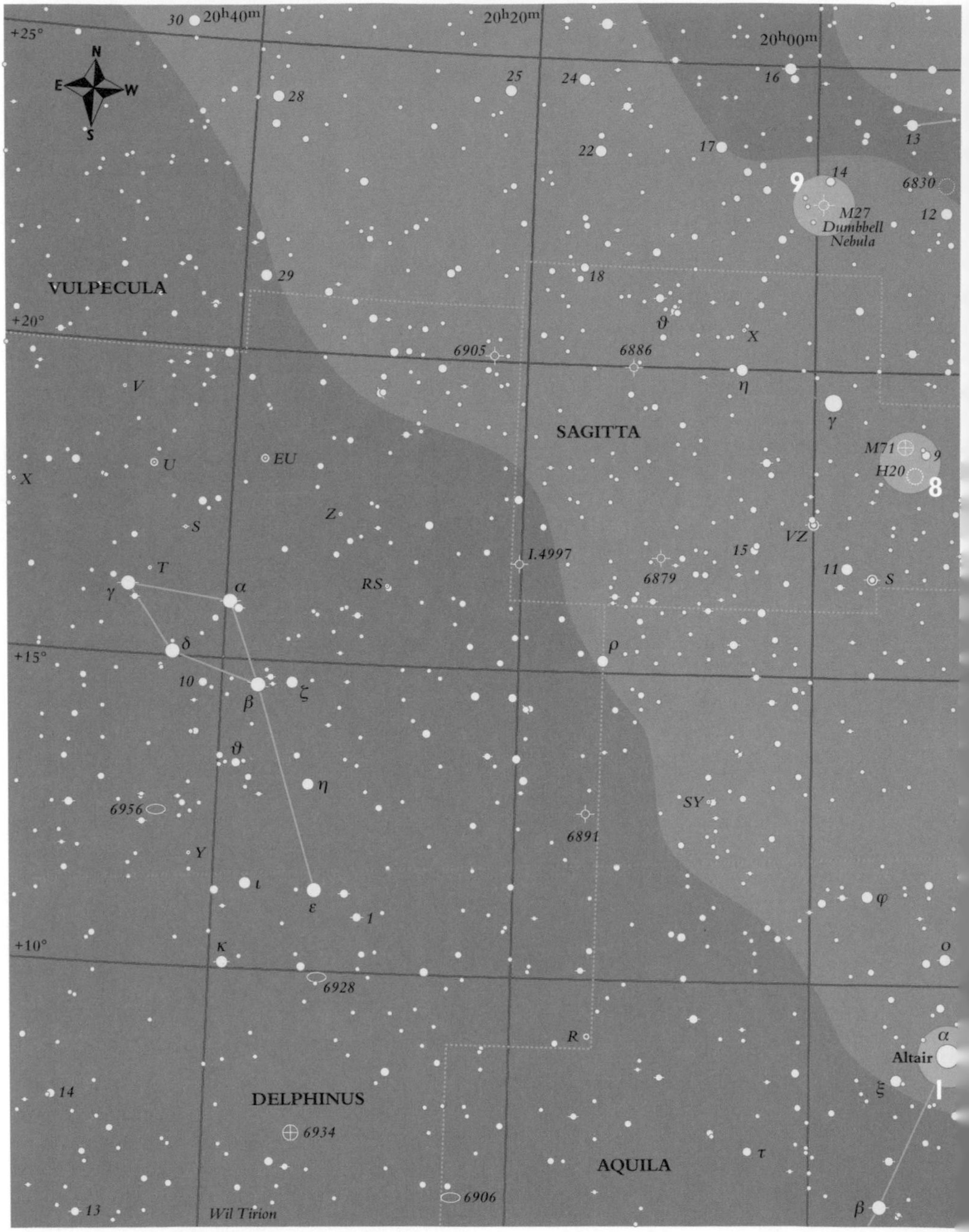

Northern and Southern Hemisphere On meridian 10 p.m. August 20

VULPECULA

SAGITTA

DELPHINUS

AQUILA

M27
Dumbbell
Nebula

M71

Altair

Wil Tirion

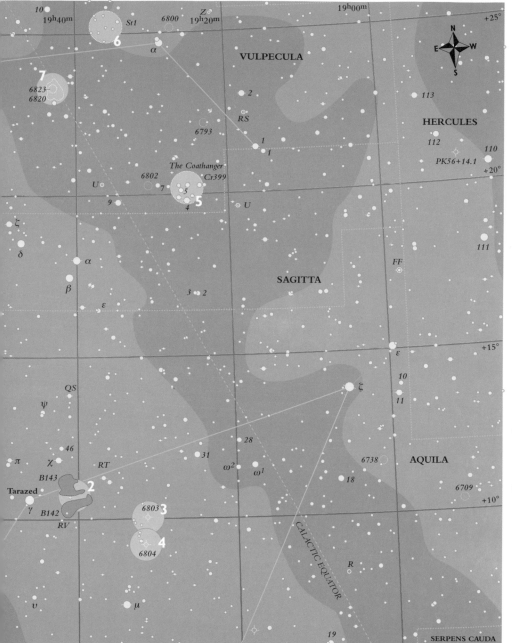

Northern and Southern Hemisphere   On meridian 10 p.m. August 20

M71, in the constellation of Sagittae, is usually classified as a loosely packed globular cluster.

1 ALTAIR
(53 ALPHA [α] AQUILAE)

👁 Our jumping-off point for this starhop is the magnitude 1 white star Altair, the brightest star in Aquila. It is also the 12th brightest star in the night sky, marking the point where the Eagle's wing attaches to its body. At some 17 light-years away, Altair is also one of our closest neighbors among all the brighter stars in the night sky.

Spectroscopic studies show that Altair is rotating at an incredible speed of 160 miles per second (258 km/s), a truly remarkable feature. One Altair "day" is completed in about 6½ hours. By comparison, the Sun takes more than 25 Earth days to complete one rotation.

To find the next object on our starhop, first nudge your scope about 2 degrees northwest of Altair, to **Tarazed (Gamma [γ] Aquilae)**, then hop 1½ degrees west to the Double Dark Nebula.

2 THE DOUBLE DARK NEBULA (B142 AND B143)

The U-shaped nebula B143 and the elongated oval nebula B142 are made up of clouds of non-luminous gas and dust and are fine examples of dark nebulas. These clouds completely blot out the grainy star fields that are thought to be located some 5,000 light-years beyond. An 8 inch (200 mm) scope or larger and a dark clear sky are usually needed to study the edges of these clouds in detail.

3 NGC 6803

About 2 degrees west and a little south of the Double Dark Nebula is a fine planetary nebula, NGC 6803, glowing at about magnitude 11. At magnitude 14, its central star is visible in telescopes that are larger than 16 inches (400 mm). NGC 6803 is only 4 arcseconds in diameter, so it is essential to use high power when observing it.

4 NGC 6804

Hop 1 degree south to NGC 6804, another planetary nebula, making a fine pair with NGC 6803. At 60 arcseconds in diameter, NGC 6804 is an easier target to locate than its close neighbor. It is dimmer overall, at magnitude 13, but its central star is a little brighter.

Both NGC 6803 and NGC 6804 look like smaller and fainter versions of the Ring Nebula (M57) in the Lyra constellation (see p. 539).

5 THE COATHANGER (COLLINDER 399)

Sweep some 10 degrees north of NGC 6804 to the spectacular open star cluster known as the Coathanger. It includes about 40 stars forming an arc of 6 bright stars running in an east-west direction, with a hook on the southern side. The Coathanger is best viewed with binoculars or a finderscope, because you can more easily orient yourself within a wider field. The magnitude 5.1 red giant at the bottom of the hook is the multiple star **4 Vulpeculae**.

6 STOCK 1

Hop 5 degrees northeast to the large, very loose open star cluster Stock 1. It contains about 40 stars that are scattered amorphously, making it a challenge to resolve individual stars from the surrounding Milky Way star field. Stock 1 is about 1 degree in diameter, so it is better to observe it with your binoculars or a finderscope, instead of with a telescope eyepiece.

7 NGC 6823

Swing your scope about 5 degrees southeast of Stock 1 to the open star cluster NGC 6823, surrounded by the elusive glow of the faint emission nebula **NGC 6820**. The 30-member cluster itself, with a combined magnitude of 7.1, is an easy binocular target.

8 M71 (NGC 6838)

Locate the 3rd magnitude stars **7 Delta [δ] Sagittae** and **12 Gamma [γ] Sagittae**, both red giant stars, about 4 degrees east of NGC 6823, to help find M71, lying midway between them. This compact cluster glows at magnitude 8.3, with many faint stars forming a triangular shape. Most astronomers consider M71 to be a loose globular rather than a compact open cluster because it contains red giant stars. However, no short-period variables, which are common to all globular clusters, have ever been detected in M71, leaving its true nature somewhat in doubt.

HARVARD 20

⊂⊙ Only 30 arcminutes southwest is the faint, sparse open cluster Harvard 20. An elongated box-like formation of 15 members, Harvard 20 is a challenge to pick out from the rich star field behind it.

9 THE DUMBBELL NEBULA (NGC 6853, M27)

⊂⊙ Return to Gamma Sagittae before hopping about 4 degrees north to the magnitude 7.6 Dumbbell Nebula. Considered by many to be one of the finest planetary nebulas, it is also one of the closest to us at 1,000 light-years away. This softly glowing, greenish, hourglass-shaped planetary nebula is best viewed with a telescope, although, at 8 arcminutes across, it is also worth a look with binoculars or a finderscope.

There is so much more to see in this part of the night sky, so plan to return and slowly scan the wonderful Milky Way star fields and dark nebulas, again and again.

Planetary Nebulas

Seen with early scopes, planetary nebulas were described as somewhat like the disks of planets, when actually, they are the last stage of a star's life.

When a star like the Sun gets old, it swells to become a red giant, soon running out of hydrogen and helium to burn in its core. Instead, it continues its nuclear reactions in shells around the core. As it does this, the star begins to pulsate, culminating in a shedding of its outer layers, which form a planetary nebula. This process reveals the hot central core which, in turn, pours ultraviolet radiation out into the expanding planetary shell, causing it to glow. This ghost-like shell survives for only about 50,000 years before it dissipates, leaving the core behind as a slowly cooling white dwarf star.

Cygnus in the Milky Way

For mid-northern observers, the two constellations traversing this region of sky hover near the zenith on July and August nights, making these the best months for viewing. This particular part of the Milky Way Galaxy is rich with a variety of celestial objects in the constellations of Cygnus, the Swan, and Lyra, the Lyre.

Cygnus forms a prominent cross shape that straddles the Milky Way at the point where the galaxy is split by a dark dust lane. It is also known as the Northern Cross—the Northern Hemisphere's answer to Crux, the Southern Cross (see p. 500). The constellation of Lyra appears as a box lying to the west of Cygnus.

Vega in Lyra, Deneb in Cygnus, and Altair in Aquila (south of this area), are the three 1st magnitude stars that form what is known in the Northern Hemisphere as the Summer Triangle.

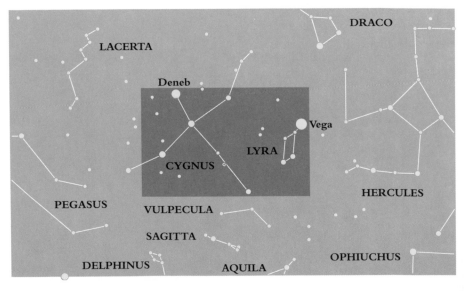

The Cross shape of Cygnus (above) with
Vega at center right. The Ring Nebula
(right) is a famous planetary nebula.

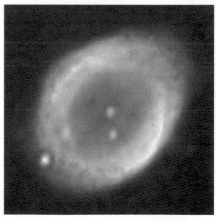

Northern and Southern Hemisphere On meridian 10 p.m. August 20

21h00m 6996 55 20h40m 20h20m o¹ 30 20h00m
+45°
α Deneb
Cr428 6997
ξ 57 56
10 7027
North America Nebula
7044 6866
7027
N
E W V
S
+40°
6910 γ
V380
61 V367 Sadr
9 Be86 19
40 M29 RS 6888 22
P I.4996 Bas6
λ 36 29 25
44 28
X 42 27
6883 6871
47 35 Bi2 η
Y T
ε χ
Gienah
6992 6979 49
6974 39
6995 48 CYGNUS
Veil Nebula 52 41 6834
6960
8
BW 6940
32 T **7** 21
31 23 15
VULPECULA
Wil Tirion V SV

+35° +30°

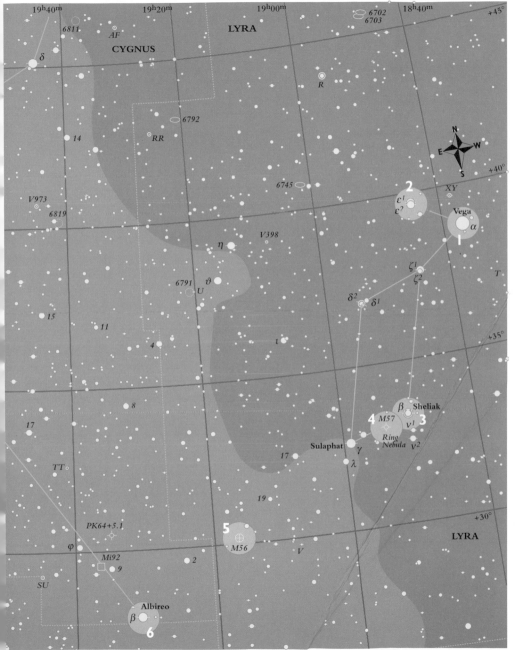

Northern and Southern Hemisphere   On meridian 10 p.m. August 20

The Visual Milky Way

One of the joys of stargazing is to sit out under a very dark sky and watch the broad swath of the faintly glowing Milky Way slowly pass overhead. Take the time to study the Milky Way without binoculars or a telescope. Look for the delicate interweaving of the bands of obscuring dust clouds and the hazy star fields. After observing the Milky Way with the naked eye, scan the band with binoculars, stopping to study the rich star fields and coal-black dark nebulas throughout it.

The plane of the Milky Way is made up of vast clouds of glowing gas and stars cut by dark lanes of dust (above). Billions of faint stars, many that are far too faint for our eyes to separate into individual points of light, merge like a mottled, grayish fog.

1 VEGA (3 ALPHA [α] LYRAE)

👁 The starting point for this tour of celestial gems in the Milky Way is the brightest star in the Northern Hemisphere's summer sky—Vega. This bright, blue-white star is very close to zero magnitude, being listed at magnitude 0.03. Vega is the fifth brightest star in the entire sky, and is estimated to be intrinsically about 58 times brighter than the Sun. It is 25 light-years away from Earth.

Vega appears in many ancient legends. Its common name comes from the Arabic *Al Nasar al Waki*, meaning "the swooping eagle." In one Greek legend, it symbolizes the lyre of Hermes, so is often called "the harp star."

Because Vega's magnitude does not vary significantly, the star is often used by astronomers when calibrating photometric equipment that is used to measure stellar brightness.

2 THE DOUBLE DOUBLE STAR (4 EPSILON¹ AND 5 EPSILON² [ε¹, ε²] LYRAE)

The famous "double double" star, lying 1½ degrees

northeast of Vega, consists of four white stars. The two primary stars are 208 arcseconds apart, and each is itself a binary star. The magnitude 6 companion of Epsilon[1] is 2.8 arcseconds from its magnitude 5.1 primary. The Epsilon[2] system is composed of two 5th magnitude stars lying 2.6 arcseconds apart.

3 SHELIAK
(10 BETA [β] LYRAE)

Hop about 6 degrees south to Sheliak, a bright eclipsing binary variable, whose magnitude fluctuates from 3.3 down to 4.4. The two unequally bright stars in this system orbit about a common center of gravity over a period of 12.9 days. The stars seem to be constantly transferring massive amounts of gas between their atmospheres. Being only about 22 million miles (35 million km) apart, the components of Sheliak have never been visually separated.

4 THE RING NEBULA
(M57, NCG 6720)

Located about midway between Sheliak and **Sulaphat (14 Gamma [γ] Lyrae)** is the famous bright planetary nebula M57. It is often referred to as the "smoke ring" or "doughnut" of the sky. M57 is the result of a star that blew off a massive amount of gas thousands of years ago. The shell of gas is easy to see through an 8 inch (200 mm) scope and has a slightly greenish cast to it. From a dark site, with a 15 inch (375 mm) scope, you can glimpse the magnitude 17 dwarf star from which the gas was expelled.

5 M56 (NGC 6779)

Some 4½ degrees southeast from Sulaphat is the globular cluster M56. This small, circular 8th magnitude mass of stars was discovered by Messier in 1779. Many faint stars around the edges of the cluster can be resolved with scopes smaller than 8 inches (200 mm).

6 ALBIREO
(6 BETA [β] CYGNI)

Continue southeast about 3½ degrees from M56 to Albireo. This is probably the finest color-contrast double star and a real showpiece at any star party. This magnitude 3.1 star appears bright yellow or topaz with a sapphire-blue companion shining at magnitude 5.1. The stars are 34.3 arcseconds apart, making them an easy pair to separate in any size telescope. While near Albireo, scan the rich star clouds with binoculars, looking for the myriad clusters and dark nebulas.

7 NGC 6940

From Albireo shift about 14 degrees east to the open cluster NGC 6940, across the border in Vulpecula. About 60 to 80 stars make up this large, scattered cluster. Nine bright stars appear centered within the cluster, while other stars seem to form chain-like strings just north of the center of the cluster.

8 THE VEIL NEBULA (NGC 6960)

Hop about 6 degrees north-east of NGC 6940 to magnitude 2.5 **Epsilon [ε] Cygni**. Three degrees due south of Epsilon is the magnitude 4.2 star **52 Cygni**, straddling the long filaments of the western side of the Veil Nebula. The nebula is the expanding shell of gas from

a supernova explosion. Your best views will be through an Oxygen III or any other high-contrast filter. To fully explore this intriguing object, trace the intertwining filaments from end to end with a 6 inch (150 mm) scope or larger.

9 M29 (NGC 6913)

Some 10 degrees northwest of the Veil Nebula is magnitude 2.1 **Sadr (37 Gamma [γ] Cygni)**. Use this star to find the open star cluster M29, about 2 degrees south. This attractive open cluster lies on the edge of one of the obscuring bands of the Great Rift dust clouds that seem to cut through the Milky Way in the Cygnus constellation. The seven brighter stars in M29 form a dipper-like asterism.

10 THE NORTH AMERICAN NEBULA (NGC 7000)

Hop about 6 degrees from Sadr to the bright magnitude 1.3 star **Deneb (50 Alpha [α] Cygni)**, "the tail of the swan."

Another 3 degrees east of Deneb is NGC 7000. From a dark site, this giant, diffuse emission nebula can just be seen with the

naked eye, glowing softly at magnitude 5.9. Its common name arises from its shape, which is very similar to that of the North American continent and Mexico.

Take your time to fly with the Swan and seek out and explore the multitude of open clusters and double stars that are embedded in the star fields of Cygnus in the Milky Way.

The North American Nebula is a mix of bright gas and dark dust lanes. The Pelican Nebula appears to its right (west).

Among the Watery Constellations

Visible from both the Northern and Southern hemispheres, this region follows the brilliant area of the galactic center across the sky. Of several water constellations, first comes Capricornus, the Sea Goat, which was depicted on charts of long ago as a goat with the tail of a fish. Following Capricornus is Aquarius, the Water Bearer, and Pisces, the Fishes, partly shown (below) on the locater map. All three are zodiacal constellations, which the planets regularly pass. Also in this region are the constellations of Cetus, the Whale, and Piscis Austrinus, the Southern Fish—the parent of Pisces, according to ancient legend.

This starhop begins at bright Fomalhaut, near the southeastern corner of the main sky chart, before going on to browse around the celestial delights of parts of three watery constellations—Aquarius, Capricornus, and Piscis Austrinus.

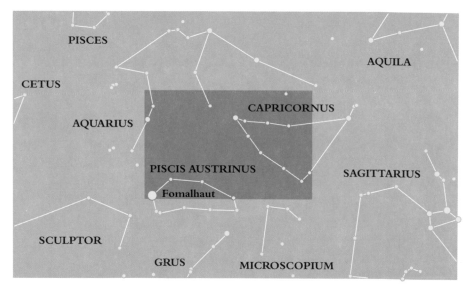

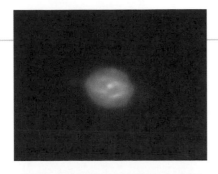

The Saturn Nebula (NGC 7009) (left) is a planetary nebula lying 3,000 light-years distant. The Helix Nebula (below) is a highlight in Aquarius.

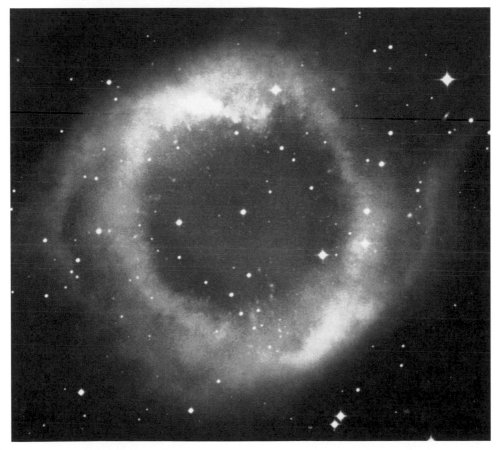

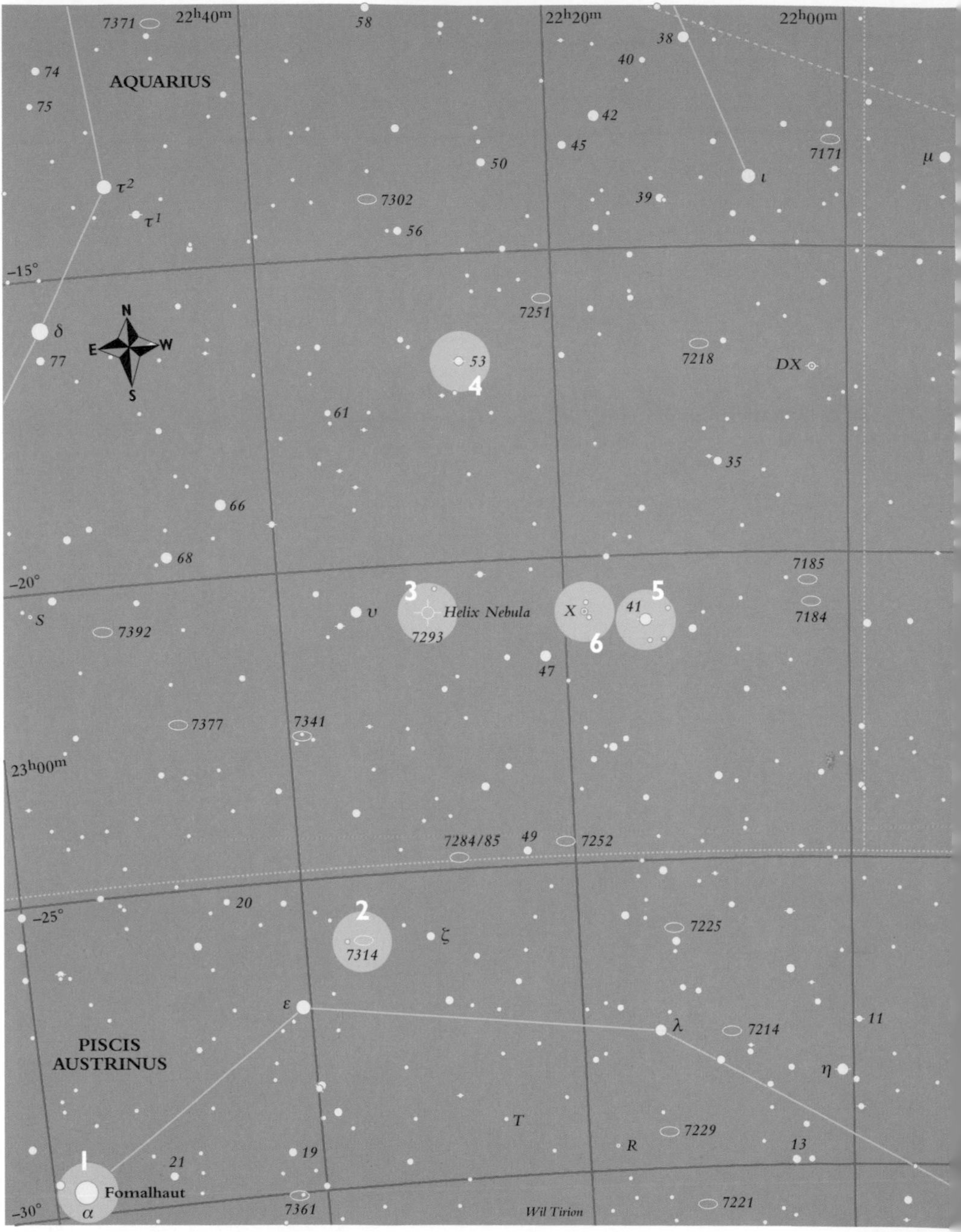

Northern and Southern Hemisphere On meridian 10 p.m. September 20

AQUARIUS

PISCIS
AUSTRINUS

Fomalhaut

Helix Nebula

Wil Tirion

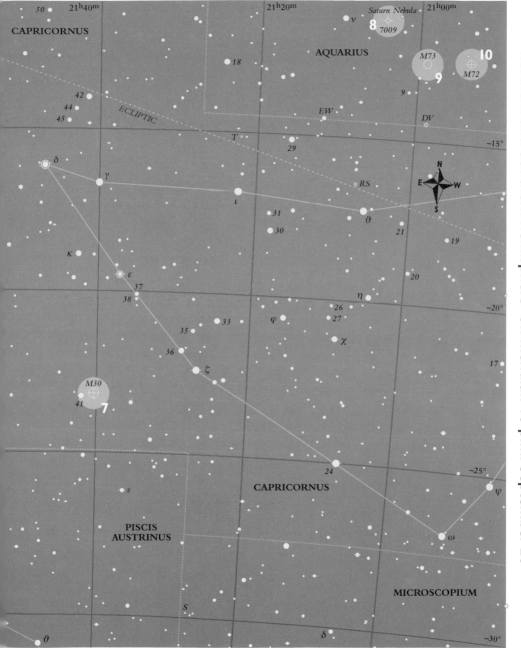

Northern and Southern Hemisphere On meridian 10 p.m. September 20

The globular cluster M30 is the only bright deep-sky object to be found in the constellation of Capricornus.

1 FOMALHAUT (24 ALPHA [α] PISCIS AUSTRINUS)

👁 Our starting point for this starhop is the brilliant magnitude 1.2 bluish star Fomalhaut, the 18th brightest star in the night sky. This star lies in quite a barren region of the southern sky and because of this has become known as "The Solitary One." Its isolation makes it very easy to find. Fomalhaut lies some 25 light-years distant from Earth and is estimated to have about twice the diameter of the Sun and to be some 14 times more luminous.

Fomalhaut's name comes from the Arabic *Fum al Hut*, meaning "mouth of the fish," as it marks the position of the Fish's mouth in the constellation of Piscis Austrinus. The Greek poet Aratos described Fomalhaut as "One large and bright by the Pourer's feet," with the pourer, of course, being Aquarius, the Water Bearer.

2 NGC 7314

To find the next object on this hop, head just over 4 degrees northwest, to **18 Epsilon [ε] Piscis Austrius**. Another 1½ degrees farther northwest will bring you to NGC 7314. In a 4 inch (100 mm) scope, this 11th magnitude spiral galaxy can be seen as a fuzzy patch of light with a small, but fairly bright, nucleus. A larger scope reveals considerably more detail surrounding its center.

3 THE HELIX NEBULA (NGC 7293)

Cross the constellation border into Aquarius and aim your scope some 5 degrees north to find the star **59 Upsilon [ʊ] Aquarii**. About 1 degree to the west of Upsilon lies the famed Helix Nebula (see Box, p. 549). The Helix is a planetary nebula— one of the best known of its type. You should just be able to capture a view of it in a good pair of binoculars on a clear, dark night, appearing as a circular patch of light about a ¼ degree in diameter. When using a scope, you need a low-power, wide-field eyepiece to really appreciate it. If you have an Oxygen III filter, you can treat yourself to a fantastic view.

4 53 AQUARII

Continue swinging your scope northward, about 4 degrees, until you find 53 Aquarii. This pretty, yellowish pair of magnitude 6 stars was much easier to separate when measured early in the last century. They were then about 10 arcseconds apart, but now the distance has shrunk to a mere 3 arcseconds. Even so, you should easily separate them with a 3 inch (75 mm) scope on a steady night.

5 41 Aquarii

⊂◎ Direct your scope 5 degrees southwest of 53 Aquarii to the next double star, 41 Aquarii. The brighter of this pair, at magnitude 5.6, has a distinctive yellow color, while its 7th magnitude companion is yellow-white. At 5 arcseconds apart, they make a fine double for small scopes.

6 X Aquarii

⊂◎ Shift your telescope 1 degree east of 41 Aquarii, then nudge it just a few arcminutes north to view the field containing X Aquarii. A long-period Mira-type variable, X is also one of the rare S-type variables, which show zirconium oxide in their spectra. This orange-red star varies between magnitude 7.5 and 14.8 over a period of 312 days, so you need to catch it near maximum to see it clearly.

7 M30 (NGC 7099)

⊂◎ To find M30, make another border crossing, into Capricornus, 8 degrees west and 2 degrees south of X Aquarii, to find the 5th magnitude 41 Capricorni. About ½ degree west of it lies the small but attractive globular cluster M30, which can just be seen with binoculars. A 3 inch (75 mm) telescope will begin to resolve some of its stars, but the view through a 6 inch (150 mm) telescope is without doubt the more attractive one.

8 The Saturn Nebula (NGC 7009)

⊂◎ Get ready to hop quite a distance to our next target. First, stop off at 4th magnitude Zeta [ζ] Capricorni, then turn northwest where, 7 degrees away, you will spot the less bright Theta [θ] Capricorni. Finally, cross back into Aquarius by moving 6 degrees farther north, to the Saturn Nebula. This delightful 8th magnitude planetary nebula, a little more than 1 degree west of Nu [ν] Aquarii, glows a beautiful blue color.

A 3 inch (75 mm) scope with moderate magnification shows the interesting elliptical shape of this object. It was given the name of the Saturn Nebula because of its almost ring-like projections that can be seen with 12 inch (300 mm) telescopes or larger.

9 M73 (NGC 6994)

Aim your scope 2 degrees southwest of the Saturn Nebula to see M73. While not exactly a spectacular sight, it has historic significance, since Charles Messier included M73 in his catalog. It is merely a tight group of four faint stars between 10th and 12th magnitude.

10 M72 (NGC 6981)

About 1 degree west of M73 is M72. Although it is moderately concentrated, 9th magnitude M72 is a relatively dim globular cluster, and one which is, unfortunately, quite difficult to resolve. A 10 inch (250 mm) scope is needed to show a hint of some of its multitude of stars, and only observers with large scopes will obtain a good view of it.

Although this patch of sky is relatively sparse, our starhop around some of the watery constellations has shown that even here there are many fascinating objects waiting to be found.

The Helix Nebula

Lying at a distance of about 450 light-years from Earth, the Helix Nebula is the closest planetary nebula to us, and therefore appears as the largest in the sky. It has been the subject of a number of serious studies.

In 1996, astronomers researching images of the Helix from the Hubble Space Telescope found thousands of comet-like gaseous fragments, especially near the inner edge of the nebula's ring. It is thought that these "knots" may have formed when new material from the star interacted with material that had been ejected earlier.

One day, billions of years from now, the Sun will have a shell, probably not unlike the Helix Nebula, but by that time, the human race will probably have long since disappeared from Earth.

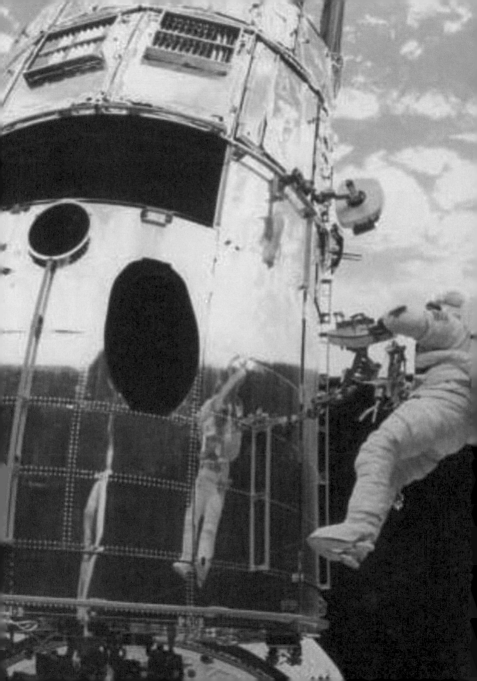

EXPLORING SPACE

*Follow in the footsteps of humankind's
explorers in the vast and dangerous
realm of space.*

HUMAN SPACEFLIGHT

Dreams of space travel became a reality in the late 1950s. As the Cold War between the United States and the Soviet Union intensified, the quest for superior spaceflight technology became another area of super-power rivalry. And a highly ambitious goal was set: putting a man on the Moon.

THE SPACE RACE

The Soviet Union took an early lead in what became known as the space race when they launched Sputnik 1 in October 1957. Sputnik 2 came a month later, carrying a live dog, Laika, into space. In 1958 the National Aeronautics and Space Admin-istration (NASA) was created in America in response to this perceived threat. And on April 12, 1961, Yuri Gagarin became the first human in space when

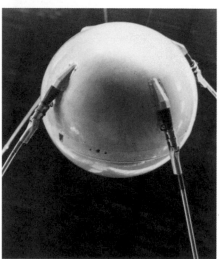

STARTING WITH SPUTNIK The launch of Sputnik 1 (left) by the Soviet Union in 1957 gave Americans a profound shock. The United States then established their own manned space program (top).

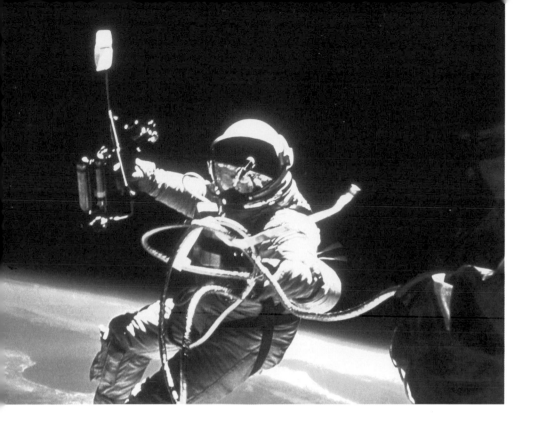

he made a single orbit of Earth aboard Vostok 1. The flight lasted only 108 minutes, from launch to landing.

Three weeks after Gagarin's feat, Alan Shepard in a U.S. Mercury spacecraft traveled beyond Earth's atmosphere but did not go into orbit. John Glenn, in another Mercury spacecraft, was the first American to reach orbit, in February 1962.

A WALK IN SPACE On June 3, 1965, Edward White in Gemini 4 became the first American to walk in space.

KENNEDY TARGETS THE MOON

In May 1961, President John F. Kennedy announced his country's goal of putting men on the Moon by the end of that decade. To achieve this, the United States laid out a complex plan. After Mercury, a two-man Gemini craft would test techniques for joining spacecraft in orbit. It would also remain aloft for two weeks, the length of a lunar trip.

However, before the first Gemini could be launched, the Soviets continued their winning streak. In 1963, Valery Bykovsky became the first person to sustain a long-duration spaceflight when he stayed in space for five days aboard Vostok 5. The first woman in space, Valentina Vladimirovna Tereshkova, launched on the final Vostok mission, Vostok 6, while Bykovsky was still in space. She orbited the Earth 48 times in 71 hours before returning safely to the surface.

In 1964, the first products of the new American push, the Gemini spacecraft, designed to carry two cosmonauts, were tested without pilots. However, in that same year, the new Soviet space-craft, Voskhod 1, performed the first two-man flight.

In 1965 Gemini 3 was the first manned Gemini flight, with Virgil Grissom and John Young.

In March, Soviet cosmonaut Alexei Leonov performed the first "space walk," drifting in space

FIRST WOMAN IN SPACE The Soviet cosmonaut, Valentina Vladimirovna Tereshkova became the first woman to reach space in 1963. The United States began a training scheme for women, but this early scheme was abandoned without one woman achieving the title of cosmonaut, despite strong performances in training. The first U.S. woman to reach space was Sally Ride in 1983.

while tethered to his spacecraft, Voskhod 2. In June, Edward White became the first American to do the same from his Gemini 4 craft.

Following Gemini, a three-man Apollo spacecraft, plus a gigantic booster rocket, was developed by the United States.

SPACE TIMELINE

1957 Launch of Sputnik 1, the first artificial satellite, by the Soviet Union starts the Space Race.

1959 First photographs of the Moon's farside by Luna 3.

1961 The Soviet Union's Yuri Gagarin becomes the first man in space.

1962 Mariner 2 discovers Venus' heavy atmosphere and hot surface.

1965 Arno Penzias and Robert Wilson discover microwave radiation left over from the Big Bang. Mariner 4 is the first spacecraft to fly past Mars.

1967 Discovery of pulsars by Jocelyn Bell-Burnell, soon identified as neutron stars.

1969 Neil Armstrong and Edwin Aldrin make the first manned landing on the Moon (Apollo 11).

1973 First flyby of Jupiter, by Pioneer 10.

1974 First close-up photos of Venus' cloud tops and Mercury's heavily cratered surface, by Mariner 10.

1975 First photos from the surface of Venus, by Venera 9.

1976 Viking 1 and 2 land on Mars in an unsuccessful attempt to detect life.

1977 Discovery of the rings of Uranus.

1978 James Christy discovers Chiron, moon of Pluto.

1979 Voyager 1 and 2 fly past Jupiter, discovering its rings. First flyby of Saturn, by Pioneer 11.

1980 Alan Guth proposes the early universe expanded extremely fast in a process called cosmic inflation. First detailed study of Saturn, by Voyager 1. Very Large Array radio telescope starts operations in New Mexico.

1983 Infrared Astronomical Satellite (IRAS) surveys the infrared sky.

1986 First flyby of Uranus, by Voyager 2.

1987 Supernova 1987A appears in the Large Magellanic Cloud.

1989 First flyby of Neptune, by Voyager 2.

1990 Hubble Space Telescope launched. Magellan spacecraft maps Venus by radar.

1991 Galileo spacecraft on the way to Jupiter makes first asteroid flyby, of 951 Gaspra. Launch of Compton Gamma-Ray Observatory.

1992 First Keck 400-inch (10-m) telescope commissioned on Mauna Kea, Hawaii.

1994 Comet Shoemaker-Levy 9 crashes into Jupiter.

1995 Galileo arrives at Jupiter. The first extrasolar planet is discovered.

1996 Milky Way found to have a massive black hole at its center.

1997 Mars Pathfinder spacecraft lands on Mars with the Sojourner rover.

1999 Launch of Chandra, X-ray satellite observatory.

2003 The first manned Chinese spacecraft, Shenzhou 5, takes off from the Gobi Desert.

The Apollo Program

■ As 1966 ended, the Gemini program showed that U.S. spacecraft could change their orbits, which the Soviet craft could not. And Apollo's booster rocket, the Saturn V, was nearing flight tests while the Soviet lunar booster was still being planned.

THE COMING OF APOLLO

The Apollo program was almost stillborn when in 1967 a fire in an Apollo craft on the ground killed all three astronauts. After a pause,

TEST FLIGHT With Earth in the background, David Scott stands in the open hatch of Apollo 9, in 1969. This flight's mission was to test the lunar lander.

missions resumed in December 1968 with the launch of Apollo 8 by the Saturn V rocket. It successfully circled the Moon for a day and returned to Earth.

Test runs The pace quickened. In March 1969, Apollo 9 tested its lunar lander in Earth orbit. This spidery craft was to take two astronauts from lunar orbit to the surface of the Moon. The two astronauts would then lift off in the upper part of the lander and rendezvous with the command module for return to Earth.

In May 1969, Apollo 10 performed a full dress-rehearsal: the crew traveled to the Moon, deployed the lunar lander, and took it to within 50,000 feet (about 15,000 m) of the surface.

SATURN V The success of the Apollo missions depended on the Saturn V rocket, which carried the crew, the lunar lander, and command module into space.

ONE GIANT LEAP

As Apollo reached its high point, the Soviet lunar program reached a new low. In early July 1969, the Soviets' lunar booster exploded on launch. Ten days later, they sent an unmanned spacecraft to the Moon, but the probe crashed.

July 16, 1969 saw Apollo 11 blast off with Neil Armstrong, Edwin Aldrin, and Michael Collins aboard. On the 20th, Armstrong and Aldrin set down on the Sea of Tranquillity. Armstrong said, "That's one small step for man, one giant leap for mankind."

Aldrin and Armstrong spent two hours on the surface collecting rock samples and setting up experiments. Their safe return to Earth marked both the end of the space race and a great scientific triumph.

MEN ON THE MOON Safety worries sent Apollo 11 to the flat Sea of Tranquillity, mirrored in Edwin Aldrin's visor (right). Later Apollos explored more interesting sites, aided by a lunar buggy (above).

LATER LANDINGS

Five more landings followed. Apollo 12 stayed longer and collected more samples. Then came the drama of Apollo 13. Only heroic efforts and ingenious improvisation saved the crew's lives after a fuel tank exploded en route to the Moon. Apollo 14 restored U.S. confidence in lunar flight, and the last three missions visited sites showing complex geology. Apollo 17 brought an end to the program in December 1972, by which time a dozen humans had walked on the Moon.

The Space Shuttle

■ After the success of the Apollo missions, the U.S. space program shifted toward developing a reusable spacecraft. Dubbed the space shuttle, this craft could orbit Earth for two weeks at a time while carrying a cargo of more than 30 tons (30 tonnes).

JUST A SPACE TRUCK

The shuttle is a "space truck." It delivers satellites into orbit and retrieves them for repair. Other payloads include scientific instrument packages for conducting experiments impossible on Earth. The Kennedy Space Center at

WEIGHTLESS PEDALING A shuttle astronaut takes his turn on an exercise bike, part of the daily routine in the spacecraft's weightless world.

A JOURNEY BEGINS The shuttle Endeavour blasts off from Cape Canaveral. Each of its three main engines has enough thrust to power two-and-a-half jumbo jets.

Cape Canaveral, on the east coast of Florida, is the center of the shuttle's operations and a major tourist attraction.

ROOM TO SPARE The shuttle's payload bay is large enough to hold a bus. The huge mechanical arm at right is used to launch, repair, and service satellites.

COMPONENTS

The shuttle has three components: the orbiter, the external tank, and the solid rocket boosters. The orbiter is the delta-wing vehicle that carries a payload into orbit. The external tank fuels the shuttle engines during launch and burns up in the atmosphere. The two solid rocket boosters that help propel the shuttle into space are ejected prior to orbit. The crew cabin is at the front of the orbiter.

THE CHALLENGER DISASTER

Columbia, the first shuttle, flew in April 1981. Three more shuttles were built and all of them flew routinely until January 28, 1986, when Challenger exploded just 73 seconds after launch, killing all seven astronauts on board,

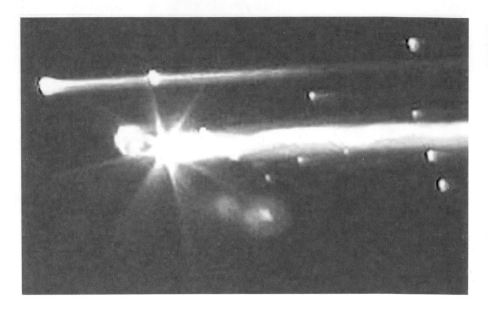

including a 37-year-old teacher, Sharon Christa McAuliffe. The fleet was grounded for two years. The cause was traced to a faulty O-ring seal on one of the solid rocket boosters, which had become brittle during a period of extreme cold at Cape Canaveral.

THE COLUMBIA The Columbia's crew (right) perished when the space shuttle disintegrated above Texas (above).

THE COLUMBIA DISASTER

In February 2003, disaster struck again when the original space shuttle, Columbia, disintegrated on reentry, killing all seven astronauts aboard. Just 15 minutes before Columbia was due to land,

while it was reentering the atmosphere at 18 times the speed of sound, spectators saw the space shuttle breaking up 39 miles (62 km) above the Earth, disintegrating into glowing trails of debris. A full NASA enquiry concluded that a piece of insulation foam, designed to protect the craft from the heat of reentry, detached from the craft at takeoff and hit the leading edge of one wing, causing the shuttle to overheat.

As a result all flights were grounded, the completion of the International Space Station was delayed, and the viability of the shuttle program was called into question.

ACCOMPLISHMENTS

Among the shuttle's many accomplishments are launching probes to Venus and Jupiter, servicing the Hubble Space Telescope, and helping to build the International Space Station.

A RUSSIAN SHUTTLE

The Soviets experimented with their own reusable space shuttle, called Buran (meaning "snowstorm"). The project began in 1976 as a response to the U.S. shuttle program. After a series of test launches the first and only orbital launch was completed successfully in 1988, without a crew, but the project lost momentum and was officially terminated in 1993. Three shuttles were built in all; one was converted into a restaurant and another was displayed in Sydney for a year during the Sydney 2000 Olympic Games.

Space Stations

■ A permanent human presence in orbit was a dream that began to come true in the early 1970s, when the Soviets launched Salyut, the first space station.

SALYUT TO MIR

Six successful Salyut missions were made between 1971 and 1986. In 1973 the U.S. launched Skylab, which made hundreds of experiments and observations before it was abandoned in 1974.

Mir The most successful space station has been the Russian Mir, launched in 1986 and occupied almost continuously until 2000. One Mir crew member spent a record 437 days in space.

MULTINATIONAL EFFORT

The International Space Station is a project using components from many countries, including the U.S., Russia, Japan, and France.

Orbital assembly began in 1998, with new modules added over following years. Its first crew took up residence in November 2000, but completion is dependent upon the space shuttle timetable. The station can house up to seven people, who will conduct experiments in manufacturing, engineering, and technology. The station will also help scientists gain biomedical knowledge for manned expeditions into the Solar System.

VISIT TO MIR A space shuttle (foreground) is just about to dock with Mir. The Russian space station was visited a number of times by shuttles in a prelude to the construction of the International Space Station. Mir was brought down from orbit in March 2001.

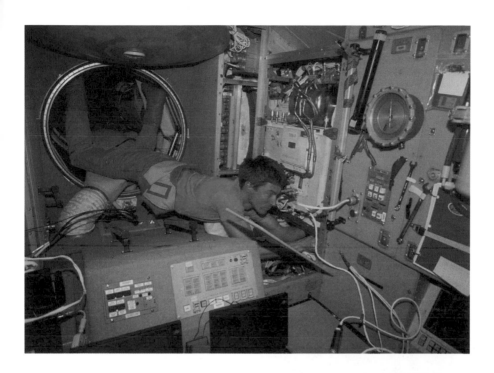

WEIGHTLESSNESS STUDY A Russian crew member of the International Space Station slides easily around the cabin in the weightless environment. The long-term effects of weightlessness—which include loss of muscle tone—will be closely studied aboard the station.

HOME IN SPACE When complete, the International Space Station will measure 356 by 290 feet (110 by 90 m), large enough for seven crew and equipment.

Human Endurance

Learning how to live in space is the major goal of the International Space Station. It circles the Earth 16 times a day at an average altitude of 250 miles (400 km). From time to time, various instrument-packed modules, experiments, and other equipment are flown up to it.

Some modules are for science, others are for manufacturing and processing materials in ways that are impossible under full gravity. These experiments will contribute to the development of science and technology. The space station's real tasks, however, revolve around the area of human health.

On March 25, 1993, cosmonaut Sergei Krikalyov returned to Earth. He had spent 311 days—more than eight months—aboard the Russian space station, Mir. (His flight lasted about as long as the travel time to or from Mars.) Krikalyov could barely stand when he first landed back on Earth, and it took a long time before his body readjusted to normal conditions.

ASTRONAUT TRAINING Long periods of training are necessary before going into space. An astronaut's training includes simulations of gravitational effects in 15-G centrifuges like this one at the training center in Cologne, Germany.

Krikalyov's experience is not unusual. Astronaut Jerry Linenger was one of five U.S. astronauts who spent time aboard Mir between 1995 and 1997; his stint lasted for four months. Linenger, a physically fit man—like most astronauts—adjusted to being weightless within a week of arriving in space, but after his return to Earth it took his body two years to recover fully.

FIGHTING BIOLOGY

Humanity evolved on a planetary surface, and we struggle against gravity from birth until death. This simple fact poses a big barrier to human spaceflight. Exploring space generally entails prolonged periods of low or zero

SUSTAINING HUMAN LIFE Biosphere experiments, such as Biosphere 2 at Oracle, Arizona, in the United States, are complex. The difficulties faced with biospheres on Earth highlight some of the problems that will be faced if humanity ever builds colonies on the Moon or another planet.

gravity, and our bodies don't know how to handle it.

Our circulation system is built to deliver blood and oxygen to a brain standing roughly 6 feet (2 m) above the toes, and to do it without putting too much or too little pressure on either extremity. In the absence of gravity the system pumps too much blood into the head, so that it grows puffy, while the legs and feet grow spindly. Muscles atrophy from lack of use. Even the body's immune system weakens for unknown reasons; colds and other infections become more prevalent and are harder to shake off.

The biggest worry, though, is bone deterioration. Every trip into space starts astronauts' bones decalcifying at an accelerated rate, and the deterioration is hard to reverse. Some astronauts have suffered up to a 20 percent reduction in bone mass (although 10 percent is more common). Besides a much-increased risk of osteoporosis, astronauts journeying eight months to Mars, say, might arrive there too weak to handle the physical effort of landing a spacecraft safely and conducting the exploration that they were sent to do. And that's without taking into account the danger if an emergency arises that requires brute strength and quick action.

To some extent, space crews have been able to counteract the problems by using treadmills, wearing elasticized clothing that forces them to exercise, and by changes in diet. Yet the experience of Sergei Krikalyov

and other astronauts on long flights is not encouraging. Much more work needs to be done before the effects are understood.

LIVING ON OTHER PLANETS

Surpassing even the difficulties of spaceflight, is the challenge of surviving on another planet, such as Mars. Mars is our closest neighbor, but the Martian environment differs greatly to that of Earth. Mars has a 24.6-hour day, a very thin carbon dioxide atmosphere, icy polar caps of water and carbon dioxide, and bracingly cool temperatures that range from 80°F (27°C) to –200°F (–130°C). Mars does appear to have near surface groundwater in some areas, which would be vital for any expedition, as the distance to Mars precludes frequent visits and large payloads.

Any of the other solid surface planets within our Solar System would pose far greater challenges than that of Mars to human habitation. Even the Moon has a much larger daily temperature fluctuation. A crewed expedition, though theoretically possible now, is unlikely to happen for decades.

PROBING SPACE

Human spaceflight is undeniably dramatic. Yet the most far-reaching discoveries about the planets have come from the data radioed back to Earth from unmanned spacecraft roaming the Solar System. Following a well-tested sequence—flybys first, then orbiters, then landers—scientists have used these robot probes to steadily increase our knowledge of Earth's neighbors.

TAKING AIM AT THE SUN
Missions that have focused on the Sun include the joint U.S. and European Solar and Heliospheric Observatory (SOHO), launched in 1995, which has studied the Sun's corona and activity from space. Ulysses (1990–), also U.S. and European, passes over the Sun's poles every five years to view it from directions we cannot see from Earth.

PROBES TO THE MOON
The Moon has been the subject of numerous probes. The Soviet Union sent the first, in 1959, and the American Pioneer 4 achieved a flyby two months later. Later that year, Luna 2 was the first probe to land on the Moon and Luna 3 was the first to see its dark side. The U.S. Lunar Observer was deliberately crashed into a polar region in 1999, searching for signs of water, but none was observed.

SCOUTING OUT MARS
Of all the planets, Mars has attracted the most attention from space agencies. When the U.S. Mariner 4 flew past in 1965, it saw a cratered landscape that resembled Earth's Moon. Later Mariners portrayed a somewhat different Mars—well cratered, but also having channels, volcanoes, and valleys.

The first successful landing on Mars was by a lander released by the Soviet Mars 3 orbiter in 1971. The Mars 2 lander had crashed into the surface a month before.

PATHFINDER Soon after touching down on Mars, the Pathfinder lander pictured a rocky red surface. The ramp (foreground) was used by the Sojourner rover.

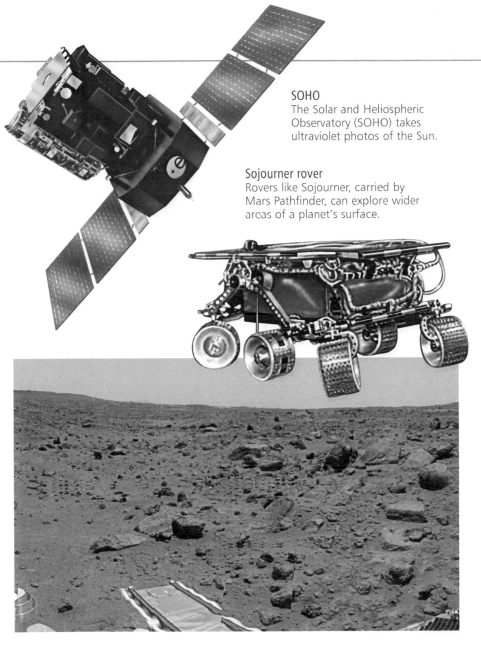

SOHO
The Solar and Heliospheric
Observatory (SOHO) takes
ultraviolet photos of the Sun.

Sojourner rover
Rovers like Sojourner, carried by
Mars Pathfinder, can explore wider
areas of a planet's surface.

Hoping to find life, NASA sent Viking 1 and 2 (1976), two pairs of orbiter and lander spacecraft. While the landers took soil samples and tested them for chemical signs of life, the orbiters took tens of thousands of photos, mapping the geology of Mars. The Viking landers found no evidence of life, past or present.

Pathfinder and Surveyor Following up on Viking, NASA's Mars Pathfinder lander and the Mars Global Surveyor orbiter arrived in 1997. Pathfinder carried a rover—Sojourner—which drove around the lander, examining rocks. Global Surveyor's detailed images are rewriting the Mars geology book, as they point to a Mars that is warmer, wetter, more volcanic, and geologically younger than scientists had previously thought.

Recent missions The Mars Climate Orbiter was launched in December 1998 but calculation errors caused a malfunction and the mission was aborted. The Mars Polar Lander then launched in January 1999, but contact was lost with the probe when it began entry into Mars' atmosphere,

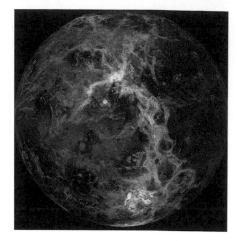

MAGELLAN'S VIEW Magellan used radar to pierce Venus's dense cloud cover and gain a detailed view of its surface.

apparently due to a software error. The Mars Odyssey 2001 met with more success, although the Mars lander portion of the project was cancelled. Odyssey is conducting mineral research and will be a communications outpost for future missions. The Mars Express Orbiter and Beagle 2 lander was launched by the European Space Agency (ESA) in June 2003 and that same month saw the launch of U.S. twin rovers, the Mars Exploration Rovers Spirit and Opportunity, in a search for water and possible signs of life.

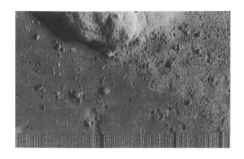

TRIUMPHS Among the success stories in recent space exploration are Magellan (being launched from a space shuttle, below), which mapped Venus, and the NEAR-Shoemaker spacecraft, which studied the asteroid Eros. NEAR sent this final image (left) before landing on the asteroid's surface.

VISITS TO HOT SPOTS

Spacecraft sent to the two planets closest to the Sun withstood scorching temperatures to radio back much of what we know about these intriguing worlds.

Mercury The planet Mercury has seen just one spacecraft, the U.S. Mariner 10, which made three flyby visits in 1974–75. Mercury was revealed as an airless Moon-like world of craters and lava plains, broiling under a Sun that makes the surface so hot (800°F/430°C) that lead would flow like water.

Venus The first attempt to reach Venus was made by the Soviet probe Venera 1 in 1961. However it was not until the next year that the first probe to reach another planet, the U.S. Mariner 2, flew past Venus. While Mariner could not see through the thick clouds shrouding the planet, its instruments detected the hot surface and dense atmosphere. Venus soon became a favorite target for Soviet spacecraft. The Venera probes included landers that radioed back photos of a surface strewn with lava rocks and gravel.

To study the planet's features, radar was used to penetrate the cloud deck from orbit. Veneras 15 and 16 (both 1983) and the U.S. Pioneer Venus (1978–92) and Magellan (1990–94) missions mapped the volcanic landscape of Venus in great detail.

EXPLORING MICRO-WORLDS

Millions of asteroids, or minor planets, orbit between Mars and Jupiter. Only a few have been visited. Bound for Jupiter, NASA's Galileo probe flew past Gaspra (1991) and Ida (1993), discovering that the latter has a tiny moon, since named Dactyl.

The NEAR-Shoemaker craft visited Mathilde in 1997 on its way to orbiting Eros in 1999. (NEAR stands for Near-Earth

---

OUT OF THIS WORLD

Voyager 1 is the most distant human-made object, at more than 7.4 billion miles (11.8 billion km) from Earth. Launched in 1977, it flew by Jupiter and Saturn in 1979–80, and is now nearing the edge of the Solar System. Voyager 1 should keep sending back data until at least 2020.

RETURN TO JUPITER Jupiter, its colorful cloud bands, the Great Red Spot, and the moon Io, can be seen in this image taken by Voyager 1 in 1979 (above). Just over 20 years later, another spacecraft— Cassini, on its way to Saturn—captured Io again, dwarfed by its mother planet (left).

VOYAGER 2 Voyager 2 was the first spacecraft to survey Uranus and Neptune. Much of what we know about these worlds comes from this single mission.

Asteroid Rendezvous.) In 2001, its mission complete, NEAR was deliberately landed on Eros, becoming the first spacecraft to touch down on an asteroid.

JUPITER AND SATURN

Beyond the asteroid belt lie the gas giants. Flight times to these distant planets are measured in years, rather than in months as for the inner planets. Only U.S. spacecraft have ventured this far.

Jupiter Pioneer 10 made the first detailed portrait of Jupiter in a 1973 flyby, measuring the planet's powerful magnetic field and imaging its turbulent atmosphere. Pioneer 11 followed the year after, sharpening the picture.

The much more sophisticated Voyager probes flew past Jupiter in 1979, sending back fascinating images of the giant planet's atmosphere and its varied family of moons. Voyager 2 also discovered that Jupiter has a thin ring system.

In 1995, the Galileo spacecraft shot an entry probe into the Jovian atmosphere. As it fell, the probe's instruments sampled gases and measured wind speeds and temperatures before being crushed after only 58 minutes by the planet's enormous gravity. The main craft then spent several years surveying Jupiter and its moons. It was perfectly placed to capture the impact of Comet Shoemaker-Levy into the clouds of Jupiter in 1994 and suffered a similar fate itself in 2003 when it was crashed into Jupiter to avoid a possible collision with Europa.

Saturn Reaching Saturn in 1979, Pioneer 11 discovered new rings and drew the first close-up portrait of the Saturnian realm.

TAKING THE PLUNGE In 1995, the Galileo spacecraft's cone-shaped probe plunged into Jupiter's atmosphere. It radioed back information for about an hour before being crushed by the atmosphere.

GANYMEDE Jupiter's moon Ganymede fascinates scientists because of its diverse surface features. An image from Galileo shows impact craters on grooved terrain.

CASSINI The Cassini orbiter carries the Huygens probe, which will slowly descend through the smoggy atmosphere of Saturn's moon Titan in July 2004.

PROBE TIMELINE

1958 The United States launch Pioneer 0. Pioneers 0 to 3 all fail.
1959 The Soviets launch the first successful space probe, Luna 1. Luna 2 is crashed onto the Moon. Luna 3 sees the lunar farside. Meanwhile, the U.S. flies Pioneer 4 past the Moon.
1961 The U.S. launches the first two Ranger probes unsuccessfully. Venera 1, the first Soviet Venus probe, also fails.
1962 The U.S. Mariner 1 fails to reach Venus, but Mariner 2 is successful.
1963 The first successful Ranger probe (Ranger 7), photographs the Moon.
1964 Mariner 4 flies past Mars. Rangers 8 and 9 photograph the Moon.
1966 The Soviets' Luna 9 lands on the Moon. Soon after, Surveyor 1 is the first U.S. Moon probe to land safely.
1967 Venera 4 reaches Venus. Mariner 5 flies past Venus. Surveyors 3, 5 and 6 land on the Moon.
1968 Surveyor 7 lands on the Moon.
1969 Veneras 5 and 6 reach Venus. Mariners 6 and 7 fly past Mars.
1970 Venera 7 is the first craft to land on another planet—Venus.
1971 Mariner 9 orbits Mars.
1972 Venera 8 lands on Venus.
1973 Pioneer 10 reaches Jupiter.
1974 Mariner 10 reaches two planets (Venus and Mercury) in a single mission. Pioneer 11 reaches Jupiter.

1975 Veneras 9 and 10 reach Venus.
1976 Vikings 1 and 2 land on Mars.
1978 Veneras 11 and 12 land on Venus.
1979 Pioneer 11 reaches Saturn. Voyagers 1 and 2 reach Jupiter.
1980 Voyager 1 reaches Saturn.
1981 Voyager 2 reaches Saturn. Veneras 13 and 14 land on Venus.
1983 Venera 15 and 16 (the last), enter orbit around Venus and map its surface.
1986 Voyager 2 reaches Uranus. Giotto and Vega 1 and 2 reach Halley's comet.
1989 Voyager 2 reaches Neptune.
1990 The Magellan probe reaches Venus.
1992 The NASA–ESA Ulysses probe arrives at Jupiter.
1994 NASA's Clementine probe orbits and maps the Moon.
1995 The Galileo probe reaches Jupiter and descends into its atmosphere.
1996 Launch of the SOHO probe.
1997 Mars Pathfinder lands on Mars. Cassini-Huygens Saturn probe launched.
1998 NASA's Mars Global Surveyor begins mapping the surface of Mars.
2000 The probe NEAR-Shoemaker becomes the first to orbit, map and land on an asteroid.
2003 Last transmission from Pioneer 10 before losing contact. Mars Express, MUSES-C (now called Hayabusa) and the Mars Exploration rovers are launched.
2004 U.S. rovers explore Mars' surface.

Voyagers 1 and 2 arrived in 1980 and 1981. As at Jupiter, they detailed Saturn's features, finding new rings and moons and mapping the racing clouds of the planet's atmosphere.

Cassini was launched in 1997 for a rendezvous with Saturn in 2004. It will orbit the ringed planet and also drop the ESA's Huygens probe onto Saturn's largest moon, Titan.

URANUS AND NEPTUNE

After their surveys of Saturn, Voyager 1 and both Pioneer probes headed out of the Solar System, while Voyager 2 took aim at Uranus and Neptune.

Uranus Arriving at Uranus in 1986, Voyager 2 found a featureless planet shrouded in a blue haze of methane. In comparison to this seemingly bland world, the satellites of Uranus were of greater interest with their distinctive and complicated geologies.

Neptune Voyager 2 completed its tour of the gas giants in 1989, when it reached Neptune. It found an active planet with giant storms in its atmosphere, and frosts and a thin atmosphere on its large moon, Triton. Its main mission completed, Voyager 2 moved out of the Solar System.

To THE EDGE

Only Pluto remains unvisited, primarily for budgetary reasons.

Comets that come relatively close to Earth are targets for study. The first rendezvous of a probe with a comet was that of Giotto with Halley's Comet in late 1985.

The Stardust spacecraft has collected particles from the tail of Comet Wild 2 in 2004 for return to Earth in 2006 and Deep Impact, launching in late 2004, will fire a projectile at Comet Tempel 1 in 2005 to observe the results.

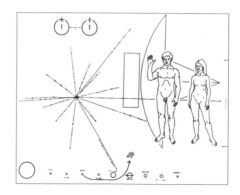

PIONEER'S MESSAGE This graphic of Earth's inhabitants and their position was sent with Pioneers 10 and 11.

FUTURE MISSIONS

If just some of the plans being made by space agencies come to pass, this century promises to be a new era of exploration.

MARS

The Mars Reconnaissance Orbiter will examine the surface of Mars in great detail in 2005. It will also be able to scan below the surface for water and ice. In 2009 the Mars Science Laboratory rover is expected to provide more detail than ever before. The Mars Reconnaissance Orbiter will aid this mission by scanning Mars' surface thoroughly for landing sites.

MARS EXPRESS The Mars Express orbiter launched from Kazakhstan in June 2003. This artist's impression shows the orbiter deploying the Beagle 2 lander.

BEAGLE 2 Once on the surface of Mars, the Beagle 2 probe will begin to collect samples from inside rocks (and under them) and test them for signs of life.

OTHER PLANNED MISSIONS

Mars is a hot-spot of future space exploration, but there are several other targets to be explored.

Comets The Deep Impact mission plans to hit the nucleus of Comet Tempel 1 in mid-2005 with a projectile and study the results.

Europa Life may be present in an ocean beneath the icy skin of Jupiter's moon, Europa. To test this, NASA is planning a Europa Orbiter, to be launched in 2006, arriving at Jupiter in 2010.

Asteroids Hayabusa (formerly known as MUSES-C)—launched by Japan in May 2003—will visit asteroid 1998 SF36 in 2005. The flightplan calls for Hayabusa to orbit the asteroid and pick up surface samples, returning them to Earth in 2007.

Mercury In 2008, a U.S. mission, Messenger, will fly to Mercury to complete Mariner 10's survey of the planet, arriving in 2009.

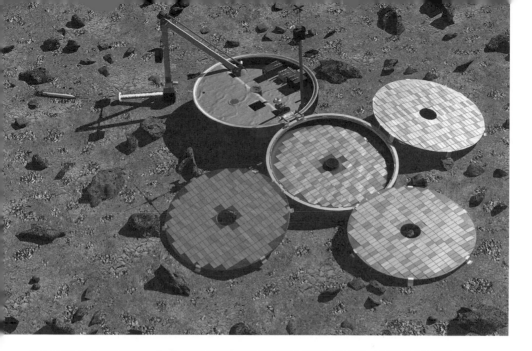

SOME FUTURE MISSIONS

SPACECRAFT	COUNTRY	TARGET	ARRIVAL
Lunar-A*	Japan	the Moon	2003
Mars Express*	Europe	Mars	2003
Mars Exploration*	USA	Mars	2004
Cassini-Huygens*	USA/Europe	Saturn and Titan	2004
Stardust*	USA	Comet Wild 2	2004
Hayabusa*	Japan	asteroid 1998 SF36	2005
Deep Impact	USA	Comet Tempel 1	2005
Mars Reconnaissance	USA	Mars	2006
Messenger	USA	Mercury	2009
Europa Orbiter	USA	Jupiter's moon, Europa	2011

* Indicates missions already in flight.

The Invasion of Mars

■ Establishing a colony on another world might be the next step for a species that seems eternally restless. Mars has always exerted a strong tug on the human imagination. How would a Martian colony establish itself? Here is one possible sequence of events, all based on the use of current technology.

SCOUTS COME FIRST

A scouting-out expedition would arrive well before the colonists. A scout rocket would contain both an Earth-return spacecraft and an atmosphere-processing factory. The factory would create methane and water using Martian air (carbon dioxide) and hydrogen brought from Earth. Methane and water could be converted into other necessities such as oxygen.

Leap-frog expeditions A crew of four to six astronauts would land two years after the rocket, and they would live on the surface in habitat modules. Launched toward Mars with them would be a second atmosphere-processing factory and Earth-return vehicle.

A LUNAR COLONY?

A human colony on the Moon is not yet deemed feasible, mainly on grounds of cost and on the Moon's lack of minerals needed on Earth. More likely is a scientific station, manned by crews in rotation.

The Moon would be an ideal site for astronomical observations. Radio telescopes could be sited on the lunar far side, shielded from Earth and its "chatter" of human broad-casting and telecommunications. Optical telescopes would also benefit from a lunar site. The lack of a filtering atmosphere means that they would enjoy the same, clear-sighted view of the universe as the orbiting Hubble Space Telescope.

This second vehicle would be set down elsewhere to begin making supplies for the next crew. The first astronauts would come back in the initial Earth-return space-craft, leaving the scene set for the second expedition's arrival.

There would probably have to to be several such "leap-frog" expeditions before Mars was ready to receive its first colonists.

Colonies follow

A colony could develop from clusters of expeditions sent to one area. Left-behind habitat modules could be recycled into living quarters for a colony. The tougher problem is of building a Martian economy. This relies largely on what minerals are available on Mars and what is needed from Earth to convert

MARTIAN CITY This artist's conception of a human settlement on Mars may seem far-fetched, but the decades ahead may well see something like it come to pass.

those minerals into a usable form. In any case, given our present knowledge of Mars, little or no technological barrier stands in the way of creating a permanent human society on the Red Planet.

The Future of Space Travel

■ We are all familiar with TV images of rockets lifting off in clouds of smoke and sheets of flame. Launching rockets this way has been going on since the 1940s. Now, however, new technologies loom on the horizon. These promise much more efficient ways of moving people and payloads through space, as once a cargo is in orbit around Earth, sending it somewhere else in the Solar System does not need the high acceleration and thrust of a chemical rocket. An engine producing a much lower thrust can do the job just as well and more efficiently. But because such an engine provides only very gentle accelerations, travel times may be long.

This "new" technology has been tested since the 1960s. It is called the ion drive.

SUCCESSFUL TEST This artist's impression shows the 1999 flyby of the Braille asteroid by Deep Space 1. The mission successfully tested an ion drive.

ION DRIVES

NASA launched Deep Space 1 in 1998 to test an ion drive engine. This works by taking atoms, giving them an electrical charge, and accelerating them in an electric field. A stream of ionized atoms shoots out the back of the engine, producing a thrust which moves the spacecraft forward. An ion drive can run for months at full throttle.

Deep Space 1 and its ion drive worked well. Engineers are soon expecting to build drives that are much more powerful.

SOLAR SAILING

Another idea for moving through space is solar sailing—using the pressure of sunlight to blow a spacecraft from one planet to the next. Such a spacecraft would have a huge sail, perhaps 1/2 mile (1 km) wide. Beyond the atmosphere, the spacecraft's computers would unfurl the sail, made from highly reflective materials. Catching sunlight in this way gives the craft a gentle but endless push.

X-33 Developers of new spacecraft contend with an array of technological, financial, and political difficulties. The sleek X-33, for example, was to be a test bed for a new generation of reusable launch vehicles. After a run of problems, the project was cancelled by NASA in 2001 before the first test flight.

NUCLEAR POWER

Another option is to develop a nuclear-powered rocket. The great advantage here is that the technology is well understood.

OLD AND NEW Visionaries and science-fiction writers have been suggesting the idea of the space elevator (above) since the 1890s. The technology to achieve this is not yet available. However, nuclear power is one option that could be used. Nuclear rocket engines (left), meant to be part of a mission to Mars, were test-fired in Nevada in the 1960s. The NERVA (Nuclear Engine for Rocket Vehicle Applications) program was abandoned in 1972 when nuclear power lost public support.

And the benefits for spaceflight are clear-cut: a nuclear rocket offers a lot of power compared with a chemical one. A trip out to Mars, for example, might last as little as four months, half the time for a low-energy trip. This means that astronauts would be exposed to zero gravity for a much shorter time. The craft would also be reusable.

A nuclear Mars rocket would not lift off from the ground. Chemical engines would get the rocket into orbit, and then it would switch to nuclear fuel.

Nuclear rocket engines were in fact tested in the 1960s, but the program ended after public support for nuclear technology development evaporated in the early 1970s.

A SPACE ELEVATOR

Another concept for the future is the "space elevator." A cable is run from Earth's surface to geostationary orbit, a point at an altitude of 22,200 miles (35,800 km). The plan is that cargoes could be shuttled along the cable. Once lifted into geostationary orbit, spacecraft could leave for destinations in the solar system using conventional rockets or other means. Much less propulsion power would be required at this elevation as spacecraft would not need to fight against the pull of Earth's gravity.

The elevator would have to be built by sending a spacecraft to geostationary orbit over the equator, that is, the satellite would remain fixed in the sky over one spot on Earth. From there, the satellite would drop a cable to the ground, and extend a cable of equal length upward from its orbit for balance. A tower 30 miles (50 km) high would then anchor the bottom of the cable.

In 1999 a NASA workshop studied the idea and developed plans for its implementation. These plans identified the necessary technologies, which include high-strength materials for the cable and for the tether tower, the ability to deploy and control such long structures and electromagnetic propulsion systems for the vehicles. The NASA workshop concluded that the project should be feasible by the end of this century.

SEARCHING FOR LIFE

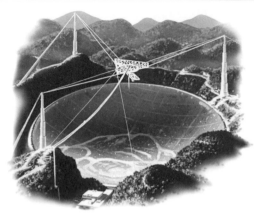

MESSAGE TO HERCULES In 1974, the Arecibo radio telescope sent a message to space about human life on Earth. It will take about 25,000 years to reach its target: the M13 star cluster in Hercules.

MARTIAN METEORITE

Sometimes evidence of possible extraterrestrial life is found very close to hand. In 1996, scientists were studying a Martian meteorite that fell in Antarctica 13,000 years ago. They discovered what appeared to be fossilized bacteria that may have originated on Mars's ancient surface. Not everyone is convinced, however. Other scientists suggest that the tube-shaped structures may be the remains of compounds that entered the rock in Antarctica. The debate continues.

A re we alone? Of all the big questions astronomers grapple with, none is bigger than the inquiry into whether or not life exists elsewhere.

SOLAR SYSTEM SEARCH

Three places in the Solar System are deemed worthy of exploration for signs of life.

Mars The Red Planet has features that seem to have been formed by flowing water. If life did develop on Mars, these "wetlands" would be prime places to look.

Europa A similar watery world may exist on the Jovian moon Europa, beneath a layer of ice.

Titan Scientists want to probe Titan, Saturn's largest satellite. A variety of organic compounds— the building blocks of living things—have been detected in Titan's thick atmosphere.

SEARCHING THE COSMOS

The search for extraterrestrial life (SETI) began in the 1960s using radio telescopes to detect unusual signals from space. A more comprehensive search began in

the 1990s with Project Phoenix. Computers sift through natural signals from space to find signals that could only have been generated artificially. At any one time, tens of millions of channels can be monitored.

Earth calling In 1974, the Arecibo radio telescope sent a complex message written in binary code to M13, the Hercules

A MARTIAN LAKE? A huge lake might once have filled the bluish area in this Viking image of Mars. Scientists are targeting such areas to search for life.

Cluster. The message included the chemical formulas for the molecular components of DNA. In effect, we were telling possible alien listeners what to expect if they dropped in for a visit.

GLOSSARY

Absolute magnitude How bright a star would appear, in magnitudes, at a standard distance of 32.6 light-years from Earth.

Active galaxy A galaxy with a central black hole that is emitting a relatively large amount of radiation.

Altazimuth mounting A simple telescope mounting that swings from side to side and up and down.

Aperture The diameter of a telescope's main light-collecting optics. Also, the diameter of a binocular lens.

Aphelion The farthest distance from the Sun on a planet or comet's orbit.

Apparent magnitude The visible brightness of a star (or any other celestial object) as seen from the Earth.

Apparition A period when a planet or comet is visible in the night sky.

Arcminute A unit of angular measure equal to $\frac{1}{60}$ of a degree; the Moon and Sun are about 30 arcminutes across.

Arcsecond A unit of angular measure equal to $\frac{1}{60}$ of an arcminute; Jupiter averages some 44 arcseconds across.

Asterism A recognizable pattern or shape created by a group of stars, smaller in area than a constellation.

Asteroid Also called a minor planet, a small rocky object with a diameter of less than 600 miles (1,000 km) orbiting the Sun.

Asteroid belt The large number of asteroids orbiting the Sun in the ecliptic between the orbits of Mars and Jupiter.

Astrometry The precise measurement of positions and motions of celestial bodies.

Astronomical unit (AU) The average distance between Earth and the Sun, about 93 million miles (150 million km).

Astrophotography Photography of the night sky.

Astrophysics The study of the dynamics, chemical properties, and evolution of celestial bodies.

Atmosphere The layer of gases attached to a planet or moon by gravity.

Aurora Curtains and arcs of light in the sky over middle and high latitudes. They are caused by particles from the Sun hitting Earth's atmosphere and causing some of its gases to glow.

Axis The imaginary line through the center of a planet, star, or galaxy around which it rotates; also, a shaft around which a telescope mounting pivots.

Big Bang The explosion of a small, very hot lump of matter about 15 billion years ago that marked the birth of the universe, according to the current theory of the universe's origin.

Binary star Two stars linked by mutual gravity and revolving around a common center of mass (see double star).

Black hole An object so dense that no light or other radiation can escape from inside it.

Bolide A very bright, long-duration fireball that explodes or appears to fragment.

Cadiotropic telescope A telescope, such as a Matsukov or Schmidt-Cassegrain, that uses both mirrors and lenses to form an image.

Celestial equator The imaginary line encircling the sky midway between the celestial poles.

Celestial poles The imaginary points on the sky where Earth's rotation axis, extended infinitely, would touch the imaginary celestial sphere.

Celestial sphere The imaginary sphere enveloping Earth upon which the stars, galaxies, and other celestial objects all appear to lie.

Chromosphere In the Sun, the thin layer of atmosphere lying just above the photosphere (visible surface) and below the corona.

Comet A small body composed of ice and dust that orbits the Sun on an elongated path.

Conjunction The moment when two celestial objects lie closest together in the sky.

Constellation One of the 88 official patterns of stars that divide the sky into sections.

Corona, solar The high temperature outermost atmosphere of the Sun, visible from Earth only during a total solar eclipse.

Declination The angular distance of a celestial object north or south of the celestial equator.

Deep-sky object A celestial object located beyond the Solar System.

Degree A unit of angular measure equal to $\frac{1}{360}$ of a circle.

Dobsonian mount A simple type of altazimuth mount.

Double star Two stars that appear close together in the sky. Optical doubles are chance alignments of the stars; binary or multiple systems are linked by gravity.

Dust lane The thin disk of a spiral galaxy has a layer of gas and dust, that, when seen edge-on, looks like a thin lane among the stars of the galaxy.

Eclipse When one celestial body passes in front of another, dimming or obscuring its light.

Ecliptic The apparent path of the Sun around the celestial sphere; marks the plane of Earth's orbit.

Ellipse The oval, closed path followed by a celestial object moving under the influence of gravity, e.g. Earth around the Sun.

Elongation The angle between Mercury or Venus and the Sun; also used for satellites and their planet. Maximum elongation describes the greatest separation.

Emission nebula A cloud of gas glowing as the gas re-emits energy absorbed from a nearby hot star.

Equatorial mount A telescope mount with one axis parallel to the Earth's rotational axis, so the motion of the heavens can be followed with a single movement.

Eyepiece A group of small lenses used as a single unit to magnify the image produced by a telescope's objective, or main, lens.

Field of view The amount of sky visible through the eyepiece of an optical instrument, such as a pair of binoculars or a telescope.

Finderscope Also called a finder, a small, low-power telescope attached to and aligned with a larger one that allows you to locate the general area of sky.

Focal length The distance between the main lens or mirror of a telescope and the point where the light from it comes to a focus.

Galaxy A huge gathering of stars, gas, and dust, bound by gravity and having a mass ranging from 100,000 to 10 trillion times that of the Sun.

Gamma rays Radiation with a wavelength shorter than X-rays.

Gas-giant planet A planet whose composition is dominated by hydrogen, e.g. Jupiter, Saturn, Uranus, and Neptune.

Gibbous The phase of a moon or a planet when it appears greater than a half disk, but less than a full disk.

Globular star cluster A spherical cluster that may contain over a million older stars.

Granulation Mottling of the Sun's photosphere caused by updwelling cells of convecting gas breaking down into smaller cells.

Infrared (IR) Radiation with wavelengths just longer than those of visible light.

Ion tail The straight, bluish tail of ionized gas that streams out behind a comet when heated.

Kuiper belt The region of the Solar System, outside the orbit of the planets, that contains icy planetesimals.

Light-year The distance that light travels in one year, about 6 trillion miles (9.5 trillion km).

Limb The edge of a celestial body such as the Sun, Moon, or planets.

Local Group A gathering of about 30 nearby galaxies, including the Milky Way.

M objects Star clusters, nebulas, and galaxies in the Messier list.

Magnitude A logarithmic unit used to measure the brightness of celestial objects. Apparent magnitude describes how bright a star looks from Earth, while absolute magnitude is its brightness if placed at a distance of 32.6 light-years. The lower the magnitude, the brighter the star.

Mare (plural Maria) A plain of congealed lava on the surface of the Moon, darker than the surrounding areas.

Meridian An imaginary line on the sky that runs due north and south, passing through the zenith.

Meteor The bright, transient streak of light produced by a meteoroid, a piece of space debris, burning up as it enters Earth's atmosphere at high speed.

Meteorite The name given to any piece of interplanetary debris that reaches Earth's surface intact.

Microwave Radiation with wavelengths measured in millimeters.

Nebula A cloud of gas or dust in space; may be dark or luminous.

Nebulosity The presence of faint gas, visible because illuminated.

Neutron star A massive star's collapsed remnant, consisting almost wholly of very densely packed neutrons. May be visible as a pulsar.

NGC objects Galaxies, star clusters, and nebulas listed in the New General Catalogue.

Nova A white dwarf star in a binary system that brightens suddenly by several magnitudes as gas pulled away from its companion star explodes in a thermonuclear reaction.

Nucleus The central core of a galaxy or comet.

Occultation The covering up of one celestial object by a larger one, such as the Moon passing in front of a star or planet, as seen from Earth.

Open star cluster A group of a few hundred relatively young stars bound together by gravity.

Opposition The point in a planet's orbit when it appears opposite the Sun in the sky.

Orbit The path of an object as it moves through space under the control of another's gravity.

Parallax The apparent change in position of a nearby object relative to a more distant background when viewed from different points; it is used to determine distances to nearby stars.

Penumbra The outer part of an eclipse shadow; and the lighter area surrounding a sunspot.

Perihelion A planet or comet's closest approach to the Sun.

Photosphere The visible surface of the Sun.

Planetary nebula A shell of gas blown off by a star late in its life.

Planetesimal A small, rocky body; one of the small bodies that coalesced to form the planets.

Precession A slow, periodic wobble in the Earth's axis caused by the pull of the Sun and Moon.

Primary star The brighter component in a double star.

Pulsar An old, rapidly spinning star that flashes bursts of radio (and occasionally optical) energy.

Quasar Short for quasi-stellar radio source, quasars are thought to be the active nuclei of very distant galaxies.

Radiant The point on the sky from where a shower of meteors appears to come.

Radio astronomy The study of celestial bodies by means of the radio waves that they emit and absorb.

Red giant A large, cool, red star in a late stage of its life.

Reflection nebula A cloud of dust or gas visible because it reflects light from nearby stars.

Reflector A telescope that forms an image using mirrors.

Refractor A telescope that forms an image using an objective lens.

Resolving power The ability of a telescope to show two closely spaced objects as separate.

Retrograde motion The apparent backward (westward) motion of a celestial body relative to the stars as the Earth overtakes it because of its greater orbital speed.

Right ascension (RA) The celestial coordinate analogous to longitude on Earth.

Satellite Any small object orbiting a larger one, although the term is most often used for rocky or artificial objects orbiting a planet.

Secondary star The companion, or less bright star, in a double star.

Seeing A measure of the steadiness of the atmosphere. Good seeing is essential to using high magnifications when observing.

Sidereal period The time needed for a planet or moon to make one rotation, or revolution around its primary body, relative to the stars.

Solar flare A sudden release of magnetic energy in or near the Sun's photosphere emitting radiation into space.

Solar wind A ceaseless, but variable, high-speed stream of charged particles flowing out into space from the Sun.

Spectroscopy The analysis of light to determine, by studying the spectral lines, the chemical composition and conditions of the object producing it, as well as that object's motion and velocity toward or away from Earth.

Sunspot A dark, highly magnetic region on the Sun's surface that is cooler than the surrounding area.

Supernova The explosion of a massive star in which it blows off its outer atmosphere and briefly equals a galaxy in brightness.

Supernova remnant An expanding cloud of gas thrown into space by a supernova explosion.

Terrestrial planet A planet with a mainly rocky composition, e.g. Mercury, Venus, Earth, and Mars.

Umbra The dark, inner part of an eclipse shadow. Also, the dark central part of a sunspot.

Variable star Any star whose brightness appears to change.

Wavelength The distance between two successive waves of energy passing through space.

White dwarf The small, very hot but faint remnant of a star that remains after the red giant stage.

X-rays Radiation with wavelengths between ultraviolet and gamma rays.

INDEX

Page numbers in *italics* indicate illustrations and photos.

Picture Credits

Key t=top; l=left; r=right; tl=top left; tc=top center; tr=top right; cl=center left; c=center; cr=center right; b=bottom; bl=bottom left; bc=bottom center; br=bottom right

AAO = Anglo-Australian Observatory; AAP = Australian Associated Press; AD = Alan Dyer; AF = Akira Fujii; ANU = Australian National University; APL/CBT = Australian Picture Library/Corbis; ARL = Ardea London; AP = Astro Photo; ASP = Astronomical Society of the Pacific; ASU = Arizona State University; BA = Bridgeman Art Library; BD = Ben Davidson; B&SF = Bill and Sally Fletcher; CFHT = Canada-France-Hawaii Telescope Corporation; CI – Celestial Image Co; COR = Corel Corp.; DMI – David Malin Images; DS = Digital Stock; ESA = European Space Agency; ESP = F. Espenak; GG = George Greaney; AIC = I.A. Crawford; JC = John Chuma; JN = Jack Newton; LCC = Lee C. Coombs; LD = Luke Dodd; MAP = D. Malin/Australian Anglo Telescope Planetarium; MIC = Meade Instruments Corporation; MSSSO = Mount Stromlo and Siding Spring Observatories; NASA/HHT = NASA and the Hubble Heritage Team; NASA/JPL = NASA/Jet Propulsion Laboratory; NASA = National Aeronautics and Space Administration; NOAO = National Optical Astronomy Observatory; NRAO/AUI = National Radio Astronomy Observatory/Associated Universities, Inc; OS = Oliver Strewe; OTB = Orion Telescopes and Binoculars; PD = Photodisc; PE = PhotoEssentials; ROE = Royal Observatory, Edinburgh; RRR = Rev. Ronald Royer; SB = Stockbyte; SCSU = South Carolina State University; SF/PE = Space Frontiers/Planet Earth Pictures; SPL = Science Photo Library; STScI = Space Telescope Science Institute; T&DH = Tony and Daphne Hallas; TPL = photolibrary.com; TSA = Tom Stack & Associates; UCO/LO = UC Regents/Lick Observatory; UA = University of Arizona;

1cl Royal Society London/BA 2c DS 3 DS 4c NASA/HHT/C.R. O'Dell/Vanderbilt University 6–7c NASA/Donald Walter (SCSU)/Paul Scowen and Brian Moore (ASU) 8–9c COR 9t DS 10–11c DS 12c NASA/HHT 23c DS 27c DS 31t DS 32bl DS 33t COR 34tr DS 35t DS 37c PD 40b MIC 41t DS 43t DS 47c NASA/HHT 48c PD 49c DS 55br, t DS 56tr NOAO 57t NASA 59c NASA/JPL 61c PE 62bl NASA/JPL 63t SB 64bl DS 65t PE 69bl, t DS 71bl DS 73t SB 74bl PE 75c DS 76br NASA 79t DS 81bl DS t NASA/JPL 83c NASA 84c DS 87t DS 89b DS 90c, cr DS **91**c NASA/JPL **93**t DS **95**b DS **97**t DS **100**c NASA/HHT/ESA and J. Hester (ASU) **101**c APL/CBT/Roger Ressmeyer **102**cl ASP **103**t DS **106**bl NASA **107**c NASA **108**bl NRAO/AUI **109**tr NASA **110**bl, tr DS **111**t DS **112**tr NASA **113**c NASA **114–115**c APL/CBT/Johnathan Blair **115**c OS **116**c NASA/HHT **117**c APL/CBT/Roger Ressmeyer **119**cr OS **121**br PD t DS **122**br, tl OS **124**bl OS **125**t DS **129**bl MIC tr OTB **130**b OS **131**bl OS t DS **133**b OS t DS **134**bl OS **135**br PD t DS **136**c NASA/HHT **137**c DS **138**b OS **145**t DS **148**br NASA **149**t PD **152**bl MIC **153**t DS **154**c TPL/SPL/NASA **155**c TPL/ESP **156**cr TPL/ESP **157**br, tr TPL/ESP **159**c UCO/LO **161**c UCO/LO **163**cl AD cl AF **165**bl TPL/ESP tr AF **166**bl TPL/ESP **167**bl TPL/Derke/O'Hara cr TPL/ESP **168**c TPL/SPL/MSSSO, ANU **169**bc AF **171**tl, tr AD **173**br TPL/SPL/John Sanford tr AF **174**bl, br AF **175**cr AD **176**br TPL/SPL/RRR **177**tr AF **178**bc, bl, br LCC **179**cr TPL/SPL/RRR tr AF **180**bl AF **181**br, cr, tr AF **182**br TSA **183**cr, tl AF **184**br Peter H Smith/UA Lunar and Planetary Laboratory/NASA **185**t SF/PE **186**bl TPL/SPL/Eurelios **187**bl TPL/SPL/John Sanford cr ARL/George Jackson **189**br TPL/SPL/Jack Finck t TPL/SPL/John Thomas **191**bl, t AF **192**c TPL/SPL/STScI/NASA **193**c TPL/SPL/Dr Rudolph Schild **194**br NOAO **195**cr TPL/SPL/CFHT/Jean-Charles Cuillandre **196**bl AAO **197**t AAO **198**tr AAO **199**br NOAO tr AAO **200**bl AF **201**br TPL/SPL/NOAO tr TPL/SPL/Dr Rudolph Schild **203**c TPL/SPL/T&DH **204**br AF **205**t TPL/SPL/CI **206**cr DMI/IAC **207**cr AD **208**bl TPL/SPL **209**bl, cr TPL/SPL/LD **211**c TPL/BA **212**c NASA/HHT **213**c NOAO **216**bl Mullard Radio Astronomy Observatory, Cambridge, David Busher, Chris Haniff, John Baldwin and Peter Warner **217**tr AAO **242**br AAO **243**tr MSSSO/SPL **268**c NASA/HHT **269**c AAO **273**tr PE **293**tl DS **305**tl PD **335**tl DS **347**tl PE **355**tl DS **365**tl DS **368–369**c AAO **375**bl AAO cr AF **376**tl BD **377**bc OS **383**cl B&SF/TSA cl AF **386**b MAP/IAC **391**t AF **396**tr GG **397**t LCC **399**b AAO/ROE t TPL/SPL/Dr Jean Lorre **402**t NOAO **407**bl AF t TPL/SPL/LD **411**tl AAO **414**br AAO **417**bl, t TPL/SPL **420**t AF **425**b AF tl TPL/SPL/John Sanford **428**t ASP/T&DH **433**br AF t TPL/JC **436**t TPL/JC tl AAO **441**tr AAO **443**bl AF t TPL/SPL/LD **446**t TPL/SPL/LD **451**b JN tl GG **456**b LCC **459**br AAO t AAO/ROE **462**t AF **467**b AF tl Martin Altman/Observatorium Hoher List of the University Bonn, Daun, Germany **470**t AAO **475**t AF t JN **480**b JN **483**b AAO/ROE t AAO **486**c TPL/SPL/NOAO t AF **489**tr AAO **493**b AAO t AF **496**c AAO **501**b, t AF **506**t AAO **509**br AAO/ROE t AF **512**t LD **517**tr AAO/ROE tr ROE/AAO **520**tl AF tr AAO **523**tr TPL/SPL **527**b GG tl Gordon Garradd tr AAO/IAC **530**c JN **535**br JN t AF **541**t B&SF/TSA **543**b TPL/SPL/CI t AF **546**t NOAO **550–551**c NASA/HHT **552**bl NASA tl PE **553**t PE **554**tr Bettmann/APL/CBT **556**bl PE **557**t NASA **558**t PE **559**c PE **560**cl PE cr DS **561**t DS **562**t AAP/ Associated Press *Tyler Morning Telegraph* **563**b NASA/Kennedy Space Center **564**bl DS **565**br, t NASA **566**b Roger Ressmeyer/APL/CBT **568**t Joseph Sohm; ChromoSohm Inc/APL/CBT **571**b SB **572**tr PD **573**b SB tl NASA **575**t PE tr NASA **577**bl German Aerospace Center and Brown University/JPL/NASA **580**bl ESA/Denmen Productions **581**tc ESA/Denman Productions **584**bl Reuters NewMedia Inc./APL/CBT **585**tr NASA Dryden Flight Research Center **586**bl APL/CBT tl NASA **589**tc DS

Illustration Credits

APL/CBT: 210; Chris Forsey: 51, 52, 53, 65, 77, 139; Clare Forte: 31; David Hardy/Wildlife Art Ltd: 1, 4, 8, 14, 15, 25, 29, 46, 58, 60, 66, 67, 71, 72, 77, 79, 82, 89, 92, 93, 94, 95, 96, 99, 119, 140, 141, 143; 571, 577; David Wood: 54, 127, 128, 132, 151, 164, 170; David Hardy: 16, 19, 119, 148, 150; Gregory Bridges: 583; Julian Baum/Wildlife Art Ltd: 577; Lee Gibbons/Wildlife Art Ltd: 21, 22, 26, 30, 38, 39, 44, 86, 87; Luigi Gallante/Wildlife Art Ltd: 144, 145, 287, 316, 349, 361; Lynnette R. Cook: 97; Mike Lamble: 13, 42, 43; Nick Farmer/Brihton Illustration: 57; Oliver Rennert: 54; Rob Mancini: 21, 36, 109, 123, 153, 369, 389, 395, 405, 413, 431, 439, 449, 455, 464, 473, 478, 490, 498, 504, 515, 525, 533, 538, 549; Tom Connell/Wildlife Art Ltd: 1, 102, 104, 105, 588; Trevor Ruth: 576; Simon Williams/Garden Studio: 20; Yirrkala/Mountford-Sheard Collection (#1480)/Special Collections, State Library of South Australia/Reproduced with the permission of the family of Wongu: 423